Paleosols and Weathering Through Geologic Time: Principles and Applications

Edited by

Juergen Reinhardt
Wayne R. Sigleo
U.S. Geological Survey
Reston, Virginia 22092

D1599884

SPECIAL PAPER
216

Published by The Geological Society of America, Inc.
3300 Penrose Place, P.O. Box 9140, Boulder, Colorado 80301

GSA Books Science Editor Campbell Craddock

Printed in U.S.A.

Library of Congress Cataloging-in-Publication Data

Paleosols and weathering through geologic time : principles and
    applications / edited by Juergen Reinhardt, Wayne R. Sigleo.
        p.   cm. -- (Special paper / Geological Society of America :
    216)
        Papers presented at a symposium held in Orlando, Fla., on Oct. 29,
    1985.
        Includes bibliographies and index.
        ISBN 0-8137-2216-0
        1. Paleopedology--Congresses.   2. Weathering--Congresses.
    I. Reinhardt, Juergen, 1946–   .   II. Sigleo, Wayne R.   III. Series:
    Special papers (Geological Society of America) : 216.
    QE473.P347   1988   87-35459
    551.7--dc19   CIP

Front Cover: White River Group (Oligocene), Badlands National Park, South Dakota. Photo by Greg J. Retallack.
Back Cover: Reconstruction of the White River Group (Oligocene), Badlands National Park, South Dakota. Reconstruction by Greg J. Retallack.

Contents

Preface

This volume is an outgrowth of papers presented on October 29, 1985, in Orlando, Florida. It represents the record of the first session dedicated to fossil soils or paleosols at a national meeting of the Geological Society of America (GSA).

The idea of organizing a symposium on paleosols for a national GSA meeting developed in the spring of 1984 during a combined meeting of the Southeastern and North-Central sections of GSA in Lexington, Kentucky. This was the first time that Wayne Sigleo and I had an opportunity to present the results of our research on Cretaceous paleosols in the southeastern United States. We were both surprised and delighted by the number of other papers presented at the same meeting that were directly related to the recognition and analysis of fossil soils.

Following the meeting, Wayne and I participated in a field trip led by Frank Ettensohn and his colleagues to look at paleosols on Mississippian limestones in east-central Kentucky. Several people on that trip had also written papers on paleosols and were focusing their attention on karst landforms, preservation of plant rootlets, and the composition of limestone residua. This trip led to wide-ranging discussions of weathering and soil features related to carbonate rock substrates and the importance of recognizing paleosols in stratigraphic analysis. A large number of geologists were beginning to focus their attention on paleosols and ancient landscapes, so we decided to raise this topic as a subject for discussion within the greater earth science community.

In response to the interest in paleosols shown at the GSA meeting in Kentucky, Wayne and I proposed to the organizing committee for the GSA meeting in Orlando that we organize a symposium dealing with: 1) the philosophy of paleosol analysis, 2) methods and techniques for analysis of various paleosol types, 3) soil processes in paleosols of different parent material, 4) paleosol recognition and stratigraphic analysis, and 5) paleosol variation as a function of paleoclimate. The last of these points, variation in paleoclimate, was to be the common thread for all of the talks.

The order of chapters in this volume follows the same general organization as the symposium. Eight of the ten papers presented at the Orlando meeting are represented in this volume. The chapter by Pinto and Holland is a substitution for the presentation on Precambrian paleosols by Holland and Zbinden in the symposium in order to broaden the scope of this volume and because of a prior publication agreement. The symposium paper on basement alteration at unconformities by M. A. Velbel was not prepared for this volume due to the author's prior commitments.

The first two chapters in the volume introduce methods and principles for studying paleosols. The lead chapter by G. J. Retallack details many of the concepts basic to the recognition and study of paleosols. Retallack's primer has allowed most of the volume's other authors the luxury of describing their paleosols without having to define many of their terms. The model presented by J. P. Pinto and H. D. Holland in the second chapter is a creative extension of previous descriptive work by Holland and Zbinden seeking to evaluate the composition of the Earth's early atmosphere through the use of geochemical signatures in Precambrian regoliths.

Although examples of paleosols from each of the geologic eras are represented, their distribution is not particularly even, either temporally or geographically. All three Paleozoic paleosols described in this volume are from the central Appalachian mountains; one focuses on an Ordovician red-bed sequence, the other two provide an interesting comparison between paleosols developed on Carboniferous carbonate and siliciclastic rocks. The chapter by C. R. Feakes and G. J. Retallack considers the characteristics and geochemistry of alluvial paleosols developed prior to the onset of abundant and diverse terrestrial vegetation. T. W. Gardner, E. G. Williams, and P. W. Helbrook elegantly describe differences in both profile horizonation and mineral composition in various Pennsylvanian underclays. The influence of tectonic elements in the Appalachian region on the nature and preservation of paleosols is the common theme of the two chapters on Carboniferous paleosols. The chapter by F. R. Ettensohn, G. R. Dever, and J. S. Grow describes the origin of various soil-related features within weathering profiles developed on Mississippian limestones in east-central Kentucky.

The two studies of Mesozoic paleosols introduce environmental settings not discussed in the chapters on Paleozoic paleosols. R. H. Blodgett describes pedogenic structures and early diagenetic features formed under semi-arid conditions in the Dolores Formation (Triassic) of southwestern Colorado. The eolian component of the Dolores deposit formation sets it apart from the other paleosols in alluvial, aggradational settings described in the volume. The chapter by W. R. Sigleo and J. Reinhardt documents the effect of parent material on the composition of paleosols formed under warm, humid conditions. This study deals with paleosols developed on three different parent lithologies below a regional Cretaceous land surface in the southeastern United States.

The chapters which discuss Cenozoic pedogenesis are concerned with sedimentation rates and surficial processes as they affect paleosols in the semi-arid parts of the western United States. M. J. Kraus and T. M. Brown present a model for relating pedogenic maturity to sedimentary cycles and proximity to alluvial channels in the Lower Eocene of Wyoming. This chapter extends their previous description of the hundreds of paleosols preserved within the Bighorn Basin. The final chapter in the volume by L. D. McFadden provides a summary of the extensive literature on Quaternary paleosols in the southwestern United States. Although the study of paleosols has become a standard stratigraphic tool for Quaternary geologists, this chapter points out the many limitations of our present state of knowledge about rates of pedogenic development even in well studied areas.

Many geomorphologists, Quaternary geologists, sedimentologists, geochemists, and soil scientists believe that the time is right to extend the use of paleosols throughout the geologic time scale. This will rely heavily on the lessons that have been learned by soil scientists and Quaternary geologists. Stratigraphers and sedimentologists have been able to help coastal geomorphologists and oceanographers to recognize what types of sedimentary bedforms and sequences have high preservation potential and require process explanations; a similar type of cross-pollination is now beginning to take place in the study of paleosols. These fascinating and complex parts of the geologic record account for so much of geologic time and provide so many clues to tectonics, structural geology, erosional history, geography, geomorphology, and climate that they cannot be ignored by the geologic community.

Since our symposium was convened, the interest and attention given to paleosols by the geological community has continued to grow. A session on "Evolution of the Regolith" at the International Association of Sedimentologists in Canberra, Australia, during August 1986 brought together French, German, American, Israeli, and Australian paleopedologists, geomorphologists, clay mineralogists, and sedimentologists, among others. A Penrose Conference on paleosols held in September 1987 in Eugene, Oregon, expanded the network of cooperating scientists. We hope that this volume will serve to introduce an even wider group of geologists to the recognition, study, and application of paleosols in their studies of the Earth's history.

Juergen Reinhardt
Reston, Virginia
October, 1987

Dedication

Paleosols are windows into the world as it was during other times. Evidence of past weathering and soil formation is found in virtually all geologic systems and is used to interpret paleoclimate and environment. Soils are complex geologic phenomena and their development and preservation depends on many factors. Consequently, there are numerous and controversial theories to explain their origin and diagenesis. Where consistent recognition of paleosols is possible, they may be useful means for stratigraphic correlation.

Wayne R. Sigleo
May 1986

Wayne Sigleo's early death of cancer on October 17, 1986, ended a career that was dedicated to first-rate science. Wayne contributed in a major way to our understanding of the value of paleosols for the interpretation of rock sequences. His work on Quaternary soils and dunes in Tasmania and on Pennsylvanian underclay soils in the Appalachian Basin led to his work on Cretaceous paleosols in the southeastern United States, and finally to the expansion of this research into the study of paleosols in the western United States.

Wayne was the moving spirit behind the Symposium on "Weathering and Paleosols through Geologic Time." As volume editor, he took on the burden of preparing the symposium proceedings for publication, and continued to work on the book until shortly before his death. Many of Wayne's contributions and aspirations are contained in this Special Paper. We believe that it is a fitting memorial to Wayne, and we dedicate it to his memory with admiration and affection.

Acknowledgments

This volume would not have been possible without the help and encouragement of many persons. Most important to the process of critically reviewing the chapters in this Special Paper were: Peter W. Birkeland, University of Colorado; Owen P. Bricker, U.S. Geological Survey (USGS); Stanley W. Buol, North Carolina State University; Henry S. Chafetz, University of Houston; C. Blaine Cecil, USGS; Steven M. Colman, USGS; Klaus W. Flach, U.S. Soil Conservation Service; David E. Grandstaff, Temple University; John W. Hosterman, USGS; Sam Johnson, USGS; A. C. Lasaga, Yale University; A. D. Miall, University of Toronto; Carolyn G. Olson, USGS; Milan J. Pavich, USGS; Joseph P. Smoot, USGS; Allan M. Thompson, University of Delaware; W. Lynn Watney, Kansas Geological Survey; and Scott L. Wing, Smithsonian Institution. We sincerely thank these reviewers for their careful consideration of the manuscripts.

I especially thank Dick Holland and Pete Birkeland for the good advice and energy that they gave this project from the onset to its conclusion. Finally, to the person most responsible for keeping projects like this alive and moving forward—my wife, Judy Reinhardt; I thank you for your constant support and devotion.

Geological Society of America
Special Paper 216
1988

Field recognition of paleosols

Greg J. Retallack
Department of Geology
University of Oregon
Eugene, Oregon 97403

ABSTRACT

Three main features of paleosols are useful for distinguishing them from enclosing rocks: root traces, soil horizons, and soil structures.

Fossil root traces are best preserved in formerly waterlogged paleosols. In oxidized paleosols their organic matter may not be preserved, but root traces can be recognized by their irregular, tubular shape, and by their downward tapering and branching. Often root traces are crushed like a concertina, because of compaction of the surrounding paleosol during burial. The top of a paleosol may be recognized where root traces and other trace fossils are truncated by an erosional surface. Root and other trace fossils are not useful for recognizing paleosols of middle Ordovician and older age, since large land organisms of such antiquity are currently unknown.

Soil horizons usually have more gradational boundaries than seen in sedimentary layering. Commonly these gradational changes are parallel to the truncated upper surface of the paleosol. Some kinds of paleosol horizons are so lithologically distinct that they have been given special names; for example, cornstone (Bk) and ganister (E); the letter symbols are equivalent horizon symbols of soil science.

Compared to sedimentary layering, metamorphic foliation, and igneous crystalline textures, soil structure appears massive, hackly, and jointed. The basic units of soil structure (peds) are defined by a variety of modified (for example, iron-stained or clayey) surfaces (cutans). Peds may be granular, blocky, prismatic, columnar, or platy in shape. Concretions, nodules, nodular layers, and crystals are also part of the original soil structure of some paleosols.

Complications to be considered during field recognition of paleosols include erosion of parts of the profile, overlap of horizons of different paleosols, development of paleosols on materials eroded from preexisting paleosols, and the development of paleosols under successive and different regimes of weathering.

INTRODUCTION

This chapter presents a personal view of the fundamental problem of recognizing paleosols in outcrop. It is not meant as a comprehensive discussion of field methods in paleopedology, nor as an outline of a "paleopedological paradigm," nor as a program for further research. The terminology and concepts used are largely those of the U.S. Department of Agriculture (Soil Survey Staff, 1951, 1962, 1975; Guthrie and Witty, 1982), with a liberal sprinkling of ideas from Brewer (1976), Buol and others (1980), and Birkeland (1984). The three main field features of paleosols are root traces, soil horizons, and soil structures. Consideration of

these features forms the bulk of this account. Also considered are complications that may affect paleosol recognition, field names for paleosols, a list of basic field equipment, and a collage of diagrams and tables useful for field reference.

ROOT TRACES

One of the most diagnostic features of paleosols is evidence of root traces in their place of growth. Even if there are no other indications of ancient soil formation, root traces are evidence that

1

the rock was exposed to the atmosphere and colonized by plants, and thus a soil by almost anyone's definition (Buol and others, 1980; Retallack and others, 1984). A gray shale with clear bedding may appear to be an ordinary sedimentary deposit, but a few fossil root traces penetrating the shale means that it was probably an alluvial paleosol similar to a Fluvent (in the classification of Soil Survey Staff, 1975).

The top of a paleosol can be recognized as the surface from which root traces emanate. Concentrations of other trace fossils, such as burrows, also can be used, a technique long recognized as an indication of omission surfaces and hardgrounds in marine sedimentary rocks (Seilacher, 1964). There are, however, situations in which sedimentation keeps pace with burrowing and vegetative growth. Where breaks in sedimentation cannot be discerned easily, paleosols are not usually developed to the extent that they can be regarded as good indicators of paleoenvironment or stratigraphic level, and so are not of great concern.

In cases where little original organic material of the root has been preserved, its remains can be considered a kind of trace fossil (Sarjeant, 1975). Unlike other trace fossils such as burrows, root traces mostly taper and branch downward. They are also very irregular in width, commonly with irregular longitudinal creasing. Large vertical roots characteristically have a concertina-like outline, because of compaction of enclosing sediments. Outward flexures of the concertina may be located at large lateral rootlets extending into the matrix. The distinction between root traces and burrows is not always easy. Roots may spread out laterally over hardpans in soils, and some kinds of roots branch upward and out of the soil (Fig. 1). Furthermore, a number of soil insects and other creatures burrow around and into roots to feed, a practice that appears to be at least as old as Triassic (Retallack, 1976).

Paleobotanical research has unearthed fossil examples of most of the major kinds of root traces; particularly well-documented examples of fossil root traces are cited herein as a guide to paleobotanical literature. Roots are downward growing plant axes, often with numerous finer branches or rootlets (Fig. 2). Both roots and rootlets are more anatomically conservative than other parts of the plants. Usually a central woody cylinder (stele) is separated by a zone (cortex) of fleshy cells (parenchyma) from a tough outer coat (epidermis) to the root (Fig. 1A; as, for example, in Late Devonian roots of *Archaeopteris*: Beck, 1981; Eocene roots of *Metasequoia*: Basinger, 1981). The central woody cylinder (stele) and tough outer layer (epidermis) often withstand decay much longer than the intervening zone (cortex) of soft cells (parenchyma, as in Late Triassic root traces studied by Retallack, 1976). Root hairs are elongate cells that gather water and nutrients from the soil. They are concentrated in zones along the finest rootlets and are preserved only under exceptional circumstances (see for example, Fig. 3, Late Carboniferous *Austroclepsis*; see also Sahni, 1929, 1932). Some very early (Silurian and Devonian) land plants and modern mosses and liverworts lack true roots. They have fine hairlike organs (rhizoids, Fig. 1E) that perform a similar function. Like

root hairs, these also are preserved under exceptional circumstances (as in Devonian *Rhynia*: Kidston and Lang, 1917).

Various kinds of roots are named for their patterns of branching and botanical origins. Many plants have several roots of equal size extending outward and downward from their base, but some have a single, thick, vertical root (tap root) similar to a carrot or turnip (Fig. 1T; a fossil example is Late Devonian *Eddya*: Beck, 1967). Other plants, especially living grasses and quillworts, have numerous fine roots (Fig. 1R, fibrous roots) radiating from the base of the plant or from a thickened stem base (a corm or rhizophore, Fig. 1G; as in Early Triassic *Pleuromeia*: Retallack, 1975). If the roots arise from the stem of the plant, rather than from its base or from other roots, they are called adventitious roots. They may arise from stems lying in or along the ground (rhizomes, Fig. 1I; as in Late Carboniferous *Calamites*: Eggert, 1962), stems scrambling along and above ground (runners or stolons, Fig. 1F; as in Pennsylvanian *Callistophyton*: Rothwell, 1975) or from erect stems and their aerial branches (prop roots, Fig. 1M; as in Early Cretaceous *Weichselia*: Alvin, 1971).

In some cases, such as modern tree ferns, a very weak stem is completely encased in numerous adventitious roots, which form a thick, soft "false trunk" (Fig. 1H, N; as in Pennsylvanian *Psaronius*: Morgan, 1959; and Early Cretaceous *Tempskya*: Andrews and Kern, 1947). Potato-like underground storage structures branching from roots or rhizomes are called tubers (Fig. 1I; as in Cretaceous *Equisetites*: Seward, 1898; Rushforth, 1971). Some plants, especially mangroves, have rootlets that extend ver-

---

Figure 1. Kinds and distribution of roots found in soils and paleosols. Plant species (and sources of these and further illustrations) follow. A, generalized dicotyledonous angiosperm morphology and anatomy; B, crack willow, *Salix fragilis* (Kawase and Whitmoyer, 1980); C, mangrove, *Avicennia marina* (Chapman, 1976); D, mangrove, *Sonneratia alba* (Chapman, 1976); E, liverwort, *Hymenophytum flabellatum* (Scagel and others, 1984); F, strawberry (*Fragaria x ananassa*) (Raven and others, 1981); G, quillwort, *Isoetes echinospora* (Seward, 1910); H, tree fern, *Dicksonia fibrosa* (Heath and Chinnock, 1974); I, horsetail, *Equisetum sylvaticum* (Andrews, 1947); J, tropical dicot, *Cariniana pyriformis* (Jenik, 1978); K, mangrove, *Avicennia germinans* (Jenik, 1978); L, tropical dicot, *Mitragyna stipulosa* (Jenik, 1978); M, screw pine, *Pandanus candelabrum* (Jenik, 1978); N, oil palm, *Elaeis guineensis* (Jenik, 1978); O, short grass prairie, southeast of Colorado Springs, Colorado, dominated by blue grama, *Bouteloua gracilis* (b), with threeawn grass *Aristida purpurea* (a) and the forbs *Artemisia frigida* (r), *Psoralea tenuiflora* (p), *Chrysopsis villosa* (c), and *Yucca glauca* (y: Weaver, 1919); P, lowland, tall grass prairie near Lincoln, Nebraska, dominated by bluestem, *Andropogon furcatus* (a), switchgrass, *Panicum virgatum* (p), and Kentucky bluegrass *Poa pratensis* (b), with cordgrass *Spartina cynosuroides* (s) and forbs *Glycyrrhiza lepidota* (g) and *Solidago altissima* (o: Weaver, 1920); Q, mountain forest near Pikes Peak, Colorado, dominated by Engelmann spruce *Picea engelmanni* (p), with limber pine *Pinus flexilis* (i), and small dicots *Chamaenerion angustifolium* (c), *Fragaria virginiana* (f), *Haplopappus parryi* (h), and *Rosa acicularis* (r: Weaver, 1919); R, threeawn grass *Aristida purpurea* (Weaver, 1919); S, mountain sage, *Artemisia frigida* (Weaver, 1919); T, 16-yr-old sugar maple *Acer saccharum* (Biswell, 1935).

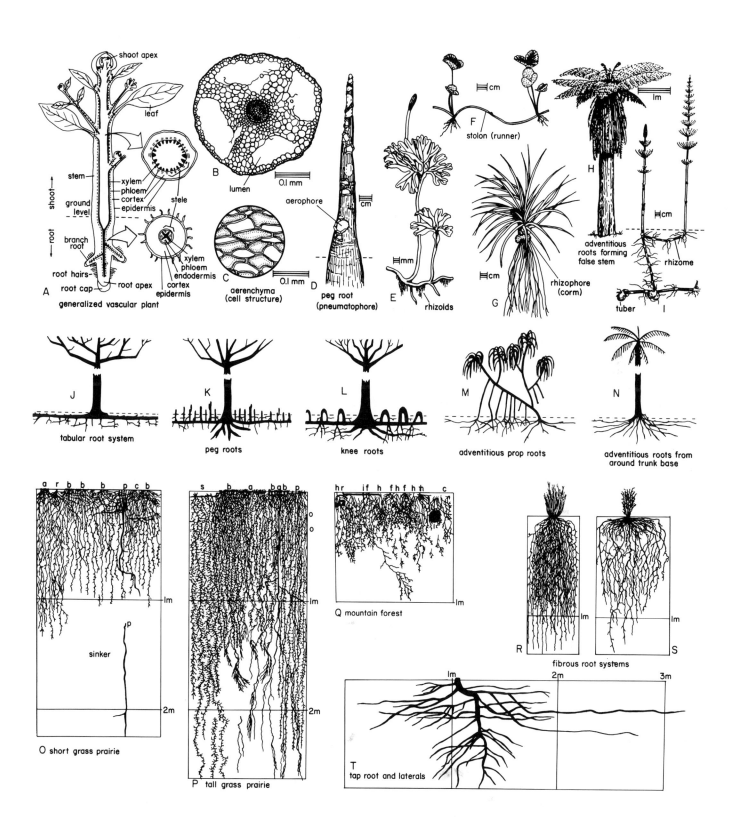

A generalized vascular plant

shoot apex
leaf
stem
shoot
ground level
root
branch root
root hairs
root cap
root apex
xylem
phloem
cortex
epidermis
stele
xylem
phloem
endodermis
cortex
epidermis

B lumen

C aerenchyma (cell structure)

D peg root (pneumatophore)
aerophore

E rhizoids

F stolon (runner)

G rhizophore (corm)

H adventitious roots forming false stem

I rhizome
tuber

J tabular root system

K peg roots

L knee roots

M adventitious prop roots

N adventitious roots from around trunk base

O short grass prairie
sinker

P tall grass prairie

Q mountain forest

R / S fibrous root systems

T tap root and laterals

Figure 2. Fossil roots and rootlets from Early Miocene, Molalla Formation on High Hill, near Scotts Mills, Oregon (Retallack specimen R261). Their original organic matter has been weakly ferruginized. Scale in both centimeters (figures) and millimeters (fine gradations).

Figure 3. Petrographic thin section of silicified root hairs radiating from hollow, adventitious root seen in transverse section in false stem of tree fern *Austroclepsis australis,* from Early Carboniferous Caroda Formation, opposite Glenidle Homestead, near Caroda Post Office, New South Wales (Retallack specimen P5580C). Scale bar = 0.1 mm.

tically upward into the air (peg roots, Fig. 1D, K; as reported from Miocene paleosols: Whybrow and McClure, 1981). Peg and prop roots often have thin-walled openings to the inside of the root (aerophores, Fig. 1D; as in Early Cretaceous *Weichselia*: Alvin, 1971), and spongy porous tissue (aerenchyma, Fig. 1C; and in Pennsylvanian *Amyelon*: Cridland, 1964). Hollow cavities in roots (lumina, Fig. 1B; as in Pennsylvanian *Stigmaria*: Stewart, 1947; and Permian *Vertebraria*: Gould, 1975) allow circulation of oxygen needed for plant respiration in waterlogged, reducing environments. Root structures such as this not only indicate the existence of paleosols, but are evidence of soil conditions.

The various kinds of roots can most easily be recognized when their original organic matter is preserved. This occurs mostly in paleosols formed in waterlogged lowland environments where the activity of microbial decomposers is limited by lack of oxygen. Many kinds of roots also are recognizable in well-drained paleosols. Rarely is there organic matter remaining in root traces of such red and variegated paleosols. All that remains are irregu-

lar tubular features filled with material different from the surrounding paleosol matrix. This filling may include several generations of clay and silt washed into the hole left by the decaying root (Fig. 4). In some cases, only soft tissues (such as the cortex of a root) may be replaced by clay within more decay resistant parts (such as the epidermis and stele: an example is figured by Retallack, 1976). Root holes also may be filled with minerals such as crystalline calcite, chalcedony, or zeolite.

Poorly preserved root traces may be accentuated by encrustations that formed around them during their growth. Roots take in water by osmosis and by maintaining a negative pressure (water potential) in their thin conducting tubes (xylem) by loss of water from leaves (transpiration). Nutrients are absorbed the same way, aided by materials exuded by roots that favor mineral weathering. The area of active nutrient uptake around a root (rhizosphere) is a gelatinous zone (mucigel) rich in bacteria and fungi. Many nutrient cations are released from soil minerals by replacement with hydrogen ions in mildly acidic solutions maintained by organic acids, and by carbonic acid arising from carbon dioxide of microbial and root respiration. Other nutrients, such as iron, are dissolved by organic reductants, such as caffeic acid, or are bonded to large organic molecules (chelates) produced by plants. This does not mean that the rhizosphere is uniformly or always chemically acidic and reducing, as was once thought (Keller and Fredericksen, 1952). Most of the time the root zone is near-neutral in pH and Eh, allowing for normal activity of both roots and microbes (Nye and Tinker, 1977). Conditions can change over short intervals of time following rainfall or nutrient starvation (Olsen and others, 1981).

With repeated cycles of wetting (making the soil mildly acidic), then drying (neutral to alkaline), plant roots growing in calcareous, friable materials such as coastal sand dunes can become heavily encrusted in thick tubes of aragonite-cemented sandstone. These calcareous rhizoconcretions become so thick and unyielding that the root eventually dies and the remaining hole fills with other materials (Semeniuk and Meager, 1981; Bown, 1982; Cohen, 1982). Similarly, iron mobilized in the drab, ferrous state within the rhizosphere may be oxidized to yellow or red ferric oxides near the root to form ferruginous rhizoconcretions (Bown, 1982). Root traces encrusted with carbonates and iron oxides are among the most prominent found in paleosols. With heavy encrustation they become increasingly difficult to distinguish from nodules and burrows.

An additional distinctive feature of root traces found in red colored paleosols is a diffuse, drab colored (bluish or greenish gray) halo extending out into the surrounding paleosol matrix (Fig. 4). Superficially, these drab, haloed root traces are similar to krotovinas and to surface-water gley in modern soils (as described by Duchafour, 1978, and Knapp, 1979). A krotovina is a tongue of material washed down into burrows and root traces from an overlying horizon of the soil or from the surface. This kind of structure differs from drab haloes in containing material of a texture different than the soil matrix, from which it is separated by a sharp boundary. Surface-water gley forms when water is perched on the surface of a clayey or indurated soil for some time, so that it becomes stagnant, and anaerobic bacterial activity initiates chemical reduction of the margins of cracks, root holes, and burrows in the soil. Surface gleying may also produce rims of iron or manganese stain around root traces, or mineralization with pyrite or sphaerosiderite, and is often found in soils with carbonaceous surface horizons. Fossil examples of both krotovinas (metagranotubules of Retallack, 1976) and surface-water gley (in Ogi Series paleosols of Retallack, 1983b) have been recognized, but these are far less common and widespread than drab-haloed root traces (Retallack, 1983b, 1985).

There are two especially promising hypotheses to explain the origin of drab-haloed root traces. Perhaps they represent the rhizosphere: the chemical microenvironment established by the living root and its associated halo of mucigel, microorganisms, and soil water. By this hypothesis it is difficult to reconcile the rarity of such features in modern red soils with their abundance in red paleosols. A second explanation for drab haloes around root

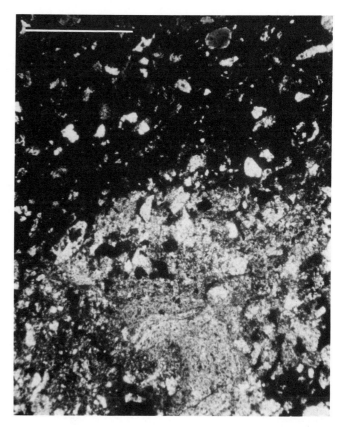

Figure 4. Petrographic thin section oriented parallel to former land surface in horizon BA of type Long Reef clay paleosol from Early Triassic, Bald Hill Claystone at Long Reef, New South Wales, showing deeply iron-stained soil matrix (dark), drab halo around root trace (light and granular), and silty clay infill of root hole (light with concentric lamination). Scale bar = 1 mm.

traces is as gley features associated with anaerobic microbial decay of organic material soon after burial of the paleosol below the water table. Also formed in this way is the gleying of surface horizons of paleosols, which commonly are bluish or greenish gray. This color is seldom seen in modern soils, even those with quite carbonaceous surface horizons. The contrast between drab-haloed root mottles and surface horizons and the red remainder of the paleosol may have been enhanced by dehydration of yellow and brown ferric oxyhydrates to brick red hematite during deep burial (Walker, 1967). Drab-haloed root traces are important not just as a common kind of root trace, but also as indicators of vegetation just before burial. They can be especially useful in distinguishing between woodland, savanna, and open grassland of the past (Retallack, 1983b). Roots and rhizospheres rapidly decay and oxidize in an exposed soil, so by either hypothesis of their origin the drab-haloed root traces represent the last crop of a paleosol.

While searching for fossil root traces it is useful to consider their arrangement (Figs. 1J–T), as this may give important clues

Figure 5. Tabular root systems of large arborescent lycopods, *Stigmaria ficoides,* in the Early Carboniferous, lower Limestone, and Coal Group, in Victoria Park, Glasgow, Scotland. Scale bar = 1 m, for
foreground only.

to the nature of former drainage, vegetation, and originally indurated parts of a paleosol. Because roots need oxygen in order to
respire, they seldom penetrate permanently waterlogged parts of
soils. Laterally spreading (tabular) root systems are characteristic
of plants growing in swampy ground (Jenik, 1978). This is a very
common configuration for fossil stumps found in sedimentary
rocks (Fig. 5), and is a part of the reason why many seat earths to
coal seams contain few root traces. In contrast, well-drained paleosols may be penetrated by roots to great depths (Sarjeant,
1975). In seasonally dry climates there may be a more complex
pattern: a copious surficial network of roots active in the wet
season, together with a few deep roots (sinkers) tapping deep
ground water during the dry season (Van Donselaar-ten Bokkel
Huininck, 1966). This is a typical pattern for root traces of savanna ecosystems in which trees are scattered among widespread
grasses. The roots of grasses are mostly of the fibrous type, and
are less than 2 mm in diameter. They tend to become less copious-
ly branched and more clumped in distribution (under individual
tussocks) in open grasslands of very dry climates (Weaver, 1968).

Root traces avoid or run along the margins of cemented horizons
or nodules, and can be an important indication that these were
originally indurated in the soil. This pattern of root traces is the
best line of evidence for recognizing duripans and fragipans (lithified horizons in soils, Soil Survey Staff, 1975) in paleosols that
are now entirely lithified. Furthermore, root traces may be better
preserved and less compacted within nodules (especially those of
siderite) than in the surrounding matrix (Retallack, 1976). This is
an indication that the nodules at least predate compaction, and
may be an original part of the soil. Many soil nodules are initiated
as unindurated chemical aggregations, easily penetrated by roots.
Later they may become hard and indurated (Gile and others,
1966).

 One limitation on the use of root traces to recognize paleosols is that they have not yet been definitely found in rocks older
than the Devonian period, when the first large woody vascular
plants appeared. There are trace fossils that may have been produced by small vascular plants in some Late Silurian paleosols
(Retallack, 1985) and reduction spots, possibly from plant or-

Figure 6. Sharp upper contact (top left) and diffuse nodular and lower horizons of modern grassland soil (upper left) and two comparable paleosols from Miocene-age (about 14 Ma) Fort Ternan Beds, in the main excavation at Fort Ternan National Monument, Kenya. Hammer handle is 25 cm.

Figure 7. Sharp upper contact and diffuse lower horizons, and drab haloed root traces (in upper part of red B horizon), in forested paleosol, type Long Reef clay paleosol (of Fig. 4). Black and white scale is 1 ft, graduated in inches.

ganic matter in Late Ordovician paleosols (Boucot and others, 1974). Other Late Ordovician paleosols have been recognized from the concentrations of burrows at specific levels, but it is only the association of these with other soil features (caliche nodules and mineral and chemical weathering trends) that allows these to be distinguished from marine trace fossils (Retallack, 1985). Nonmarine metazoan trace fossils are unlikely to be much older than this, but their antiquity has received little serious scientific attention.

SOIL HORIZONS

A second general feature of paleosols is their soil horizons. The exact nature of paleosol horizons varies considerably, but there are some consistent features useful for recognizing them in the field. The top of the uppermost horizon of a paleosol is usually truncated sharply by an erosional surface. Below that, by contrast, boundaries between different horizons and the underlying parent material are usually gradational (Figs. 6, 7). The dis-

tinction between sharp and diffuse contacts can be made only in outcrops at least a few tens of centimeters wide. If there are no extensive sea cliff or roadcut exposures, as in a weathered badlands slope, some digging may be needed to improve exposure. It is worth considerable effort to be sure of the nature of the boundaries of soil horizons in the field, as this will determine where samples are taken, and is something that cannot be redeemed by later laboratory studies.

Exceptions to the sharp top of the upper horizon and gradational boundaries to other horizons are not common in my experience, but do occur. Some lowland soils receive thin increments of sediment through which vegetation continues to grow (a cumulative horizon of Birkeland, 1984). These cumulative surface horizons are more bioturbated than a purely sedimentary shale or siltstone. Usually, however, they are less bioturbated than most of the paleosol just below. Generally, there is a more or less abrupt change in the density of bioturbation that can be taken as the approximate top of the profile. Other exceptions to the generalization of gradational horizon boundaries are sharp contacts between layers within a paleosol. Most commonly these are relict beds from sedimentary parent material, not yet obliterated by soil formation. Associated sedimentary features, such as bedding, ripple marks, or load casts, allow confident identification of such relict bedding. There also may be erosional surfaces within a profile, where a preexisting paleosol has been substantially eroded, and soil development proceeded on an additional layer of sediment. These cases may be more difficult to detect in the field, but may be revealed by chemical or petrographic anomalies.

In some cases, soil horizons are so striking that they have specific geological names, such as cornstone (a nodular calcareous, usually Bk horizon; Steel, 1974) and ganister (a silicified sandy, usually E horizon; Retallack, 1976). Strongly contrasting colors from one horizon to the next are common. Successions of paleosols with grey green near-surface (A and E) horizons and red to purple subsurface (Bt and Bs) horizons form especially scenic sequences, as gaudy as a barber pole or candy cane (Retallack, 1984). Sequences of calcareous paleosols are often more subdued and lighter in color, with alternating brown surface (A) and cream subsurface (Bk) horizons (Retallack, 1983b). Some Precambrian paleosols have surface (A) horizons of a very distinctive lime green color (Retallack and others, 1984).

A wide variety of horizons are recognized in modern soils, and these are labeled with a system of letters and numbers (such as A and Bt) in a kind of shorthand system of description (Table 1). Although laboratory reassessment may force changes in a horizon designation, it is best to interpret paleosol horizons in the field. Such field observations will determine the way a paleosol is sampled, and perhaps ultimately its interpretation and identification in classifications of modern soils. Compared to the numerous systems for classification of soils, the field nomenclature for soil horizons has remained fairly stable over the years. Some minor changes are now being proposed in revision of the U.S. Department of Agriculture's Soil Survey Manual (Guthrie and Witty, 1982). These are contrasted with nomenclature of an earlier edition of the Soil Survey Manual in Table 1. A distinctive feature of the new scheme is its conflation of accumulations of carbonate, clay, sesquioxides, and humus as equally valid indicators of B horizons. Thus, horizons formerly labeled "Cca" should now be "Bk."

In order to characterize soil horizons, their grain size, color, reaction with acid, and the nature of their boundaries must all be recorded in the field. Grain size can be reassessed by laboratory studies, but color cannot. Samples of well-indurated or partly metamorphosed paleosols may hold their color well, but little-altered clayey paleosols of the kind widespread in scenic badlands of Mesozoic and Cenozoic rocks in the western United States change color on exposure and laboratory storage. In the Badlands of South Dakota, rock samples became paler (Munsell value became higher) after a few hours of drying in the sun, and after six months of laboratory storage, greenish gray parts of the samples became discernibly more yellowish (change in Munsell hue) because of oxidation of their reduced iron-bearing minerals (Retallack, 1983b). It is best to record color using a comparative chart (Munsell Color, 1975) on fresh rock within a few minutes of exposure. In some cases it is useful to take the weathered color of the adjacent unexcavated exposure of color-banded badlands, because these colors are useful for locating similar paleosols in unexcavated weathered slopes.

The carbonate content of a horizon, as a guide to its base saturation, can be determined in the laboratory, and may be useful in identifying the paleosol within a classification of modern soils. It also is helpful to determine carbonate content in the field by applying drops of dilute (about 10%) hydrochloric acid. In recent fieldwork, I was especially interested in carbonate content as a guide to the preservation of bone (following general models of Retallack, 1984), and used an expanded scale of acid reaction to approximate carbonate content (Table 2). A final feature of horizons that must be recorded in the field is the nature of their contact with adjacent horizons. Only one contact needs to be specified for each horizon—the upper one if systematically describing a profile up section or the lower one if working downward. Two aspects of the contact are of interest: whether one horizon changes into another within a narrow (abrupt) or broad (diffuse) vertical distance, and whether the contact is laterally planar (smooth) or somehow disrupted (broken). The U.S. Department of Agriculture has adopted official terms for the National Cooperative Soil Survey to describe these various degrees of sharpness and lateral continuity (Table 3). I have used these in published descriptions of paleosols, but have often found my memory of them uncertain in the field and measured the transition distances and spacing of irregularities. Such measurements can easily be translated later into categories.

The nature of soil horizons provides important clues to past vegetation of paleosols and the time available for formation. As a soil develops so does the complexity of its vegetation and the degree of differentiation of its horizons. Soils of young land surfaces, such as recent flood deposits, or landslide debris, have persistent features betraying their origin, such as bedding. They support early successional vegetation and have only an organic (A) horizon over mildly weathered parent material (C horizon). This simple structure (A horizon over C) is also seen in some grassland soils (Fig. 6). These also may have a calcareous subsurface horizon (Bk) that is closer to the surface in grassland soils of progressively drier climates (Jenny, 1941; Arkley, 1963) and that becomes thicker and more massive with time (Table 4). A full sequence of horizons (A–Bt or Bs–C) is formed under stable, mature woody vegetation. Leached (eluvial or E) horizons form under closed canopy forest, woodland, and heath, in which rainfall leachates from the leaves, as well as root action and other agents, translocate organic matter, clay, or sequioxides of iron into a distinctive subsurface (Bt or Bs) horizon (Fig. 7). With time this subsurface horizon becomes thicker and more enriched in organic matter, clay, or sesquioxides. The differentiation horizons can be used to assess the relative degree of development of paleosols (Table 5). Rough estimates in years can be gleaned from current studies of modern soils of various ages (chronosequences: Birkeland, 1984).

Dr. Steven Bill

Soil horizons are also the bas[...] of soils. Because each system of [...] strengths and weaknesses, it is best t[...] several classifications. The classifica[...] Cooperative Soil Survey of the Unite[...] 1975) is based largely on experience [...] and volcanic soils of North Americ[...] concepts are now gaining widesprea[...] classification of the Food and Agricul[...] UNESCO (summarized by Fitzpatri[...] rience of soils in tropical regions. Th[...] the Australian CSIRO (Stace and o[...] soils of the stable and largely unglac[...] and employs many old and familia[...] and Chernozem. Tentative field identification of paleosols within such classifications serves to focus attention on those features that are diagnostic.

SOIL STRUCTURE

A final field characteristic of paleosols is soil structure. This forms at the expense of bedding, crystal structure, and schistosity of parent materials, because of bioturbation by plants and animals, wetting and drying, and other soil-forming processes. Compared to sedimentary, metamorphic and igneous textures, soil structure appears massive or hackly at first sight. On closer inspection it can be seen to be complexly organized, with particular structures indicative of particular soil conditions.

The hackly appearance of much soil structure (for example, Fig. 8) is caused by a network of irregular planes (cutans, in soil terminology) surrounding more stable aggregates of soil material (peds). A common kind of cutan is clay skins (or illuviation argillans, in the terminology of Brewer, 1976), formed where clay has washed down into and lined cracks within the soil. These should be restricted to a pedogenic, clayey B horizon, as opposed to a subsurface clayey bed in the parent material of the soil. Cutans also can be ferruginized planes (diffusion ferrans), manganese encrusted surfaces (mangans) or cracks filled with sand (skeletans of soil science, which is the same thing as "sandy clastic dikes" of geological nomenclature). Soils may also contain sheets of crystalline calcite, barite, or gypsum. The network of cutans found in soils, especially if mineralized with crystals such as barite, may appear similar to the boxwork veining of some hydrothermal ores. In general, however, cutans are less regularly boxlike, less sharply bounded (on one side at least), and are restricted to narrow, stratabound horizons of considerable lateral extent.

Stable aggregates of soil material (peds) are bounded by both cutans and open spaces (voids) in the soil. Since open spaces are usually crushed or filled within paleosols, recognition of fossil peds in them depends on recognizing cutans. In cases where peds have been strongly compressed against each other during burial, slickensides form. These also form in surface soils of clayey texture with shrinking and swelling of clay on wetting and drying. Unlike slickensides associated with faults, those around peds are randomly oriented and restricted to particular (usually clayey)

[...]ed according to size and shape (Fig. 9). [...]eds in the field. Many kinds of peds are [...]se they are only weakly defined or dis-[...]d during burial.

[...]s of specific minerals (glaebules, in the [...]976) are also common in soils. Usually [...]lcareous, ferruginous, or sideritic lumps. [...] nodules and concretions of sedimentary [...] homogeneous internal texture, they are [...] with concentric internal lamination are [...]rewer, 1976). Nodules also may be [...]r has proposed calling these "papules," a [...] those cases where it is unclear whether [...]f a partly brecciated parent material or whether they were cavity fills or other local pedogenic accumulations of clay. If aggregations of material are especially diffuse, irregular, or weakly mineralized, they are termed mottles. Both mottles and glaebules can be categorized in terms of their visibility and abundance (Table 7). As with other such classifications used by the U.S. Department of Agriculture (Soil Survey Staff, 1975), this provides a degree of uniformity for published descriptions. Glaebules and mottles are irregularly shaped and have minerals that are either amorphous or very finely crystalline. Tubular mineral segregations (pedotubules) and a variety of crystals are found in soils and have a terminology of their own (Brewer, 1976). Glaebules, tubular features, and crystals are found in marine sedimentary rocks as well as in soils, and so are not as diagnostic of paleosols as peds and cutans. Nevertheless, glaebules, tubular features, and crystals are abundant and varied in paleosols, and form an important part of their structure.

Soil structures are important to the interpretation of paleosols, especially their drainage and chemical behavior. Clay skins, for example, form in soils in which the water table is below the surface for some part of the year. Soils formed under waterlogged swampy conditions may lack soil structure, showing little more than root traces. Granular and crumb structures are indications of copious biological activity. This is evidence for high soil fertility, and is characteristic of the surface (A) horizons of grassland soils (Mollisols). Domed columnar peds form in soils in which the clays are saturated with sodium cations. This structure is most commonly found in marine-influenced soils of mangal and salt marsh, and also in desert soils formed around salt pans. The mineralogy of nodules and related features may be a guide to former pH and Eh of the paleosol (using the well-known stability fields for minerals proposed by Krumbein and Garrels, 1952), provided these features can be shown to be original from their relationship to root traces and burrows. In general, ferric nodules and concretions form in well-drained, oxidized soils. Siderite nodules are characteristic of neutral to alkaline, waterlogged soils. Some waterlogged soils, especialy those which are marine-influenced, may have pyrite nodules. Calcareous nodules are found in well-drained alkaline soils. Consideration of these various interpretative possibilities may be useful in framing and further field-testing hypotheses about paleosols.

COMPLICATIONS IN
FIELD-SETTING OF PALEOSOLS

The recognition of root traces, soil horizons, and soil structure in paleosols may seem complex enough, but there are additional general complications that need to be considered during field examination of paleosols. These have to do with the way in which paleosols fit into rock sequences (Fig. 10).

In subsiding river valleys and coastal plains, of the sort in which many thick sedimentary sequences accumulate, soils are periodically covered by sediment. If a flood is especially catastrophic, and vegetation or engineering works are unable to contain it, a considerable amount of flood alluvium (a meter or so) may cover the soil. It then becomes a buried soil, a term I regard as synonymous with "fossil soil" and "paleosol."

If only thin increments (a few millimeters or centimeters) of sediment are deposited on a soil, most plants continue to grow and incorporate this material into the soil. Such cumulative horizons may blur the upper boundary of a paleosol, but these kinds of paleosols commonly show a break in the density of bioturbation, which can be taken as the top of the profile.

A more serious problem is the covering of a soil with an intermediate thickness of sediment (a few tens of centimeters) so that the younger soil that developed on the surface above the paleosol overlaps the paleosol. The remaining structures of the older surface (A) horizon in the subsurface (B) horizon of the younger soil are called pedorelicts. This is a general term for soil features believed to have formed in a soil (or paleosol) different from the one in which they are present (Brewer, 1976). Other examples of pedorelicts include nodules weathered out of older soils and incorporated into and persisting within the parent material of younger soils.

A pedorelict is not the same as a relict soil, which refers to a whole or partly eroded profile. Relict soils are surface soils in which the same soil material appears to have been modified by several different regimes of soil formation. This can be because the soil was buried and then uncovered by erosion at a later date (exhumed soil), or because it simply remained at the surface while climate, vegetation, or other soil-forming factors changed. Most fossil soils below major unconformities involving millions of years of nondeposition are relict soils to some extent. This, as well as the possibility of subsurface modification by ground water running along the unconformity, should be considered in interpreting their paleoenvironment (Pavich and Obermeier, 1985). For all paleosols it is prudent to consider the kind of paleoenvironment indicated by root traces, soil horizons, and soil structure in the field. Conflicting indications may arouse suspicion that the soil or some features are relict, and stimulate the search for evidence of the order of environmental change. The distinction between relict and exhumed soils may be difficult to determine, but can be settled by tracing the paleosol laterally to where it is buried (Ruhe, 1965). Thus, it is best to keep general the term relict paleosol, and to use the term exhumed paleosol only for those paleosols in which burial and uncovering can be demonstrated.

Soil material is not only eroded, but also deposited. The term pedolith (in the sense of Gerasimov, 1971) is convenient for deposits with a sedimentary organization, such as bedding or ripple marks, but with individual grains of soil mineralogy and microstructure. Most sediment is ultimately derived from soil, and so is pedolithic in a strict sense. In many sedimentary sequences (such as those discussed by Retallack, 1976, 1977), however, sediment from distant sources is quite distinct from that eroded out of local soils. In such cases, the term and the concept of pedolith are useful.

FIELD NAMES FOR PALEOSOLS

Many names for particular paleosols and kinds of paleosols are now finding their way into print. While some regard these names as an intolerable burden to already overloaded geological nomenclature, experience with other materials, such as trace fossils, has shown that informal number or letter designations tend to be ignored by future scientists working with comparable material.

Three systems for naming paleosols are available for the three different purposes of stratigraphic correlation, geological mapping, and paleoenvironmental interpretation of paleosols. It is not necessary to decide on final names during fieldwork, but potential names and relevant data for the particular system of naming should be considered in the field.

Paleosols have long been used for stratigraphic correlation in Quaternary sediments (Morrison, 1976); this technique is now being applied to much older rocks (Ortlam, 1971). The basic units of this technique have been called a number of different names in the past, but are now widely called geosols; for example, the Sangamon Geosol (North American Commission on Stratigraphic Nomenclature, 1982). A geosol defines a recognizable land surface. It may consist of different kinds of paleosols along strike, but is recognized by a comparable degree of development and other regionally consistent (especially climate-related) features.

Some paleosols, especially the thick remnants of paleosols at major unconformities such as laterite, silcrete, and caliche, are so widespread and well developed that they cover significant areas of geological maps. These also have been names after localities where they are best exposed and given the name profile, as in Curalle silcrete profile (Senior and Mabbutt, 1979).

For interpretative studies of paleosols, names are needed for kinds of paleosols as well as for selected specific profiles. Often in paleosol sequences, many examples of the same kind of paleosol may be found, reflecting persistence of broadly similar soil-forming conditions as the sequence accumulated (Retallack, 1983a,b). In situations such as this, I have used conventional soil mapping units (Soil Survey Staff, 1951, 1962). The basic field unit is termed the series, representing a consistently recognizable kind of paleosol. Series are named after a locality, or other feature if localities are not available (for example, Zisa and Gleska Series paleosols mean "red" and "mottled" series in the local Sioux Indian language: Retallack, 1983b). Each series is based on a representative paleosol (type profile), which should be carefully studied and documented. Individual paleosols may be named from the petrographic texture of their surface horizon or from other features (for example, the type Zisa clay and Gleska silty clay loam thick petrocalcic phase paleosols of Retallack, 1983b). There is also scope for grouping series of paleosols into larger units (associations) based on shared features, such as similar parent material. Paleosol series names are not yet formal geological names in the same way as geosols, but some effort should be made to avoid names that could be confused with other soil or rock units by checking compilations of these names (for example, by Luttrell and others, 1986; by Huddleston, 1979; or the computer data base available from the offices of the U.S. Soil Conservation Service).

A PERSONAL FIELD KIT

A good deal of equipment is now available to aid geological fieldwork. The following checklist outlines my own basic kit.

1. My digging and sampling equipment always includes a geological hammer. Some Quaternary paleosols may be too friable to sample directly with a hammer, but a hammer is still useful for forcing opened tin cans or pipe into the outcrop for extraction of samples showing soil fabric. If eroded badlands are to be sampled, it may be necessary to dig through the weathered surface to fresh rock using picks, shovels, or backhoes.

2. Recording equipment includes cameras, lenses, pencils, pencil sharpener, pens, and a field notebook. I prefer to make copious longhand notes and pencil sketches. This requires a larger-than-usual field notebook; quarto-sized, hardbound exercise books, with pages ruled into half-centimeter squares have proven best. The manner of describing sections of paleosols is just as it would appear in publications (Table 8), using my own modifications of the graphic presentation recommended by Selley (1978; Fig. 11).

3. The best available soil color charts are manufactured by Munsell Color (1975). Because diagenetic reddening of ferric oxyhydrate minerals and diagenetic pseudogley are so widespread in paleosols, the additional pages for tropical (hues 7.5R and 5R) and gley (chroma of 1) soil colors are strongly recommended. Soil color should always be taken on fresh rock within minutes of exposure, because colors change as rock samples dry and oxidize.

4. Dilute (about 10%) hydrochloric acid carried in an eyedropper bottle is needed for testing the carbonate content of samples by their effervesence of reaction (Table 2).

5. Marker pens with felt tips are useful for labeling hand specimens of different parts of a paleosol. It is also advisable to mark the top of hand specimens so that oriented petrographic thin sections can later be prepared. This is best marked by drawing a large (3 to 4 cm in diameter) circle on the upper portion of the sample in such a way that it forms a plane parallel to the top of the paleosol.

6. My measuring equipment includes tape and ruler. A Brunton compass may be useful for measuring dips and strikes of surfaces, and orientation of special features. Long sections designed to show the setting of paleosols within a sequence may be measured by the method of eye heights using a Brunton compass or other leveling device, such as an Abney level.

7. Packaging materials are needed for protection of samples of soil horizons, soil structures, and associated fossils during transport from the field. Newspaper is useful for wrapping. Small, delicate items may require boxes, bottles, or film canisters to prevent crushing.

8. Also useful are reminder sheets of information, such as the collage of diagrams included here (Figs. 8 through 11 and Tables 1 through 8). When working in a field camp, the following few books serve as an excellent research library: those by Stace and others (1968), Soil Survey Staff (1975), Buol and others (1980), Fitzpatrick (1980), and Birkeland (1984).

CONCLUSIONS

The basic question addressed in this chapter is an apparently simple one. Is it a paleosol? To deal with even such a simple question, some concept of the characteristic features and settings of paleosols is needed. As discussed at length, fossil root traces, soil horizons, and soil structures are especially characteristic. The settings of paleosols include unconformities of all kinds, from major erosional gaps in the rock record to minor breaks between beds of alluvial sediments. More than any other piece of field equipment, it is these concepts that enable the field recognition of paleosols. Even in finding paleosols, which are much more abundant than generally suspected, fortune favors the prepared mind.

Another question is worth asking in the field, and has not been addressed in detail here. What else could it be, if not a paleosol? A number of geologic phenomena may mimic some features of paleosols: mylonitized and brecciated fault zones; reaction rims around and on top of pillow lava; graded beds that fine upward from conglomerate or sandstone to claystone; strongly bioturbated marine or lacustrine sediments; or marine hardgrounds. These have only a superficial resemblance to paleosols and are very different in setting. As dissimilar as they may seem in comparison to paleosols, these other phenomena can appear similar, especially on first inspection and in small outcrops. It is possible also for a particular outcrop to show a combination of a paleosol and one of these other phenomena, for example, a paleosol developed on an alluvial graded bed or a paleosol altered by ground-water flow beneath an impermeable capping rock. There has been no attempt to catechize these various alternatives here, because each case is different and provides its own challenge to one's powers of observation and reason.

Other questions also arise during fieldwork. In terms of modern soil classification, what kind of soil was this paleosol? What was its former climate, vegetation, topographic position, parent material, or time for formation? How should it be mapped and named? My own answers to some of these questions have

12   *G. J. Retallack*

been scattered through this description of basic features of paleosols in an attempt to show why these things are of interest. Complex interpretative questions also can be tested by field
observations. Later, laboratory data on grain size, mineralogy,
and chemical composition may provide invaluable quantification
or validation of field ideas. Since samples analyzed are collected
on the basis of field observations, such laboratory data may considerably refine field observations, but only rarely will overturn
all the assumptions made then. Thus, the most crucial phase in
the investigation of a natural phenomenon as complex as a paleosol is its field examination and description. Take care then, for
paleopedology is fundamentally a field science.

ACKNOWLEDGMENTS

Many colleagues have helped shape my ideas concerning
interpretation of paleosols, but with only a few have I had the
pleasure of extended discussions in the field: D. L. Dilcher (Indi-
ana University), A. K. Behrensmeyer (Smithsonian Institution),
L. Tauxe (Scripps Institution of Oceanography), P. V. Wright
(University of Bristol), and J. H. Anderson (Botanical Research
Institute, Pretoria). This chapter also answers probing questions
from my students during classes and field excursions in paleopedology at the University of Oregon, especially P. Miller, M.
Spoon, C. Feakes, J. Battista, and S. Radosevich. Production of
the manuscript was assisted by National Science Foundation
Grant EAR 8503232.

Figure 8. Granular ped structures outlined by clay skins (argillans, espe-
cially prominent at arrow) from type Conata clay paleosol of mid-
Oligocene (Orellan or about 32 m.y.), Scenic Member of Brule
Formation, in Pinnacles area, Badlands National Park, South Dakota.
Scale in both centimeters (figures) and millimeters (fine gradations).

TYPE	PLATY	PRISMATIC	COLUMNAR	ANGULAR BLOCKY	SUBANGULAR BLOCKY	GRANULAR	CRUMB
SKETCH							
DESCRIPTION	tabular and horizontal to land surface	elongate with flat top and vertical to land surface	elongate with domed top and vertical to surface	equant with sharp interlocking edges	equant with dull interlocking edges	spheroidal with slightly interlocking edges	rounded and spheroidal but not interlocking
USUAL HORIZON	E,Bs,K,C	Bt	Bn	Bt	Bt	A	A
MAIN LIKELY CAUSES	initial disruption of relict bedding; accretion of cementing material	swelling and shrinking on wetting and drying	as for prismatic, but with greater erosion by percolating water, and greater swelling of clay	cracking around roots and burrows; swelling and shrinking on wetting and drying	as for angular blocky, but with more erosion and deposition of material in cracks	active bioturbation and coating of soil with films of clay, sesquioxides and organic matter	as for granular; including fecal pellets and relict soil clasts
SIZE CLASS	very thin <1mm	very fine <1cm	very fine <1cm	very fine <0.5cm	very fine <0.5cm	very fine <1mm	very fine <1mm
	thin 1 to 2mm	fine 1 to 2cm	fine 1 to 2cm	fine 0.5 to 1cm	fine 0.5 to 1cm	fine 1 to 2mm	fine 1 to 2mm
	medium 2 to 5mm	medium 2 to 5cm	medium 2 to 5cm	medium 1 to 2cm	medium 1 to 2cm	medium 2 to 5mm	medium 2 to 5mm
	thick 5 to 10mm	coarse 5 to 10cm	coarse 5 to 10cm	coarse 2 to 5cm	coarse 2 to 5cm	coarse 5 to 10mm	not found
	very thick >10mm	very coarse >10cm	very coarse >10cm	very coarse >5cm	very coarse >5cm	very coarse >10mm	not found

Figure 9. Classification of soil peds (simplified from Soil Survey Staff, 1975; Birkeland, 1984).

TABLE 1. DESCRIPTIVE SHORTHAND FOR LABELING PALEOSOL HORIZONS

Category	New Term	Description	Old Term
Master Horizons	O	Surface accumulation of organic materials (peat, lignite, coal), overlying clayey or sandy part of soil	O
	A	Usually has roots and a mixture of organic and mineral matter; forms the surface of those paleosols lacking an O horizon	A
	E	Underlies an O or A horizon and appears bleached because it is lighter colored, less organic, less sesquioxidic, or less clayey than underlying material	A2
	B	Underlies an A or E horizon and appears enriched in some material compared to both underlying and overlying horizons (because it is darker colored, more organic, more sesquioxidic or more clayey) or more weathered than other horizons	B
	K	Subsurface horizon so impregnated with carbonate that it forms a massive layer (developed to stage III or more of Table 4)	K
	C	Subsurface horizon, slightly more weathered than fresh bedrock; lacks properties of other horizons, but shows mild mineral oxidation, limited accumulation of silica carbonates, soluble salts or moderate gleying	C
	R	Consolidated and unweathered bedrock	R
Gradations Between Master Horizons	AB	Horizon with some characteristics of A and B, but with A characteristics dominant	A3
	BA	As above, but with B characteristics dominant	B1
	E/B	Horizon predominantly (more than 50%) of material like B horizon, but with tongues or other inclusions of material like an E horizon	A&B
Subordinate Descriptors	a	Highly decomposed organic matter	—
	b	Buried soil horizon (used only for pedorelict horizons with paleosols; otherwise redundant)	b
	c	Concretions or nodules	cn
	e	Intermediately decomposed organic matter	—
	f	Frozen soil, with evidence of ice wedges, dikes, or layers	f
	g	Evidence of strong gleying, such as pyrite or siderite nodules	g
	h	Illuvial accumulation of organic matter	h
	i	Slightly decomposed organic matter	—
	k	Accumulation of carbonates less than for K horizon	ca
	m	Evidence of strong original induration or cementation, such as avoidance by root traces in adjacent horizons	m
	n	Evidence of accumulated sodium, such as domed columnar peds or halite casts	sa
	o	Residual accumulation of sesquioxides	—
	p	Plowing or other comparable human disturbance	p
	q	Accumulation of silica	si
	r	Weathered or soft bedrock	ox
	s	Illuvial accumulation of sesquioxides	ir
	t	Accumulation of clay	t
	v	Plinthite (in place, pedogenic laterite)	—
	w	Colored or structural B horizon	—
	x	Fragipan (a layer originally cemented by silica or clay, and avoided by roots)	x
	y	Accumulation of gypsum crystals or crystal casts	cs
	z	Accumulation of other salts or salt crystal casts	sa

Note: This table has been adapted for use with paleosols from one by Guthrie and Witty (1982), showing proposed terminology from the new edition of the USDA *Soil Survey Manual*, compared to that of the 1951 edition. Some of the subordinate descriptors are considered more important than others; these letters (a, e, i, h, r, s, t, v, w) should all be written first after the master horizon if in combination with other letters, and they should not be used in combination with each other. Master horizons can be subdivided by numbers (e.g., B1, B2, B3). If the parent material of a paleosol consists of interbedded shale and sandstone, these will show different kinds of alteration in the same profile. Such different layers separated by discontinuities are numbered from the top down, without using the number 1; for example, A, E, E/B, Bt, 2Bt, 2BC, 2C, 3C. If you can form a clear mental picture of this profile, you are well on the way to mastering this pedological shorthand.

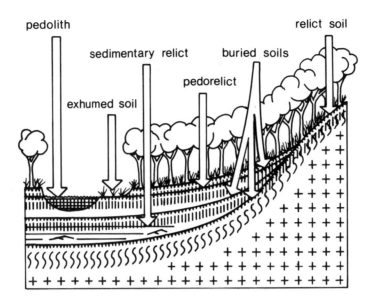

Figure 10. Important terms and concepts for recognition of fossil soils (from Retallack, 1983a, with permission from the Geological Society of America).

TABLE 2. SCALE OF ACID REACTION TO APPROXIMATE CARBONATE CONTENT OF PALEOSOLS	
Carbonate Content	Reaction with Dilute Acid
Noncalcareous	Acid unreactive; often forms an inert bead
Very weakly calcareous	Little movement within the acid drop, which could be flotation of dust particles as much as bubbles
Calcareous	Numerous bubbles, but not coalescing to form a froth
Strongly calcareous	Bubbles forming a white froth, but drop of acid not doming upward
Very strongly calcareous	Drop vigorously frothing and doming upward

Note: This table, developed during recent fieldwork, has been amplified from a scale proposed by Birkeland (1984).

TABLE 3. SHARPNESS AND LATERAL CONTINUITY OF PALEOSOL HORIZON BOUNDARIES		
Category	Class	Features
Sharpness	Abrupt	Transition from one horizon to another completed within 1 in (2cm)
	Clear	Transition completed within 1-2.5 in (2-5 cm)
	Gradual	Transition spread over 2.5-5 in (5-15 cm)
	Diffuse	One horizon grading into another over more than 5 in (15 cm)
Lateral Continuity	Smooth	Horizon boundary forms an even plane
	Wavy	Horizon boundary undulates, with pockets wider than deep
	Irregular	Horizon boundary undulates, with pockets deeper than wide
	Broken	Parts of the adjacent horizon are disconnected, e.g., by deep and laterally persistent clastic dikes in Vertisols

Note: This table is slightly modified from one of Birkeland (1984).

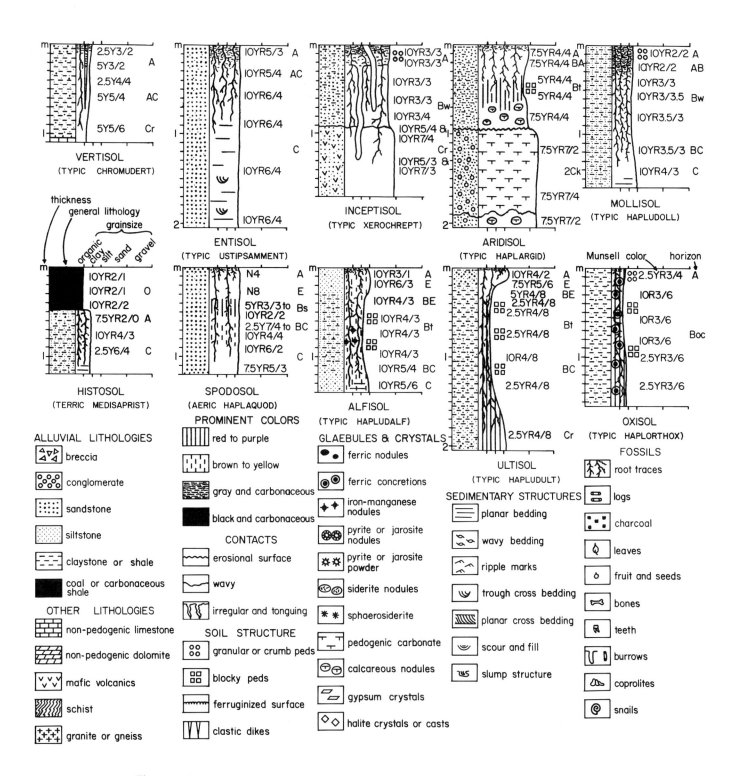

Figure 11. Suggested symbols and style for representing columnar sections of paleosols (adapted from scheme of Selley, 1978), with 10 profiles of modern soils thought to be representative of USDA taxonomic orders (by Buol and others, 1980, Appendix 1) as examples. Symbols not exhaustive; may need to be adapted or augmented to particular circumstances.

G. J. Retallack

TABLE 4. STAGES OF CARBONATE ACCUMULATION IN PALEOSOLS

Stage	Paleosols Developed in Gravel	Paleosols Developed in Sand, Silt, or Clay
I	Thin, discontinuous coatings of carbonate on underside of clasts	Dispersed powdery and filamentous carbonate
II	Continuous coating all around, and in some cases, between clasts: additional discontinuous carbonate outside main horizons	Few to common carbonate nodules and veinlets, with powdery and filamentous carbonate in places between nodules
III	Carbonate forming a continuous layer enveloping clasts: less pervasive carbonate outside main horizon	Carbonate forming a continuous layer formed by coalescing nodules; isolated nodules and powdery carbonate outside main horizon
IV	Upper part of solid carbonate layer with a weakly developed platy or lamellar structure, capping less pervasively calcareous parts of the profile	
V	Platy or lamellar cap to the carbonate layer strongly expressed; in places brecciated and with pisolites of carbonate	
VI	Brecciation and recementation, as well as pisoliths common in association with the lamellar upper layer	

Note: This table includes modifications (Machette, 1985) to the scheme proposed by Gile and others (1966).

TABLE 5. STAGES OF PALEOSOL DEVELOPMENT

Stage	Features
Very weakly developed	Little evidence of soil development apart from root traces: abundant sedimentary, metamorphic, or igneous textures remaining from parent material
Weakly developed	With a surface rooted zone (A horizon), as well as incipient subsurface clayey, calcareous, sesquioxidic, or humic, or surface organic horizons, but not developed to the extent that they would qualify as USDA argillic, spodic, or calcic horizons or histic epipedon
Moderately developed	With surface rooted zone and obvious subsurface clayey, sesquioxidic, humic, or calcareous or surface organic horizons: qualifying as USDA argillic, spodic or calcic horizons or histic epipedon, and developed to an extent at least equivalent to stage II of calcic horizons (Table 4)
Strongly developed	With especially thick, red, clayey, or humic subsurface (B) horizons, or surface organic horizons (coals or lignites), or especially well-developed soil structure, or calcic horizons at stages III to IV (Table 4)
Very strongly developed	Unusually thick subsurface (B) horizons, or surface organic horizons (coals or lignites), or calcic horizons of stage VI: such a degree of development is mostly found at major geologic unconformities

Note: This scale is modified from a version of Retallack (1984) to include coal-bearing paleosols.

TABLE 6. A SHORT AND SUPERFICIAL KEY TO SOIL ORDERS OF THE U.S. DEPARTMENT OF AGRICULTURE
FOR FIELD IDENTIFICATION OF PALEOSOLS

Features	Order
If paleosol has:	*It may be a(n):*
• Abundant swelling clay (mainly smectite) to a presumed uncompacted depth of 1 m or to a bedrock contact, together with hummock and swale structure (mukkara), especially prominent slickensides or clastic dikes	Vertisol
• No horizons diagnostic of other orders, and very weak development (Table 5)	Entisol
• No horizons diagnostic of other orders, but weak development (Table 5)	Inceptisol
• Light coloration (high Munsell value), thin calcareous layer (calcic horizon) close to surface of profile and developed to stage II or more (Table 4), or evidence of pedogenic gypsum or other evaporite minerals	Aridisol
• Organic (but not carbonaceous or coaly), well-structured (usually granular) surface (A) horizon (*mollic epipedon*), usually with evidence of copious biological activity (such as abundant fine root traces and burrows) and with subsurface horizons often enriched in carbonate, sometimes enriched in clay	Mollisol
• Surface organic (O) horizon of carbonaceous shale, peat, lignite, or coal (*histic epipedon*) originally (before compaction) at least 40 cm thick	Histosol
• Thick, well-differentiated (A, Bt, and C horizons) profile, with subsurface (Bt) horizon appreciably enriched in clay (*argillic horizon*) and often red with sesquioxides or dark with humus, and also with evidence (such as effervescence in acid or calcareous nodules or abundance of easily weathered minerals such as feldspar) for high concentrations of nutrient cations (such as Ca^{++}, Mg^{++}, Na^+, and K^+)	Alfisol
• Thick, well-differentiated (A, Bt, and C horizons) profile, with subsurface (Bt) horizon appreciably enriched in clay (*argillic horizon*) and often red with sesquioxides or dark with humus, but also with evidence (such as lack of reaction with acid or abundant quartz or kaolinite) for low concentrations of nutrient cations	Ultisol
• Thick, well-differentiated (A, Bs, and C horizons), with sandy subsurface (Bs or Bh) horizon cemented with opaque iron or aluminum oxyhydrates or organic matter (*spodic horizon*), and always with little or no clay or carbonate	Spodosol
• Thick, well-differentiated to uniform profile, clayey texture, with subsurface horizons highly oxidized and red, and almost entirely depleted of weatherable minerals (*oxic horizon*)	Oxisol

Note: This key has been simplified for field observation. Precise identification of soils and their diagnostic horizons requires laboratory work and careful reference to Soil Survey Staff (1975).

TABLE 7. SIZE, ABUNDANCE, AND CONTRAST OF MOTTLES IN PALEOSOLS

Category	Class	Features
Contrast	Faint	Indistinct mottles or glaebules visible only on close examination: both mottles and matrix have closely related hues and chromas
	Distinct	Mottles are readily seen, with hue, value, and chroma different from that of surrounding matrix
	Prominent	Mottles are obvious and form one of the outstanding features of the horizon; their hue, value, and chroma differing from that of the matrix by as much as several Munsell color units
Abundance	Few	Mottles occupy less than 2% of the exposed surface
	Common	Mottles occupy about 2 to 20% of the exposed surface
	Many	Mottles occupy more than 20% of the exposed surface. This class can be subdivided according to whether (a) the mottles are set in a definite matrix, or (b) the sample is almost equally two or more kinds of mottle
Size	Fine	Mottles less than 5 mm diameter in greatest visible dimension
	Medium	Mottles between 5 and 15 mm in greatest dimension
	Coarse	Mottles greater than 15 mm in greatest dimension

Note: These terms are little modified from those of Soil Survey Staff (1975). They may also be used for describing pedotubules and glaebules.

TABLE 8. SUGGESTED FORMAT FOR DESCRIPTION OF PALEOSOL HORIZONS

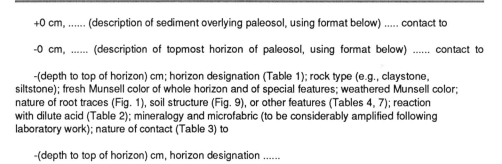

+0 cm, ... (description of sediment overlying paleosol, using format below) ..... contact to

-0 cm, ... (description of topmost horizon of paleosol, using format below) ...... contact to

-(depth to top of horizon) cm; horizon designation (Table 1); rock type (e.g., claystone, siltstone); fresh Munsell color of whole horizon and of special features; weathered Munsell color; nature of root traces (Fig. 1), soil structure (Fig. 9), or other features (Tables 4, 7); reaction with dilute acid (Table 2); mineralogy and microfabric (to be considerably amplified following laboratory work); nature of contact (Table 3) to

-(depth to top of horizon) cm, horizon designation ......

Note: Examples of this kind of description are given in Retallack (1983b). Usually they are published as a sentence fragments connected by colons and semicolons, but I find it best in the field to write longhand paragraphs on each horizon, discussing field interpretations and subsequent efforts to test them.

REFERENCES CITED

Alvin, K. L., 1971, *Weichselia reticulata* (Stokes et Webb) Fontaine, from the Wealden of Belgium: Institut Royal des Sciences Naturelles de Belgique Memoire, v. 33, no. 166, 33 p.

Andrews, H. N., 1947, Ancient plants and the world they lived in: Ithaca, New York, Comstock, 279 p.

Andrews, H. N., and Kern, E. M., 1947, The Idaho tempskyas and associated fossil plants: Missouri Botanical Garden Annals, v. 34, p. 119–186.

Arkley, R. J., 1963, Calculation of carbonate and water movement in soil from climatic data: Soil Science, v. 96, p. 239–248.

Basinger, J. F., 1981, The vegetative body of *Metasequoia milleri*, from the middle Eocene of southern British Columbia: Canadian Journal of Botany, v. 59, p. 2379–2410.

Beck, C. B., 1967, *Eddya sullivanensis* gen. et sp. nov.; A plant of gymnospermic morphology from the Upper Devonian of New York: Palaeontographica, v. B121, p. 1–22.

———, 1981, *Archaeopteris* and its role in vascular plant evolution, *in* Niklas, K. J., ed., Paleobotany, paleoecology and evolution: New York, Praeger, p. 193–230.

Birkeland, P. W., 1984, Soils and geomorphology: New York, Oxford University Press, 372 p.

Biswell, H. H., 1935, Effects of environment upon the root habits of certain deciduous forest trees: Botanical Gazette, v. 96, p. 676–708.

Boucot, A. J., Dewey, J. F., Dineley, D. L., Fletcher, R., Fyson, W. K., Griffin, J. G., Hickox, C. F., McKerrow, W. S., and Zeigler, A. M., 1974, The geology of the Arisaig area, Antigonish County, Nova Scotia: Geological Society of America Special Paper 139, 191 p.

Bown, T. M., 1982, Ichnofossils and rhizoliths of the nearshore Jebel Quatrani Formation (Oligocene), Fayum Province, Egypt: Palaeogeography, Palaeoclimatology, and Palaeoecology, v. 40, p. 255–309.

Brewer, R., 1976, Fabric and mineral analysis of soils: New York, Krieger, 482 p.

Buol, S. W., Hole, F. D., and McCracken, R. J., 1980, Soil genesis and classification: Ames, Iowa State University Press, 406 p.

Chapman, V. J., 1976, Mangrove vegetation: Vaduz, West Germany, Cramer, 447 p.

Cohen, A. S., 1982, Paleoenvironments of root casts from the Koobi Fora Formation, Kenya: Journal of Sedimentary Petrology, v. 52, p. 401–414.

Cridland, A. A., 1964, *Amyelon* in American coal balls: Palaeontology, v. 7, p. 186–209.

Duchafour, P., 1978, Ecological atlas of soils of the world (Mehnys, G. R., de Kimpe, C. R., and Martel, Y. A., transl.): New York, Masson, 178 p.

Eggert, D. A., 1962, The ontogeny of Carboniferous arborescent Sphenopsida: Palaeontographica, v. B110, p. 99–127.

Fitzpatrick, E. A., 1980, Soils: London, Longman, 353 p.

Gerasimov, I. P., 1971, Nature and originality of paleosols, *in* Yaalon, D. H., ed., Paleopedology—Origin, nature and dating of paleosols: Jerusalem, International Society for Soil Science and Israel University Press, p. 15–27.

Gile, L. H., Peterson, F. F., and Grossman, R. B., 1966, Morphologic and genetic sequences of carbonate accumulation in the desert soils: Soil Science, v. 101, p. 347–360.

Gould, R. E., 1975, A preliminary report on petrified axes of *Vertebraria* from the Permian of eastern Australia, *in* Campbell, K.S.W., ed., Gondwana geology: Canberra, Australian National University Press, p. 109–123.

Guthrie, R. L., and Witty, J. E., 1982, New designations for soil horizons and the new *Soil Survey Manual:* Soil Science Society of America Journal, v. 46, p. 443–444.

Heath, E., and Chinnock, R. J., 1974, Ferns and fern allies of New Zealand: Wellington, New Zealand, Reed, 48 p.

Huddleston, J. H., 1979, Soils of Oregon; Their classification, taxonomic relationships and physiography: Oregon State University Extension Service Special Report, v. 535, 121 p.

Jenik, J., 1978, Roots and root systems in tropical trees—Morphologic and ecologic aspects, *in* Tomlinson, P. B., and Zimmermann, M. H., eds., Tropi-

cal trees as living systems: Cambridge, England, Cambridge University Press, p. 323–349.

Jenny, H., 1941, Factors of soil formation: New York, McGraw-Hill, 281 p.

Kawase, M., and Whitmoyer, R. E., 1980, Aerenchyma development in waterlogged plants: American Journal of Botany, v. 67, p. 18–22.

Keller, W. D., and Fredericksen, A. F., 1952, Role of plants and colloidal acids in the mechanism of weathering: American Journal of Science, v. 250, p. 594–608.

Kidston, R., and Lang, W. H., 1917, On Old Red Sandstone plants showing structure from the Rhynie chert bed, Aberdeenshire. Pt. I: *Rhynia Gwynne-Vaughani*, Kidston and Lang: Royal Society of Edinburgh Transactions, v. 51, p. 761–784.

Knapp, B. J., 1979, Soil processes: London, Allen and Unwin, 73 p.

Krumbein, W. C., and Garrels, R. M., 1952, Origin and classificaiton of chemical sediments in terms of pH and oxidation-reduction potential: Journal of Geology, v. 60, p. 1–33.

Luttrell, G. W., Hubert, M. L., and Jussen, V. M., 1986, Lexicon of new formal geologic names of the United States 1976–1980: U.S. Geological Survey Bulletin, v. 1564, 191 p.

Machette, M. N., 1985, Calcic soils of the southwestern United States, *in* Weide, D. L., ed., Soils and Quaternary geology of the southwestern United States: Geological Society of America Special Paper 203, p. 1–21.

Morgan, J., 1959, The morphology and anatomy of American species of the genus *Psaronius:* Illinois Biological Monograph, v. 27, 108 p.

Morrison, R. B., 1976, Quaternary soil stratigraphy—Concepts, methods and problems, *in* Mahaney, W. C., ed., Quaternary soils: Norwich, England, Geoabstracts, p. 77–108.

Munsell Color, 1975, Munsell soil color charts: Baltimore, Maryland, Munsell Color, 24 p.

North American Commission on Stratigraphic Nomenclature, 1982, North American stratigraphic code: American Association of Petroleum Geologists Bulletin, v. 67, p. 841–875.

Nye, P. H., and Tinker, P. B., 1977, Solute movement in the soil-root system: Oxford, England, Blackwell, 324 p.

Olsen, R. A., Clark, R. B., and Bennett, J. H., 1981, The enhancement of soil fertility by plant roots: American Scientist, v. 69, p. 378–384.

Ortlam, D., 1971, Paleosols and their significance in stratigraphy and applied geology in the Permian and Triassic of southern Germany, *in* Yaalon, D. H., ed., Paleopedology—Origin, nature and dating of paleosols: Jerusalem, International Society for Soil Science and Israel University Press, p. 321–327.

Pavich, M. J., and Obermeier, S. F., 1985, Saprolite formation beneath Coastal Plain sediments near Washington, D.C.: Geological Society of America Bulletin, v. 76, p. 886–900.

Raven, P. H., Evert, R. F., and Curtis, H. A., 1981, Biology of plants: New York, Worth, 686 p.

Retallack, G. J., 1975, The life and times of a Triassic lycopod: Alcheringa, v. 1, p. 3–29.

———, 1976, Triassic palaeosols in the upper Narrabeen Group of New South Wales. Pt. I, Features of the palaeosols: Geological Society of Australia Journal, v. 23, p. 383–399.

———, 1977, Triassic palaeosols in the upper Narrabeen Group of New South Wales. Pt. II, Classification and reconstruction: Geological Society of Australia Journal, v. 24, p. 19–35.

———, 1983a, A paleopedological approach to the interpretation of terrestrial sedimentary rocks; The mid-Tertiary fossil soils of Badlands National Park, South Dakota: Geological Society of America Bulletin, v. 94, p. 823–840.

———, 1983b, Late Eocene and Oligocene paleosols from Badlands National Park, South Dakota: Geological Society of America Special Paper 193, 82 p.

———, 1984, Completeness of the rock and fossil record; Some estimates using fossil soils: Paleobiology, v. 10, p. 59–78.

———, 1985, Fossil soils as grounds for interpreting the advent of large plants and animals on land: Royal Society of London Philosophical Transactions, v. B309, p. 105–142.

Retallack, G. J., Grandstaff, G. E., and Kimberley, N. M., 1984, The promise and problems of Precambrian paleosols: Episodes, v. 7, p. 8–12.

Rothwell, G. W., 1975, The Callistophytaceae (Pteridospermopsida). I, Vegetative structures: Palaeontographica, v. B151, p. 171–196.

Ruhe, R. V., 1965, Quaternary paleopedology, *in* Wright, H. E., and Frey, D. G., eds., The Quaternary of the United States: Princeton, New Jersey, Princeton University Press, p. 755–764.

Rushforth, S. R., 1975, A flora from the Dakota Sandstone Formation (Cenomanian) near Westwater, Grand County, Utah: Brigham Young University Science Bulletin, Biological Series, v. 14, no. 13, 44 p.

Sahni, B., 1929, On *Clepsydropsis australia*, a zygopterid tree-fern with *Tempskya*-like false stem, from the Carboniferous rocks of Australia: Royal Society of London Philosophical Transactions, v. B217, p. 1–37.

—— , 1932, On the genera *Clepsydropsis* and *Cladoxylon* of Unger and on a new genus *Austroclepsis:* New Phytologist, v. 31, p. 270–278.

Sarjeant, W.A.S., 1975, Plant trace fossils, *in* Frey, R. W., ed., The study of trace fossils: New York, Springer, p. 163–179.

Scagel, R. F., Bandoni, R. J., Maze, J. R., Rouse, G. E., Schofield, W. B., and Stein, J. R., 1984, Plants; An evolutionary survey: Belmont, California, Wadsworth, 756 p.

Seilacher, A. 1964, Biogenic sedimentary structures, *in* Imbrie, J., and Newell, N., eds., Approaches to paleoecology: New York, Wiley, p. 296–315.

Selley, R. C., 1978, Ancient sedimentary environments: Ithaca, New York, Cornell University Press, 287 p.

Semeniuk, V., and Meagher, T. D., 1981, Calcrete in Quaternary coastal dunes in southwestern Australia—A capillary rise phenomenon associated with plant roots: Journal of Sedimentary Petrology, v. 51, p. 47–68.

Senior, B. R., and Mabbutt, J. A., 1979, A proposed method of defining deeply weathered rock units based on regional mapping in southeast Queensland: Geological Society of Australia Journal, v. 26, p. 237–254.

Seward, A. C., 1898, Fossil plants, v. I: Cambridge, England, Cambridge University Press, 452 p.

—— , 1910, Fossil plants, v. II: Cambridge, England, Cambridge University Press, 624 p.

Soil Survey Staff, 1951, Soil survey manual: U.S. Department of Agriculture Handbook 18, Washington, D.C., Government Printing Office, 503 p.

—— , 1962, Supplement to USDA Handbook 18, Soil Survey Manual: Washington, D.C., Government Printing Office, replacing p. 173–188.

—— , 1975, Soil taxonomy: U.S. Department of Agriculture Handbook 436, Washington, D.C., Government Printing Office, 754 p.

Stace, H.C.T., Hubble, G. D., Brewer, R., Northcote, K. H., Sleeman, J. R., Mulcahy, M. J., and Hallworth, E. G., 1968, A handbook of Australian soils: Adelaide, Australia, Rellim, 435 p.

Steel, R. J., 1974, Cornstone (fossil caliche)—Its origin, stratigraphic and sedimentologic importance in the New Red Sandstone, Scotland: Journal of Geology, v. 82, p. 351–369.

Stewart, W. N., 1947, A comparative study of stigmarian appendages and *Isoetes* roots: American Journal of Botany, v. 34, p. 315–324.

Walker, T. R., 1967, Formation of red beds in modern and ancient deserts: Geological Society of America Bulletin, v. 78, p. 353–368.

Van Donselaar-ten Bokkel Huinink, W.A.E., 1966, Structure, root systems and periodicity of savanna plants and vegetation in northern Surinam: Amsterdam, New Holland, 162 p.

Weaver, J. E., 1919, The ecological relations of roots: Carnegie Institution of Washington Publication, v. 286, 128 p.

—— , 1920, Root development in the grassland formation: Carnegie Institution of Washington Publication, v. 292, 151 p.

—— , 1968, Prairie plants and their environments: Lincoln, University of Nebraska Press, 276 p.

Whybrow, P. J., and McClure, H. H., 1981, Fossil mangrove roots and paleoenvironments of the Miocene of the eastern Arabian peninsulas: Palaeogeography, Palaeoclimatology, and Palaeoecology, v. 32, p. 213–225.

MANUSCRIPT ACCEPTED BY THE SOCIETY JULY 1, 1987

Geological Society of America
Special Paper 216
1988

Paleosols and the evolution of the atmosphere; Part II

Joseph P. Pinto
Ames Research Center
Moffett Field, California 94035

Heinrich D. Holland
Department of Earth and Planetary Sciences
Harvard University
Cambridge, Massachusetts 02138

ABSTRACT

Coupled, one-dimensional transport equations for CO_2 and O_2 in pre-Middle Ordovician soils have been developed. The value of the ratio $\Delta P_{O_2}/\Delta P_{CO_2}$, where ΔP_{O_2} is the difference between the O_2 pressure in the atmosphere and at any level in a particular soil profile, and where ΔP_{CO_2} is the difference between the CO_2 pressure in the atmosphere and at the same level in the same soil profile, depends on the relative importance of O_2 and CO_2 transport by diffusion and transport by advection in soils.

The transport equations were solved in closed form for a particularly simple soil model. Numerical solutions were obtained for more complex soil profiles, and the sensitivity of the P_{O_2} profile in soils to changes in a variety of parameters was explored. The results indicate that free oxygen has been present in the atmosphere at least since early Proterozoic time. The range of atmospheric oxygen pressure permitted by the available paleosol data is large. Our currently preferred range of the oxygen pressure in the atmosphere between ca. 2.5 and 1.8 Ga is between 5×10^{-4} and 1×10^{-3} atm.

INTRODUCTION

In a previous paper, which is referred to herein as Part I (Holland and Zbinden, 1987), criteria for identifying paleosols were explored, and methods for reconstructing the nature of paleosols prior to diagenesis were outlined. The relationship between the composition of the atmosphere at the time of soil formation and the behavior of iron and manganese during weathering, when the gradient of the O_2 and CO_2 content in soil air is constant was also explored. This is a rather special case. In this chapter we treat the problem of the O_2 and CO_2 distribution in pre-Middle Ordovician soils much more generally. The basic differential equations are well known. In a few cases they can be solved in closed form. We solve these, and then describe the results of computer runs, in which we define the distribution of O_2 and CO_2 in more complicated model soils. The results are compared with those of Part I, and are applied to the interpretation of the chemical composition of known and inferred paleosols that developed before the advent of higher land plants during the Ordovician period (Gray, 1985).

CONTROLLING EQUATIONS FOR O_2 AND CO_2 PROFILES IN SOILS

In present-day soils, the distribution of O_2 and CO_2 is strongly influenced by the presence of plants. O_2 is consumed, and CO_2 is released by plant decay in such large quantities that biological processes dominate the concentration and the fluxes of these gases in soils. Prior to the development of vascular land plants, the magnitude of biologic fluxes must have been much smaller, perhaps negligible compared to the magnitude of inorganic fluxes of O_2 and CO_2. In the present analysis we first assume that soil biology can be neglected; we then assess the possible influence of soil biology on the results of our analysis.

Figure 1 shows a small volume element in a soil profile. Oxidants, reductants, and weathering acids are supplied to this volume element by vertical diffusion through the soil pores and by advection as constituents of soil water. Reactions occur within the soil volume, so that the flux of these constituents out of the volume differs from the influx. Horizontal fluxes are set equal to zero, a condition that is only realistic for soils developed in areas

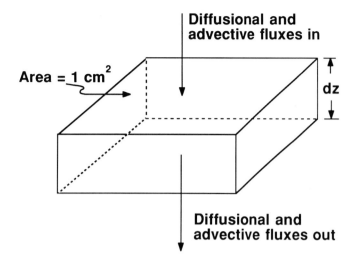

Figure 1. Small soil element within which CO_2 and O_2 are lost by weathering reactions.

of low relief. The concentration of a mobile constituent, i, is described by a one-dimensional diffusion-advection equation with a reaction term. The difference between the diffusive flux into and out of the soil volume of a constituent i, is

$$-D_i(z)\frac{\partial P_i}{\partial z} \times \frac{3.1 \times 10^7 \text{ sec/yr}}{2.2 \times 10^4 \text{ cc/mol at STP}} \times dz \text{ mol/yr,} \quad (1)$$

if the cross sectional area is 1 cm². The units of $D_i(z)$ are cm²/sec, and the pressue P_i is in atmospheres. $D_i(z)$ includes a factor determined by the soil porosity.

The difference between the advective flux of a constituent i into the soil volume and the advective flux out is given by the expression

$$-r\left(\frac{\partial m_i}{\partial z}\right) dz \quad \text{mol/yr,} \quad (2)$$

where r is the velocity of soil water in liters per year, which passes through the soil volume, and where m_i is the concentration of component i in the soil water. The concentration of many of the important reactants can be related to their partial pressure in soil air, P_i, via their Henry's Law constant B_i

$$m_i = B_i P_i \quad (3)$$

The advective flux of such a component *i* can therefore be written in the form

$$-rB_i\left(\frac{\partial P_i}{\partial z}\right) dz. \quad (4)$$

The loss of any constituent i by reaction in the soil volume is normally a complicated function of the concentration of this constituent, the concentration of the other constituents of the soil

air and soil water, and the nature of the soil. The reactive flux can be given by the expression

$$-k_i f(P_i) dz, \quad (5)$$

where the parameter k_i is a complicated function of the state of the system. The three terms can be combined to yield the equation

$$1.4 \times 10^3 \frac{\partial}{\partial z}[D_i(z)\frac{\partial P_i}{\partial z}] - r B_i(\frac{\partial P_i}{\partial z}) - k_i f(P_i) = \frac{\partial M_i}{\partial t} \quad (6)$$

where M_i is the number of moles of component i per cm³ in the soil atmosphere and water. It can be shown that the magnitude of the term $\partial M_i/\partial t$ in most soils is very small compared to the magnitude of the terms on the left side of the equation. Hence equation 6 can be reduced without serious loss of precision to the steady-state form:

$$1.4 \times 10^3 \frac{\partial}{\partial z}[D_i(z)\frac{\partial P_i}{\partial z}] - r B_i \frac{\partial P_i}{\partial z} - k_i f(P_i) = 0. \quad (7)$$

In general, this equation cannot be solved in closed form, since D_i and k_i are normally strong functions of depth in soils. Profiles of the partial pressure of gases in soils must therefore be computed numerically, except in soils where D_i is constant, and where the use term $k_i f(P_i)$ is a simple function of P_i and z.

The behavior of iron and manganese in soils where biological processes are unimportant depends on the availability of oxidants in the soil profile. When oxidants are available in sufficient quantity throughout a soil profile, these elements tend to be oxidized and retained as oxides and/or hydroxides. When all of the oxidants supplied from the atmosphere are exhausted within a soil profile, iron and manganese tend to be mobile, to move downward with soil water, and to be either lost completely from the soil or to be reprecipitated below the water table as compounds of Fe^{+2} and Mn^{+2} (see, for instance, Holland, 1984, Ch. 7, and Part I).

The loss of oxidants in soils is coupled to the loss of weathering acids, since silicate minerals have to dissolve before their contained Fe^{+2} and Mn^{+2} can be oxidized (see Part I). CO_2 is the dominant weathering acid today, and has apparently played this role during most, if not all, of geologic time. Acids are generated by photochemical processes in the atmosphere (Kasting and others, 1985) but in concentrations that are small compared to the probable concentration of CO_2 in Precambrian rain water. The flux of weathering acids is therefore given reasonably precisely by equation (7) when component i is CO_2.

Today, the dominant oxidant is molecular oxygen. In low-O_2 atmospheres the concentration of photochemically produced oxidants and reductants in rain water is apt to be equal to or greater than that of molecular oxygen (Kasting and others, 1985). H_2O_2 is the most important of the oxidants, and H_2CO is probably the most important reductant produced by photochemical reactions in the atmosphere. The oxidative capacity of rain water is therefore approximately equal to

$$(m_{O_2} + \frac{1}{2} m_{H_2O_2} - m_{H_2CO}). \tag{8}$$

The factor $1/2$ precedes $m_{H_2O_2}$, because the oxidative capacity of one mole of H_2O_2 is only that of $1/2$ mole of O_2:

$$H_2O_2 \rightleftharpoons H_2O + 1/2\ O_2. \tag{9}$$

The rate of oxidant use in soils is related to the rate of acid use via the value of the ratio R, the ratio of the oxidant demand to the acid demand during the weathering of a parent rock. The calculation of R values and the variations of the effective value of R during the evolution of soil profiles have been discussed previously (Holland, 1984, Ch. 7, and Part I). When oxidants are present in soil water, their rate of use in the small volume of Figure 1 is:

$$R\ k_{CO_2}\ f(P_{CO_2})\ dz, \tag{10}$$

where the value of R is the effective value of this parameter in the small volume. When oxygen is the only oxidant, it follows that this is the rate of loss of O_2 within the volume. When the concentrations of H_2O_2 and H_2CO are nonneglible,

$$R\ k_{CO_2}\ f(P_{CO_2}) = \frac{dm_{O_2}}{dt} + \frac{1}{2}\frac{dm_{H_2O_2}}{dt} - \frac{dm_{H_2CO}}{dt}, \tag{11}$$

where m refers to the number of moles of O_2, H_2O_2, and H_2CO, respectively, per cm^3 of soil. If the rate of use of H_2O_2 and H_2CO is proportional to that of O_2, we can write:

$$R\ k_{CO_2}\ f(P_{CO_2}) = \frac{dm_{O_2}}{dt}(1 + \xi), \tag{12}$$

where

$$\xi = \frac{\frac{1}{2}\frac{dm_{H_2O_2}}{dt} - \frac{dm_{H_2CO}}{dt}}{\frac{dm_{O_2}}{dt}} = constant. \tag{13}$$

The rate of O_2 use then becomes:

$$\frac{dm_{O_2}}{dt} = \frac{R}{(1 + \xi)} k_{CO_2}\ f(P_{CO_2}). \tag{14}$$

The value of ξ can be either positive or negative.

Since the rate of O_2 use in soils is coupled to the rate of CO_2 use, the relationship between the O_2 and CO_2 profiles can be predicted. The equations that govern the profiles of the two gases are

$$1.4 \times 10^3 \frac{\partial}{\partial z}[D_{CO_2}\frac{\partial P_{CO_2}}{\partial z}] - r\ B_{CO_2}\frac{\partial P_{CO_2}}{\partial z} - k_{CO_2}\ f(P_{CO_2}) = 0 \tag{15}$$

and

$$1.4\ 10^3 \frac{\partial}{\partial z}[D_{O_2}\frac{\partial P_{O_2}}{\partial z}] - r\ B_{O_2}\frac{\partial P_{O_2}}{\partial z} - \frac{R}{(1 + \xi)} k_{CO_2}\ f(P_{CO_2}) = 0, \tag{16}$$

respectively. Consider first a soil in which the diffusive flux supplies most of the O_2 and CO_2 used in weathering reactions.

The second term in both equations can then be set equal to zero. If equations 15 and 16 are rearranged, and equation 15 is divided by equation 16, we obtain

$$\frac{\partial}{\partial z}[D_{CO_2}\frac{\partial P_{CO_2}}{\partial z}] = \frac{(1 + \xi)}{R}\frac{\partial}{\partial z}[D_{O_2}\frac{\partial P_{O_2}}{\partial z}]. \tag{17}$$

The ratio of D_{CO_2} to D_{O_2} is very close to unity in soils, and $\xi \ll 1$ when the supply of oxidants in solution is very small compared to the supply of O_2 by diffusion. Hence, for constant R, D_{CO_2}, and D_{O_2}

$$D_{CO_2}\frac{\partial^2 P_{CO_2}}{\partial z^2} = \frac{D_{O_2}}{R}\frac{\partial^2 P_{O_2}}{\partial z^2} \tag{18}$$

on double integration with respect to z from 0 to z, we obtain

$$D_{CO_2}\left[(P_{CO_2})_z - (P^o_{CO_2}) - (\frac{\partial P_{CO_2}}{\partial z})_o\ z \right]$$

$$= \frac{D_{O_2}}{R}\left[(P_{O_2})_z - (P^o_{O_2}) - \frac{\partial P_{O_2}}{\partial z})_o\ z \right], \tag{19}$$

where $P^o_{O_2}$ and $P^o_{CO_2}$ are the partial pressures of O_2 and CO_2 in the atmosphere, and where $(P_{O_2})_z$ and $(P_{CO_2})_z$ are the partial pressures of these gases in the soil atmosphere. The term $D_{CO_2} \times (\partial P_{CO_2}/\partial z)_o$ represents the diffusive flux of CO_2 across the soil-atmosphere boundary. The term $D_{O_2}(\partial P_{O_2}/\partial z)_o$ represents the diffusive flux of O_2 across this boundary. Both gases are used in weathering reactions within the soil. At constant R, the ratio of the rate of O_2 use to the rate of CO_2 use in these reactions is equal to R. Hence, at steady state

$$D_{CO_2}\left(\frac{\partial P_{CO_2}}{\partial z} \right)_o = \frac{D_{O_2}}{R}\left(\frac{\partial P_{O_2}}{\partial z} \right)_o, \tag{20}$$

as long as O_2 is not exhausted within a soil profile. If O_2 is exhausted within the soil profile, then for the soil as a whole

$$D_{CO_2}\left(\frac{\partial P_{CO_2}}{\partial z} \right)_o > \frac{D_{O_2}}{R}\left(\frac{\partial P_{O_2}}{\partial z} \right)_o. \tag{21}$$

When O_2 is present in sufficient quantities, equation (19) reduces to the form:

$$\Delta P_{O_2} = P^o_{O_2} - (P_{O_2})_z = R\ [P^o_{CO_2} - (P_{CO_2})_z]. \tag{22}$$

Consider next a soil in which the advective flux of oxidants and weathering acids is much greater than the diffusive flux. In this case, the first term in equations 15 and 16 can be dropped. If we again rearrange and divide equation 16 into equation 15, we obtain

$$\left(\frac{\partial P_{O_2}}{\partial z} \right) = \frac{R}{(1 + \xi)}\frac{B_{CO_2}}{B_{O_2}}\left(\frac{\partial P_{CO_2}}{\partial z} \right). \tag{23}$$

Upon integration this becomes

$$\Delta P_{O_2} = P^o_{O_2} - (P_{O_2})_z = \frac{R}{(1+\xi)} \frac{B_{CO_2}}{B_{O_2}} [P^o_{CO_2} - (P_{CO_2})_z]. \qquad (24)$$

The ratio B_{CO_2}/B_{O_2} is a weak function of temperature, and has a value close to 30 between 0° and 30°C (Holland, 1984, Ch. 7).

Oxidants and weathering acids are supplied to soils in part by diffusion and in part by advection. The ratio of the O_2 gradient to the CO_2 gradient within pre-Middle Ordovician soils in which O_2 is not exhausted, tends to be limited by its value in equations (22) and (24). Hence

$$\frac{R}{(1+\xi)} \frac{B_{CO_2}}{B_{O_2}} \geq \frac{\Delta P_{O2}}{\Delta P_{CO2}} \geq R. \qquad (25)$$

Iron and manganese are apt to be lost from soils when P_{O_2} in soils falls below certain low values P'_{O_2} (see below). An interesting boundary is therefore set by the condition that $P_{O_2} = P'_{O_2}$ at the water table. Under these conditions,

$$P^o_{O_2} - P'_{O_2} = A(P^o_{CO_2} - P^L_{CO_2}), \qquad (26)$$

where $P^L_{CO_2}$ is the CO_2 pressure in soil air at the water table, and where

$$\frac{R}{(1+\xi)} \frac{B_{CO2}}{B_{O2}} \geq A \geq R. \qquad (27)$$

COMPUTATION OF O_2 AND CO_2 PROFILES

Equations 15 and 16 can be solved in closed form for certain very simple cases. If, for instance, D_{CO_2} and k_{CO_2} in these equations are independent of depth in a soil, and if $f(P_{CO_2}) = P_{CO_2}$, equation 15 becomes

$$1.4 \times 10^3 D_{CO_2} \frac{\partial^2 P_{CO_2}}{\partial z^2} - r B_{CO_2} \frac{\partial P_{CO_2}}{\partial z} - k_{CO_2} P_{CO_2} = 0. \qquad (28)$$

The solution of this equation when P_{CO_2} approaches zero as z approaches infinity is

$$(P_{CO_2})_z = P^o_{CO_2} e^{-bz}, \qquad (29)$$

where

$$b = \frac{-r B_{CO_2} + \sqrt{r^2 B^2_{CO_2} + 5.6 \times 10^3 k_{CO_2} D_{CO_2}}}{2.8 \times 10^3 D_{CO_2}}. \qquad (30)$$

In general, P_{CO_2} does not go to zero as z approaches infinity, since at equilibrium with all common rock types, P_{CO_2} will be substantially greater than zero when $P^o_{CO_2} \geq$ the present-day value. If we let the equilibrium value of P_{CO_2} be $P^\infty_{CO_2}$, and if the rate of reaction is proportional to the difference $(P_{CO_2} - P^\infty_{CO_2})$, then equation (28) becomes

$$1.4 \times 10^3 D_{CO_2} \frac{\partial^2 P_{CO_2}}{\partial z^2} - r B_{CO_2} \frac{\partial P_{CO_2}}{\partial z} - k_{CO_2} (P_{CO_2} - P^\infty_{CO_2}) = 0, \qquad (31)$$

and its solution becomes

$$P_{CO_2} = (P^o_{CO_2} - P^\infty_{CO_2}) e^{-bz} + P^\infty_{CO_2}. \qquad (32)$$

In areas where a reasonably thick soil is present, most of the CO_2 loss takes place above the water table. Thus, where the depth to water table is 10 m, the value of P_{CO_2} at this level, $(P_{CO_2})_{10m}$, is nearly the same as $P^\infty_{CO_2}$. The possible range of the parameter b is very wide, but values can be proposed that are probably close to that for an average soil. The average rainfall today is about 100 cm^3/cm^2yr. This is probably not very different from rainfall on the pre-Middle Ordovician Earth. If half the rainfall penetrated into soils, the value of r was 50×10^{-3} ℓ/yr. The Henry's Law constant for CO_2 is 0.04 at 20°C. The diffusion constant of CO_2 in soils is highly variable (see Part I). In air, D_{CO_2} between 0° and 50°C is (0.17 ± 0.03) cm^2/sec. In water-saturated soils, D_{CO_2} is about 2×10^{-6} cm^2/sec, i.e., close to the diffusion constant of CO_2 in liquid water. In many soils the value of D_{CO_2} is about 2×10^{-2} cm^2/sec above the water table (Taylor, 1949; Lai and others, 1976; Richter and Grossgebauer, 1978; De Jong and others, 1983), and this value is adopted here.

The value of k_{CO_2} can be computed in a somewhat roundabout fashion. In many areas the HCO_3^- concentration in ground waters is about 2×10^{-3} mol/ℓ. This is generated largely by the neutralization of carbonic acid. If the penetration rate of water is 50 cm^3/cm^2yr, the annual CO_2 use rate is

$$2 \times 10^{-3} \frac{mol}{\ell} \times 0.050 \frac{\ell}{cm^2yr} = 1 \times 10^{-4} \frac{mol}{cm^2yr}. \qquad (33)$$

If the soil thickness in which most of the reaction takes place is 10 m, then the rate of CO_2 neutralization is 1×10^{-7} mol/cm^3yr. The CO_2 pressure in many soils is about 1×10^{-2} atm. Thus

$$k_{CO_2} \approx \frac{1 \times 10^{-7} \text{ mol/}cm^3yr}{1 \times 10^{-2} \text{ atm}} = 1 \times 10^{-5} \frac{mol}{cm^3yr \text{ atm}}. \qquad (34)$$

It should be emphasized that this is a reasonable value for k_{CO_2}, but that the actual value of k_{CO_2} must vary considerably from soil to soil, as well as with depth within any particular soil.

For our model soil,

$$b = 5.5 \times 10^{-4} cm^{-1}.$$

The CO_2 pressure in a soil that obeys equation (29) decreases exponentially with depth; at a depth of 10 m, P_{CO_2} in the model soil has therefore fallen to about 60 percent of the CO_2 pressure in the ambient atmosphere.

The rate of O_2 use is coupled to the rate of CO_2 use. Equation 16 in the simplified soil model therefore becomes

$$1.4 \times 10^3 D_{O_2} \frac{\partial^2 P_{O_2}}{\partial z^2} - r B_{O_2} \frac{\partial P_{O_2}}{\partial z} - \frac{R}{(1+\xi)} k_{CO_2} P_{CO_2} = 0. \qquad (35)$$

This equation can be solved in closed form. The solution is:

$$P_{O_2} = \alpha\, e^{-bz} + \beta\, e^{r\,B_{O_2}\,z/1.4 \times 10^3 D_{O_2}} \qquad (36)$$

where

$$\alpha = \frac{\dfrac{R}{(1+\xi)}\, k_{CO_2}\, P^o_{CO_2}}{1.4 \times 10^3\, D_{O_2}\, b^2 + r\, B_{O_2}\, b} \qquad (37)$$

and

$$\beta = P^o_{O_2} - \frac{\dfrac{R}{(1+\xi)}\, k_{CO_2}\, P^o_{CO_2}}{1.4 \times 10^3\, D_{O_2}\, b^2 + r\, B_{O_2}\, b} \qquad (38)$$

The second term on the right side of equation (36) is zero, since P_{O_2} does not go to infinity as z approaches infinity. Physically, this is true, because O_2 that is added to soils advectively and that is not used in oxidation reactions passes out of soils as a dissolved constituent of ground waters, and ultimately reappears at the Earth's surface.

If D_{O_2} is set equal to D_{CO_2} in the calculation above, and if ξ is set equal to zero, the value of α becomes 5×10^{-4}. It can be shown that the solution of equation 36 then reduces to the form

$$P_{O_2} \approx P^o_{O_2} - 5 \times 10^{-4}\,(1 - e^{-bz}). \qquad (39)$$

At a depth of 10 m,

$$P_{O_2} \approx P^o_{O_2} - 5 \times 10^{-4}\,(1 - 0.6)\ \text{atm} \approx P^o_{O_2} - 2 \times 10^{-4}\ \text{atm}. \qquad (40)$$

If the oxygen pressure in the atmosphere is 2×10^{-4} atm, then P_{O_2} at 10 m is just zero.

The value of the ratio $\Delta P_{O_2}/\Delta P_{CO_2}$ in this soil is

$$\frac{\Delta P_{O_2}}{\Delta P_{CO_2}} = \frac{2 \times 10^{-4}}{0.4 \times 10^{-2}} = 0.050. \qquad (41)$$

This value is only slightly greater than 0.045, the R value of many basaltic rocks. Diffusional transport of O_2 and CO_2 is therefore much more important than advective transport in this soil. The same relationship seems to prevail in many soils (see Part I).

Although the above calculations are instructive, they are not particularly satisfactory, because unrealistic assumptions were required to permit the integration of equations 15 and 16 in closed form. It is unlikely, for instance, that R, D_{O_2}, and D_{CO_2} are independent of depth in soils, and that the rates of oxidant and acid demand are simple functions of P_{CO_2}. We have therefore obtained numerical solutions of equation 7, the one-dimensional equation of continuity, to define P_{O_2} profiles of soils in which the diffusivity of gases and the rate of cation release change with depth.

For each model soil, oxygen profiles were calculated iteratively for a range of values of atmospheric oxygen pressures to determine at which value of $P^o_{O_2}$ the oxygen content of soil air just goes to zero at the base of the soil profile. Typically, on the order of 30 iterations were required until a given O_2 profile converged to better than 1 part in 10^6. The equations were solved

with a zero flux lower boundary condition; this differs from the lower boundary condition used above in deriving closed solutions for equations 15 and 16.

The value of the parameters used in solving the continuity equations are listed in Table 1. In our standard case (case 1), the diffusivity of oxygen in the upper 5 m of soil was set equal to 1.6 $\times 10^{-2}$ cm^2/sec, the nominal value used in Part I. Between 5 and 10 m, the value of D_{O_2} was allowed to decrease exponentially with depth of 1.6×10^{-6} cm^2/sec, a value appropriate for water-logged soils. In several other cases (2 through 5, 8 through 10), the D_{O_2} profile was chosen to be identical to that in the standard case. In the model soil of Run #6, the value taken for D_{O_2} at the surface was one-tenth that of the standard case; in Run #7, the value chosen for D_{O_2} at the surface was six times higher than in the standard case.

The infiltration rate of rainwater was taken to be 50 cm/yr for the standard case as well as for most of the other runs. In a few cases an infiltration rate of 100 cm/yr was used. Two sets of figures were used for the flux of photochemical products from the atmosphere. In the standard case, and in most of the other soil models we considered, the concentration of photochemical products in rain water was assumed to be equal to that calculated by Kasting and others (1985) for each particular value of $P^o_{O_2}$. In a few cases the net concentration of photochemical oxidants was set equal to zero. We assumed that the photochemical products did not react until they reached a depth of 4 m in the soil. They were then supplied uniformly with depth between 4 m and the base of the profile.

The O_2 demand and its variation with depth were set equal to the R value of the parent rock times the CO_2 demand. This is reasonable, as long as Fe^{+2} released by carbonic acid attack is oxidized within the soil profile (see below). For cases 1 through 10, the value of R was taken to be 0.045—a value close to that of the Hekpoort Basalt (2.2 Ga; South Africa) and many other basaltic rocks. For cases 11 through 16, the value of R was taken to be 0.01, which is typical of granites.

Several sets of depth variations were used for the CO_2 demand of our model soils. In the standard case, the CO_2 demand was taken to be constant throughout the soil, and this pattern was used in several of the other cases. In some model soils a step function was used for the CO_2 demand. In others, the CO_2 demand increased linearly with depth, and in still others the CO_2 demand increased exponentially with depth.

For each of the model soils described in Table 1, O_2 profiles were calculated for a wide range of atmospheric oxygen pressures. At the base of each soil profile, oxygen was observed to be present in soil air when $P^o_{O_2}$ was greater than a certain minimum value. The $P^o_{O_2}$ (min) values for the 16 model soils are listed in the last column of Table 1. The pressures vary a good deal from case to case, and reflect the differences in the values of the parameters that were chosen for the model soils. When the oxygen pressure in the atmosphere above a model soil is less than $P^o_{O_2}$ (min), O_2 is completely consumed above the base of the soil profile. Below the soil depth where O_2 is exhausted, Fe^{+2} will not

TABLE 1. INPUT PARAMETERS AND VALUES OF $P_{O_2}^o$ (min) FOR MODEL SOILS DEVELOPED ON BASALTS AND GRANITES

Case No.	D_{O_2} (cm²/sec) (z in cm)	Infiltration Rate (cm/yr)	Photochemical Inputs	CO_2 Demand (mol/cc yr)	O_2 Demand (mol/cc yr)	$P_{O_2}^o$ (min) (atm)
A. Values for Soils Developed on Basalts (R = 0.045)						
1	0-5 m: 1.6×10^{-2}; 5-10 m: $1.6 \times 10^{-2} e^{-(z-500)/54.5}$	50	K.H.P.*	3.1×10^{-8}	1.4×10^{-9}	2.0×10^{-3}
2	"	"	0	"	"	2.4×10^{-3}
3	"	100	K.H.P.*	0-4 m: 5.5×10^{-9}; 4-10 m: 5.5×10^{-8}	0-4 m: 2.5×10^{-10}; 4-10 m: 2.5×10^{-9}	1.2×10^{-3}
4	"	50	"	3.1×10^{-7}	1.4×10^{-8}	3.0×10^{-3}
5	0-5 m: 1.6×10^{-3}; 5-10 m: $1.6 \times 10^{-3} e^{-(z-500)/72}$	"	"	3.1×10^{-8}	1.4×10^{-9}	3.0×10^{-2}
6	"	"	"	"	"	3.4×10^{-3}
7	0-5 m: 0.10; 5-10 m: $0.10 \, e^{-(z-500)/45}$	"	"	$6.2 \times 10^{-11} z$	$2.8 \times 10^{-12} z$	1.2×10^{-3}
8	0-5 m: 1.6×10^{-2}; 5-10 m: $1.6 \times 10^{-2} e^{-(z-500)/54.5}$	"	"	"	"	3.4×10^{-3}
9	"	"	"	$8.6 \times 10^{-8} e^{2.303 \times 10^{-3}(z-1000)}$	$3.6 \times 10^{-9} e^{2.303 \times 10^{-3}(z-1000)}$	4.0×10^{-3}
10	"	"	"	$2.2 \times 10^{-7} e^{6.91 \times 10^{-3}(z-1000)}$	$9.9 \times 10^{-9} e^{6.91 \times 10^{-3}(z-1000)}$	1.1×10^{-2}
B. Values for Soils Developed on Granites (R = 0.01)						
11	0-5 m: 1.6×10^{-2}; 5-10 m: $1.6 \times 10^{-2} e^{-(z-500)/54.5}$	50	K.H.P.*	3.1×10^{-8}	3.1×10^{-10}	1.1×10^{-4}
12	"	"	0	"	"	5.4×10^{-4}
13	"	100	K.H.P.*	"	"	3.4×10^{-5}
14	"	50	"	3.1×10^{-7}	3.1×10^{-9}	3.4×10^{-3}
15	0-5 m: 1.6×10^{-3}; 5-10 m: $1.6 \times 10^{-3} e^{-(z-500)/72}$	"	"	3.1×10^{-8}	3.1×10^{-10}	4.0×10^{-4}
16	0-5 m: 0.10; 5-10 m: $0.10 \, e^{-(z-500)/45}$	"	"	"	"	1.1×10^{-4}

*K.H.P.: Total photochemical inputs as computed by Kasting and others (1985); they were supplied uniformly between 4 and 10 m.

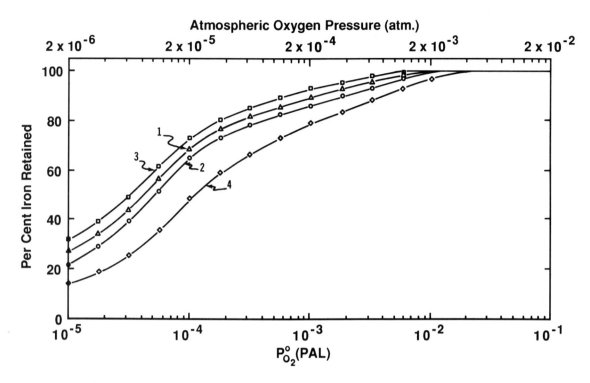

Figure 2. Relationship between the O_2 content of the atmosphere and the percentage of iron retained in model soils through 4.

be oxidized, and generally moves downward in solution as a constituent of soil water. The fraction of Fe^{+2} retained is the ratio of the quantity of Fe^{+2} oxidized to the total quantity of Fe^{+2} released by acid attack. This parameter is plotted in Figures 2 through 5 for all 16 model soils. When $P^o_{O_2} > P_{O_2}$ (min), 100 percent of the released Fe^{+2} is retained if the kinetics of Fe^{+2} oxidation are sufficiently rapid. The percentage that is retained decreases quite rapidly as $P^o_{O_2}$ drops below the value of $P^o_{O_2}$ (min) of each model soil. The value of $P^o_{O_2}$ (min) for each of the model soils is plotted in Figure 6.

The CO_2 demand in the standard soil model was chosen, so that the HCO_3^- content in soil water at the base of this profile was 1 m mol/ℓ, i.e., equal to that of average river water today. The value of $P^o_{O_2}$ (min) for this case was 2.0×10^{-3} atm. In soil model 2 we assumed that the net contribution of photochemical oxidants was zero. The value of $P^o_{O_2}$ (min) was therefore higher than for case 1, but only marginally so. In case 3, all of the soil parameters had the same value as in case 1, but the infiltration rate of rainwater was chosen to be 100 cm/yr. The value of P_{O_2} (min) dropped from 2.0×10^{-3} atm, since the influx of O_2 and photochemical oxidants was significantly greater at the more rapid infiltration rate chosen for case 3. In case 4 the demand for CO_2 and O_2 was set 10 times higher (between a depth of 4 and 10 m) than between 0 and 4 m. The average demand for these gases was the same as in the first three cases. The value of $P^o_{O_2}$

(min) was found to be somewhat higher than for case 1, since so much of the O_2 demand was now in the lower part of the soil profile.

Case 5 was identical to the standard case, but the CO_2 and O_2 demand was an order of magnitude greater. Understandably, the minimum value of $P^o_{O_2}$ for case 5 was somewhat more than an order of magnitude greater than that for case 1. Case 6 explored the effect of reducing the gas diffusivity, and case 7 the effect of increasing the gas diffusivity with respect to the standard case. The decrease in $P^o_{O_2}$ increased P_{O_2} (min) by a factor of 1.7. The increase in D_{O_2} reduced $P^o_{O_2}$ (min) by a factor of 0.6.

Cases 8, 9, and 10 explored the effect of increasing the CO_2 and O_2 demand with depth. In all three cases the demand for the soil profile as a whole was the same as in the standard case, and in all three cases the value of $P^o_{O_2}$ (min) was greater than that for the standard case. $P^o_{O_2}$ (min) increased progressively with increasing O_2 demand in the lower part of the soil profiles.

These computations show that the minimum value of $P^o_{O_2}$ required to retain all of the Fe^{+2} released during weathering 10 m thick soils developed on basalts and described by the rather wide range of parameters used in cases 1 through 4 and 6 through 10 is between 1×10^{-3} and 1×10^{-2} atm. It is likely that the range of parameters used in our computations includes those of the Hekpoort paleosol (see Part I) and other thick Proterozoic soils developed on basalts. If this is correct, the value of $P^o_{O_2}$ at

Pinto and Holland

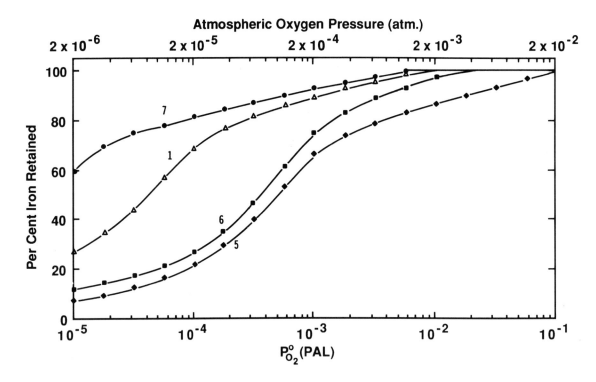

Figure 3. Relationship between the O_2 content of the atmosphere and the percentage of iron retained in model soils 5 through 7.

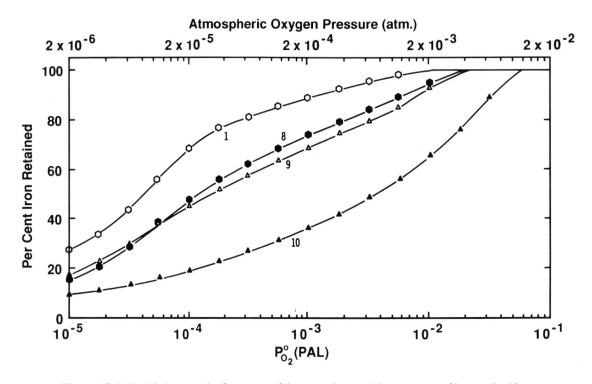

Figure 4. Relationship between the O_2 content of the atmosphere and the percentage of iron retained in model soils 1, 8, 9, and 10.

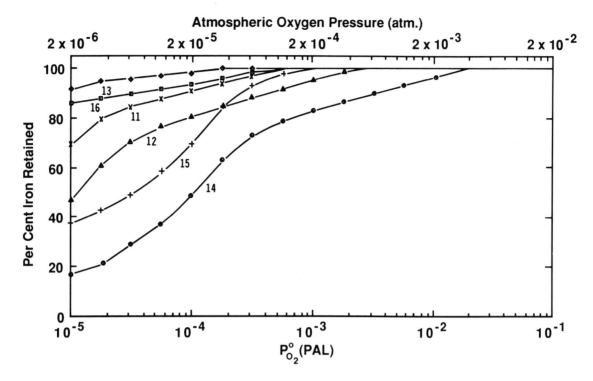

Figure 5. Relationship between the O_2 content of the atmosphere and the percentage of iron retained in model soils 11 through 16.

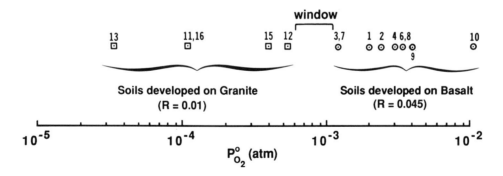

Figure 6. Value of the minimum oxygen pressure in the atmosphere P_{O_2} (min), required for the retention of all of the iron released during weathering in the model soils of Table 1 for which the integrated CO_2 demand is 3.1×10^{-5} moles/cm²yr.

the time of formation of the Hekpoort paleosol 2.2 b.y. ago was less than 1×10^{-2} atm, and probably less than 2×10^{-3} atm.

Cases 11 through 16 were run for soils developed on parent rocks with an R value of 0.01, a value typical of granites. Intermediate igneous rocks have R values between 0.01 and 0.045. Since the O_2 demand of soils developed on rocks with an R value of 0.01 is so much less than that of soils developed on basalts, the value of $P_{O_2}^o$ (min) for a given CO_2 demand profile is much lower. The effect of a lower R value is accentuated by the progressively greater share of photochemical oxidants in the total supply of oxidants by rain water at low values of $P_{O_2}^o$. For an O_2 demand equal to that of the standard case, the value of $P_{O_2}^o$ (min) for soils developed on rocks with an R value of 0.01 ranged from 3×10^{-5} to 5×10^{-4} atm. If the cases examined to date span the range of $P_{O_2}^o$ (min) values for 10-m-thick soils developed on granitic rocks, the $P_{O_2}^o$ (min) must have been greater than 3×10^{-5} atm and could well have been required to be greater than 5×10^{-4} atm. As shown in Figure 6, there is a gap between the upper limit of $P_{O_2}^o$ (min) required for the retention of iron in soils developed on granites (5×10^{-4} atm), and the lower limit for the value of $P_{O_2}^o$ (min) at which iron can be retained in soils developed on basalts (1×10^{-3} atm). At values of $P_{O_2}^o$ within this gap, iron is retained in all of the model soils developed on granites and is lost in all of the model soils developed on basalts when the integrated acid demand within the soil profiles is equal to the present-day average.

AN EXAMINATION OF TWO ASSUMPTIONS

In the treatment of soil chemistry above, we assumed that the oxidation of Fe^{+2} and perhaps of Mn^{+2} is rapid in soils, even at very small values of P_{O_2} in soil air. We also assumed that the effects of biology were minor. Both assumptions are in need of examination. If the rate of oxidation of Fe^{+2} and Mn^{+2} is slow compared to the rate of movement of water through soils, then these elements are lost even when free oxygen is present in soil air. The behavior of iron and manganese in soils can therefore be used to define the composition of their contemporary atmosphere only if the relationship between the O_2 content of soil air and the kinetics of Fe^{+2} and Mn^{+2} oxidation are understood. The rate of oxidation of Fe^{+2} to Fe^{+3} in aqueous solutions has been studied quite thoroughly. Singer and Stumm (1970) have shown that when pH > 5, the rate of Fe^{+2} oxidation in homogeneous solutions is governed by the equation

$$\frac{-d[Fe^{+2}]}{dt} = k[Fe^{+2}] [OH^-]^2 P_{O_2}. \qquad (42)$$

It follows that

$$\frac{[Fe^{+2}]}{[Fe^{+2}]_o} = e^{-\lambda t}, \qquad (43)$$

where, at constant P_{O_2},

$$\lambda = k [OH^-]^2 \cdot P_{O_2}. \qquad (44)$$

Singer and Stumm (1970) proposed a value of $(8 \pm 2.5) \times 10^{13}$ min^{-1} atm^{-1} mol^{-2} for k at 20°C. Sung and Morgan (1980) have summarized the more recent measurements of k, and have provided a considerable quantity of new data. They have shown that k is a function of the ionic strength of the solutions in which Fe^{+2} is oxidized, and that it may decrease in the presence of complexing agents for Fe^{+2} other than OH^-.

Sung and Morgan (1980) also showed that the oxidation products of Fe^{+2} catalyze the oxidation of Fe^{+2}, especially when the pH of the solutions is greater than about 7. The catalytic effects do not seem to be very large in aqueous solutions. They could, however, be important in soils, where the surface area of FeOOH per cm^3 of soil water can be very high. A much more spectacular increase in the rate of oxidation can be achieved by iron-oxidizing bacteria. In solutions at a pH of 3.5 to 4.0, where the half life of the oxidation of Fe^{+2} in aqueous solutions is several years in the presence of atmospheric oxygen (Stumm and Morgan, 1981, p. 467), iron-oxidizing bacteria can oxidize Fe^{+2} to Fe^{+3} in a matter of minutes to hours (K. H. Nealson, personal communication). No quantitative measurements seem to have been made of the rate of Fe^{+2} oxidation by bacteria at lower O_2 pressures, although such bacteria are apparently active even at very low values of P_{O_2} (R. Mitchell, personal communication).

The oxidation of Mn^{+2} in homogeneous aqueous solutions is even slower than that of Fe^{+2}. Diem and Stumm (1984) have shown that Mn^{+2} oxidation by O_2 does not occur even after several years in solutions that are sterile and not supersaturated with respect to $MnCO_3$ or $Mn(OH)_2$. In the presence of $MnCO_3$ and other surface catalysts and in waters contaminatd with "Mn-bacteria," Mn^{+2} oxidation takes place in a matter of days. Similar results have been obtained by Emerson and others (1982). The rate of Mn^{+2} removal from waters containing low levels of oxygen in Saanich Inlet, British Columbia, is on the order of days. Electron micrographs of particulates from this area revealed structures characteristic of bacterially formed Mn precipitates. The mechanism of manganese removal in Saanich Inlet is not well known, but manganese removal is at least in part the result of bacterial catalysis. Sung and Morgan (1981) have shown that the oxidative removal of manganese can be catalyzed by γ-FeOOH. The presence of γ-FeOOH in millimolar levels was shown to reduce the half life of Mn^{+2} in 0.7 molar NaCl from hundreds of hours to hours. Heterogenous reactions may also play a role in the removal of manganese from lakes, estuaries, and ground waters.

The rate of oxidation of Fe^{+2} in ancient soils must have been at least as rapid as the rate of oxidation of Fe^{+2} in homogeneous aqueous solutions; the rate could have been many orders of magnitude faster. If we accept the value of Singer and Stumm (1970) for the rate constant of Fe^{+2} oxidation in aqueous solutions, the half life of Fe^{+2} in soils where inorganic oxidation is the rate limiting step is

$$\tau_{Fe^{+2}} = \frac{0.693}{\lambda} = \frac{0.693}{8 \times 10^{13} [OH^-]^2 P_{O_2}} \; min \qquad (45)$$

$$= \frac{1.7 \times 10^{-20}}{[OH^-]^2 P_{O_2}} \text{ yr.} \qquad (46)$$

In sandy-loamy soils water moves downward at a rate of about 1 m/yr (Matthess, 1982, p. 173). The residence time of water in a 10-m-thick soil of this type is therefore approximately 10 yr. Fe^{+2} released in such a soil during weathering will be oxidized quantitatively only if $\tau_{Fe^{+2}}$ is considerably less than 10 yr. If we set the requirement that $\tau_{Fe^{+2}} < 1$ yr, then

$$[OH^-]^2 P_{O_2} > 1.7 \times 10^{-20}. \qquad (47)$$

The activity of H^+ in rain water in which CO_2 is the only acid is given by the expression

$$[H^+] = \sqrt{K_1 B_{CO_2} P_{CO_2}}, \qquad (48)$$

where K_1 is the first ionization constant of carbonic acid. During much of the Precambrian, P_{CO_2} was almost certainly in the range of 10^{-3} to 10^{-1} atm (Kasting, 1987, and Part I). When P_{CO_2} is 10^{-2} atm, the pH of pure rain water at 20°C is 4.9, and the activity of OH^- is $10^{-9.1}$. Thus, the oxidation of Fe^{+2} in such a solution is sufficiently rapid only when

$$P_{O_2} > 2.7 \times 10^{-2} \text{ atm.}$$

This is an embarrassingly large oxygen pressure. However, the pH of soil waters rises rapidly with depth, and usually reaches values ≥7.0 by the time soil waters reach the water table. At this pH the minimum value of P_{O_2} is 2.7×10^{-6} atm, a pressure that is much lower than current estimates of the actual value of P_{O_2} in the Proterozoic atmosphere (see Part I and below). It follows that the rate of Fe^{+2} oxidation may have been too slow to prevent iron loss from the uppermost portions of Precambrian soils, but that the rate of Fe^{+2} oxidation in the middle and lower parts of thick Precambrian soils was almost certainly sufficiently rapid, so that significant iron loss occurred only when P_{O_2} in the soil atmosphere had been reduced to a very small fraction of the oxygen prssure in the atmosphere above the soil.

It is probable that the oxidation of Fe^{+2} in soils was actually much more rapid than suggested by the above calculation, since the catalytic effect of FeOOH was probably significant, and iron-oxidizing bacteria were probably present in soils as early as 2.0 Ga. Their presence is suggested by the discovery of Eoastrion in the Gunflint Iron Formation and in several other Proterozoic iron formations (A. H. Knoll, personal communication). If iron-oxidizing bacteria were present in Proterozoic soils, then iron was almost certainly retained when P_{O_2} in air was in excess of about 10^{-6} atm. Similar but less convincing arguments can be made for the oxidation and retention of manganese in Proterozoic soils.

Another major assumption remains to be examined before the calculations presented above can be used to interpret the chemical composition of paleosols in terms of the composition of their contemporary atmosphere. The effects of a possible land biota have been neglected, an omission that must be justified. A significant quantity of soluble organic compounds is produced during the decay of modern land plants. Thurman (1985a,b) has recently summarized the available data for the concentration of dissolved organic carbon (DOC) in soil waters. DOC in soil waters decreases from a median of about 20 mg/ℓ in the A horizon to a median of about 2 mg/ℓ in the C horizon. The DOC concentration of ground waters in the United States has been studied by Leenheer and others (1974), who found a median DOC value of 0.7 mg/ℓ for samples collected at 100 sites in 27 states. These data indicate that approximately

$$\frac{20 \times 10^{-3} \text{ gm/ℓ} \times 50 \times 10^{-3} \text{ ℓ/cm}^2\text{yr}}{12 \text{ gm/mol}} = 83 \text{ } \mu\text{mol DOC/cm}^2\text{yr}$$

are added to and largely removed from soil solutions today. The mechanisms by which DOC is removed from soil water are not well defined, but polymerization and precipitation, adsorption on clay minerals, and oxidation are almost certainly the most important. If oxidation is the dominant mechanism, the oxygen flux required to destroy the DOC produced in the upper soil layers is very much larger than the flux of O_2 that was required in our model soil to oxidize Fe^{+2} released during weathering. If the HCO_3^- concentration in a soil water at the base of a soil profile is 2 mmol/ℓ, the flux of soil water 50×10^{-3} ℓ/yr, and, the R value of the parent rock 0.045, the required flux of O_2 is

$$2 \times 10^{-3} \text{ mol/ℓ} \times 50 \times 10^{-3} \text{ ℓ/yr} \times 0.045 = 4.5 \text{ } \mu\text{mol/ℓ.}$$

The O_2 flux required for Fe^{+2} oxidation is therefore only 5 percent of the O_2 flux that would be required to oxidize the present-day flux of DOC. The analysis presented above can therefore be valid only if the flux of DOC in soil waters was at least two orders of magnitude smaller than at present, or if the DOC generated by a cover of primitive plants was not oxidized in the underlying soils. If either of these conditions was not met, our analysis underestimates the amount of oxygen required for Fe^{+2} oxidation.

There is still room for doubt that the continents possessed a plant cover at all prior to the development of higher land plants. However, Campbell (1979) has made a good case for the proposition that the continents were colonized by terrestrial blue-green algal mats during the early Precambrian, and Beeunas and Knauth (1985) have interpreted the isotopic composition of 1.2-b.y.-old Mescal Limestone below a dissolution zone in terms of the presence of a subaerial vegetative cover. The concentration of DOC in soils below blue-green algal mats has not been measured and is difficult to predict; however, a rough estimate can be made. The net primary productivity of dry organic matter in a variety of modern ecosystems is about 10 tons/ha yr (Smil, 1985, p. 26), or about 40 mg of carbon/cm²yr. About 2 percent of this primary productivity is converted into DOC. The primary productivity of terrestrial algal mats is not known; it is probably less than that of aqueous algal mats, since the growth of terrestrial mats ceases during desiccation (Campbell, 1979). N. Pearl (personal communication, 1986) has observed that algal mats along the coast of North Carolina fix carbon at a rate of about 2 to 4 mg C/cm^2yr, i.e., at a rate some 5 to 10 percent of the figure cited above for the primary productivity in many terrestrial ecosystems today. If the fraction of algal productivity converted into DOC was the same as the fraction of primary productivity converted to DOC today, the flux of DOC would have been on the order of 3 to 6 $\mu mol/cm^2yr$. This is almost certainly a strong upper limit, because the productivity of terrestrial algal mats is probably lower than that of aqueous algal mats, and because today DOC is generated in the A horizon of soils, which frequently contains several percent of organic matter. Such highly carbonaceous A horizons have not been found and are not expected in Precambrian paleosols.

If these order-of-magnitude calculations are valid, the downward flux of oxygen required to destroy the flux of DOC from terrestrial algal mats was smaller than and possibly trivial compared to the oxygen flux required to oxidize Fe^{+2} released during the weathering of many igneous rocks. It is clear, however, that there is ample room to doubt the validity of the above calculations. Experiments should be carried out in a suitably designed "Precambrian garden" to determine the actual magnitude of the DOC flux below terrestrial algal mats in a variety of climatic settings. With such experiments it should also be possible to determine whether the chelation of iron and manganese by DOC compounds might have influenced the behavior of these elements in Precambrian soils.

IMPLICATIONS FOR THE EVOLUTION OF THE ATMOSPHERE

A compilation of the available data for the composition of ancient paleosols in Part I showed that Fe^{+2} was apparently oxidized and retained as Fe_2O_3 in paleosols developed on low-R rocks younger than about 3.0 Ga, but that a good deal of Fe^{+2} was apparently lost from soils formed during the weathering of high-R rocks before about 1.8 Ga.

Figure 7 is a slightly updated version of the corresponding figure in Part I. Supporting data for points 1 through 14 are given in this chapter. Point 15 in Figure 7 represents the Flagstaff Mountain paleosol near Boulder, Colorado. This paleosol was developed during the pre-Fountain (Pennsylvanian) and probably post-Madison weathering of a granodiorite (Wahlstrom, 1948); the weathering zone extends to a depth of approximately 80 ft beneath and normal to the contact of the granodiorite with the overlying sediments. Point 16 represents the Sturgeon River paleosol (Zbinden and others, in preparation), which is developed on hydrothermally altered Keweenawan basalt in the Upper Peninsula of Michigan and which is overlain by the Jacobsville Sandstone. Point 17 represents the Sishen paleosol, which is developed along the contact of the Olifantshoek (Waterberg) sequence with the Ongeluk lavas of the Transvaal sequence in Griqualand West (Van Wyk and Beukes, 1982; Beukes, 1985).

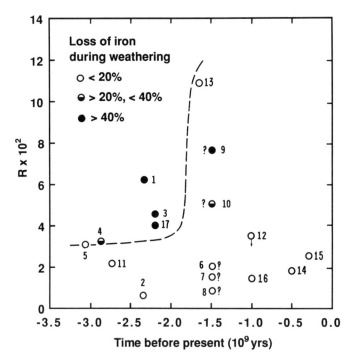

Figure 7. R value of the parent rocks of paleosols and the percentage of iron loss during soil formation.

The Ongeluk lavas are time equivalents of the Hekpoort basalt. In the area of the Sishen iron ore deposits, these lavas contain 8 percent Fe_2O_3 as well as 8 percent FeO. During weathering, the lavas retained their Fe_2O_3 but lost about 70 percent of their FeO.

The new data points are consistent with and corroborate the earlier data. However, geologic evidence for the identification of many of these units as paleosols is not particularly convincing. Very few have been shown to meet the criteria outlined in Part I, and it is likely that some of the points in Figure 7 will not appear in future versions of this diagram. Clearly, much more work is needed to define the position of the curve separating paleosols that have lost little or no iron during weathering from those that have lost a sizable fraction of their iron. If we accept the data in Figure 7, the transition between the two groups of paleosols occurred at an R value of about 3×10^{-2} in the time interval of 1.8 to 2.5 Ga.

In this chapter we have developed two semi-independent approaches to the problem of extracting information regarding the composition of the atmosphere from paleosols at the time of their formation. The first is quite general, and the results are summarized in equations 26 and 27. The arguments presented above suggest that the value of P_{O_2}' was very small during pre-Middle Ordovician time. Hence,

$$P_{O_2}^o \approx A(P_{CO_2}^o - P_{CO_2}^L). \tag{49}$$

If we use 0.03 as the value of R for the transition of paleosols that have retained iron to those that have lost iron, the value of A is within the limits

$$\frac{0.9}{(1 + \xi)} > A > 0.03. \qquad (50)$$

The lower values of A are valid for paleosols in which much of the gas transfer was by diffusion, the higher values for paleosols in which much of the gas transfer was by advection. The CO_2 content of the atmosphere during this period of Earth history is not well constrained. In Part I we showed that $P^o_{CO_2}$ values of $10^{-3 \pm 1}$ atm were consistent with the inferred rates of chemical weathering. However, Kasting (1987) has proposed that CO_2 pressures of $10^{-1.5 \pm 0.5}$ may have been required to supply a sufficient greenhouse effect, so that the surface of the Earth was maintained at a reasonable temperature despite the lower luminosity of the sun 1.5 to 2.5 b.y. ago. Both estimates are vulnerable, since they are based on uncertain assumptions, and we propose to take a value of 10^{-2} atm as a reasonable compromise between the two uncertain numbers.

The value of $P^L_{CO_2}$ must have been quite variable. For the model discussed in connection with equations 32 and 39, $P^L_{CO_2}$ was approximately 60 percent of $P^o_{CO_2}$. Similar results were obtained in numerical calculations with some of the model soils of Table 1. Thus the value of $P^o_{O_2}$ is roughly bounded by the relationship

$$4.5 \times 10^{-3} > P^o_{O_2} > 1.2 \times 10^{-4} \text{ atm.} \qquad (51)$$

In the second approach developed in this chapter, we related the O_2 profile in soils to their physical and chemical properties via the use rate of CO_2 in weathering. No claim for complete coverage of the choice of soil parameters can be claimed, but it is reassuring to note that the range of values of P_{O_2} obtained in this fashion is consistent with that of equation 51. Perhaps the "window" in Figure 6 spans a particularly likely portion of the range of atmospheric oxygen pressures that is permitted by the results of both approaches.

SUMMARY

We have tested a number of analytical and numerical solutions of the one-dimensional transport equation for CO_2 and O_2 in ancient soils. The analytical approach is appealingly simple, but the results may be inadequate because modeling of physical parameters, such as the diffusivity profile in soils, was necessarily oversimplified. The soil models that we have studied numerically are more realistic, although to date we have examined only a relatively small number of models to define the sensitivity of our solutions to the choice of physical parameters.

The results from both sets of calculations indicate that free oxygen has been present in the atmosphere from at least early Proterozoic time. The range of atmospheric oxygen pressure permitted by the available paleosol data is large. Our currently preferred value for the range of P_{O_2} between 2.5 and 1.8 Ga is 5×10^{-4} to 1×10^{-3} atm. Additional paleosol data, studies of Precambrian gardens, and support from independent lines of evidence are needed to confirm these figures.

ACKNOWLEDGMENTS

We have benefited a great deal from discussions of the contents of this paper with a number of colleagues, particularly A. H. Knoll, J. F. Kasting, D. E. Grandstaff, S. Golubic, K. H. Nealson, D. Des Marais, and R. Mitchell. A. C. Lasaga and H. H. Hummel provided incisive reviews of the manuscript. The work was supported by the National Aeronautics and Space Administration under Grant NAGW-599 to Harvard University, and by the Pennsylvania State University with funds from the Earth Systems Science Center. H.D.H. is particularly indebted to Penn State for the hospitality enjoyed as a visiting professor during the academic year 1985–86.

REFERENCES CITED

Beeunas, M. A., and Knauth, L. P., 1985, Preserved stable isotope signature of subaerial diagenesis in the 1.2 b.y. Mescal Limestone, central Arizona; Implications for the timing and development of a terrestrial plant cover: Geological Society of America Bulletin, v. 96, p. 737–745.

Beukes, N. J., 1985, Final report on the geology of the Sishen iron ore and Kalahari manganese deposits: Pretoria, C.S.I.R., C.S.P., Open-File Report, 49 p.

Blaxland, A. B., 1974, Geochemistry and geochronology of chemical weathering, Butler Hill Granite, Missouri: Geochimica et Cosmochimica Acta, v. 38, p. 843–852.

Campbell, S. E., 1979, Soil stabilization by a prokaryotic desert crust; Implications for Precambrian land biota: Origins of Life, v. 9, p. 335–337.

De Jong, E., Douglas, J. T., and Goss, M. J., 1983, Gaseous diffusion in shrinking soils: Soil Science, v. 136, p. 10–18.

Diem, D., and Stumm, W., 1984, Is dissolved Mn^{+2} being oxidized by O_2 in absence of Mn-bacteria or surface catalysts?: Geochimica et Cosmochimica Acta, v. 48, p. 1571–1573.

Emerson, S., Kalhorn, S., Jacobs, L., Tebo, B. M., Nealson, K. H., and Rosson, R. A., 1982, Environmental oxidation rate of manganese; II, Bacterial catalysis: Geochimica et Cosmochimica Acta, v. 46, p. 1073–1079.

Gray, J., 1985, The microfossil record of early land plants; Advances in understanding of early terrestrialization, 1970–1984: Philosophical Transactions of the Royal Society of London, Ser. B., v. 309, p. 167–192.

Holland, H. D., 1984, The chemical evolution of the atmosphere and oceans: Princeton, New Jersey, Princeton University Press, 582 p.

Holland, H. D., and Zbinden, E. A., 1987, Paleosols and the evolution of the atmosphere, Part I, *in* Lerman, A., and Meybeck, M., eds., Physical and chemical weathering in geochemical cycles: NATO ASI Institute, Dordrecht, D. Reidel.

Kasting, J. F., Holland, H. D., and Pinto, J. P., 1985, Oxidant abundances in rainwater and the evolution of atmospheric oxygen: Journal of Geophysical Research, v. 90, p. 10497–10510.

Kasting, J. F., 1987, Theoretical constraints on oxygen and carbon dioxide concentrations in the Precambrian atmosphere: Precambrian Research, v. 34,

p. 205–229.

Lai, S. H., Tiedje, J. M., and Erickson, A. E., 1976, In situ measurement of gas diffusion coefficient in soils: Soil Science Society of America Journal, v. 40, p. 3–6.

Leenheer, J. A., Malcolm, R. L., McKinley, P. W., and Eccles, L. A., 1974, Occurrence of dissolved organic carbon in selected ground-water samples in the United States: U.S. Geological Survey Journal of Research, v. 2, p. 361–369.

Matthess, G., 1982, The properties of ground water: New York, John Wiley & Sons, 405 p.

Richter, J., and Grossgebauer, A., 1978, Untersuchungen zum Bodenlufthaushalt in einem Bodenbearbeitungsversuch; 2, Gasdiffusionskoeffizienten als Strukturmasse für Böden: Z. Pflanzenernaehr. Bodenkd., v. 141, p. 181–202.

Singer, D. C., and Stumm, W., 1970, Acid mine drainage; The rate-determining step: Science, v. 167, p. 1121–1123.

Smil, V., 1985, Carbon-nitrogen-sulfur; Human interference in grand biospheric cycles: New York, Plenum Press, 476 p.

Stumm, W., and Morgan, T. T., 1981, Aquatic chemistry, 2nd ed.: New York, John Wiley & Sons, 780 p.

Sung, W., and Morgan, J. J., 1980, Kinetics and product of ferrous iron oxygenation in aqueous solutions: Environmental Science and Technology, v. 14, p. 561–568.

—— , 1981, Oxidative removal of Mn(II) from solution catalyzed by the γ-FeOOH (lepidocrocite) surface: Geochimica et Cosmochimica Acta, v. 45, p. 2377–2383.

Taylor, S. A., 1949, Oxygen diffusion in porous media as a measure of soil aeration: Soil Science Society of America Proceedings, v. 14, p. 55–61.

Thurman, E. M., 1985a, Humic substances in ground water, *in* Aiken, G. R., McKnight, D. M., Wershaw, R. L., and MacCarthy, P., eds., Humic substances in soil, sediment, and water: New York, John Wiley & Sons, 692 p.

—— , 1985b, Organic geochemistry of natural waters: Dordrecht, Martinus Nijhoff/Dr. W. Junk Publishers, 497 p.

Van Wyk, T. P., and Beukes, N. J., 1982, The geology of the Sishen iron ore deposit, *in* Glen, H. W., ed., Proceedings; 12th Congress of the Council of Mining and Metallurgical Institutions: Marshalltown, South Africa, South Africa Institute of Mining and Metallurgy, p. 203–211.

Wahlstrom, E. E., 1948, Pre-Fountain and recent weathering on Flagstaff Mountain near Boulder, Colorado: Geological Society of America Bulletin, v. 59, p. 1173–1190.

MANUSCRIPT ACCEPTED BY THE SOCIETY JULY 1, 1987

Geological Society of America
Special Paper 216
1988

Recognition and chemical characterization of fossil soils developed on alluvium; A Late Ordovician example

C. R. Feakes
Department of Earth and Planetary Sciences
Harvard University
Cambridge, Massachusetts 02138

G. J. Retallack
Department of Geology
University of Oregon
Eugene, Oregon 97403

ABSTRACT

Fossil soils in alluvial red beds from the Juniata Formation, near Potters Mills, in central Pennsylvania, provide evidence of soil-forming processes during Late Ordovician time. Paleogeographic and facies considerations indicate that the fossil soils formed on flood plains west of the Taconic uplift.

Most studies of paleosols of this age or older have considered soils developed on metamorphic or igneous basement rock. Alluvial fossil soils provide evidence of conditions during shorter intervals of weathering without problems of overprinting by successive and different weathering regimes. They can be recognized by the presence of trace fossils and the development of soil horizons and structures. Problems associated with such fossil soils include establishing the nature of the parent material and distinguishing clay formation in the soil from originally deposited fining-upward cycles.

These difficulties can be overcome by comparing paleosols in different stages of development, as indicated by degree of ferruginization, density of trace fossils, amount of clay, and abundance and size of caliche nodules. In modern soils, caliche forms in alkaline conditions under which TiO_2 is stable. Gains and losses of oxides (measured in grams per cubic centimeters) relative to TiO_2 in a strongly developed paleosol were compared with those of a weakly developed paleosol, taken to approximate the compositional range of the parent material. Concentration ratios indicate significant soil development of the strongly developed paleosol beyond the compositional range of the weakly developed paleosol. There was depletion of SiO_2 and enrichment of Fe_2O_3, Al_2O_3, and K_2O relative to TiO_2. Anomalous enrichment of K_2O has been documented in other fossil soils. Both x-ray diffraction studies and a strong correlation between K_2O and Al_2O_3 are evidence that most of the potassium is contained in sericitized illite.

INTRODUCTION

Identification of Tertiary and Quaternary paleosols is usually straightforward because of their distinctive root traces, profile development, color, and mineralogical variations. Yet paleosols older than Silurian are much more difficult to recognize, especially within alluvial sequences. In large part this is because vascular land plants were not yet available to stabilize, bioturbate, and chemically alter the land surfaces. This chapter provides a detailed description of Late Ordovician soil development on alluvial parent materials. Because little evidence of plant activity is apparent in these paleosols, evaluation of soil formation is based primarily on chemical analyses and on the study of trace fossils.

Early Paleozoic and Precambrian paleosols developed on

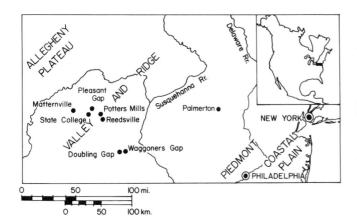

Figure 1. Location of Potters Mills, and other mentioned localities in Pennsylvania.

Figure 2. Roadcut, 4.2 km southeast of Potters Mills. Arrow indicates the top of Potters Mills clay. Scale on left is in feet.

unconformities between igneous or metamorphic basement rocks and overlying sediments are easy to recognize and are now studied using a variety of geochemical approaches (Holland, 1984; Retallack, 1986a; Retallack and others, 1984). Yet these paleosols are difficult to understand because they have been subjected to several cycles of weathering during their long exposure. This study seeks to apply comparable methods of paleopedological analysis to paleosols developed within ancient alluvium. A vexing problem in analysis of such paleosols is the identification of a uniform parent material. Both fining-upward cycles and interlayered shaly and sandy beds characteristic of alluvium could be confused for soil horizons if partly bioturbated. In addition, in well-indurated rocks it is very difficult to distinguish clays and micas originally present from those produced by soil formation, and then by late diagenesis and metamorphism. Despite these difficulties, paleosols developed on alluvial lowlands may provide more reliable paleoenvironmental information than paleosols, which formed at major geologic unconformities.

LOCATION AND GEOLOGICAL SETTING

The Juniata Formation is one of several red beds of Paleozoic age exposed in the Valley and Ridge Province of the Appalachian orogen (Meckel, 1970). It is Late Ordovician (Ashgillian, or 438 to 448 Ma) in age (Ross, 1982). Paleosols in the Juniata Formation are especially well exposed within a roadcut 4.2 km southeast of Potters Mills along U.S. 322, in Center County, Pennsylvania (Figs. 1, 2). The type profile of the Potters Mills clay paleosol (Retallack, 1985) overlies the type Faust Flat silty clay paleosol (named here) 200 m east of the western end of the southern cutting, at a stratigraphic level of 75 to 76 m (245–250 ft) in a measured section with its base at the western end of the roadcut (Fig. 3). There are numerous other Potters Mills and Faust Flat Series paleosols in this sequence.

This part of Pennsylvania was removed from the regions of intense metamorphism and structural deformation due to Appalachian mountain building. The outcrops examined are folded into a shallow, asymmetrical syncline that plunges gently to the westsouthwest (Fig. 2). The degree of alteration of conodonts in Ordovician limestones of Pennsylvania and the illitic and chloritic composition of the Juniata paleosols are compatible with lower greenschist facies burial metamorphism. The Potters Mills clay and the Faust Flat silty clay appear to have escaped intense structural or metamorphic alteration (Retallack, 1985).

Fossil soils of the upper Juniata Formation are within alluvial red beds that are part of a large wedge of clastic sediments derived from the Taconic uplift to the southeast (Thompson, 1970a). Cross-bedding, maximum pebble size, and isopach data, along with the lack of marine fauna and the presence of mudcracks and ripple marks, are evidence that this part of the clastic wedge was nonmarine. Fining-upward sequences of red-maroon sandstones and shales within this part of the Juniata Formation were deposited by loosely sinuous streams that drained the ancestral Appalachian highlands (Thompson, 1970b). Marine rocks of comparable age are 260 km northwest of these paleosols in the Juniata Formation (Yeakel, 1962). Thus, the paleosols reported here formed on inland portions of a coastal plain.

DESCRIPTION AND INTERPRETATIONS OF THE PALEOSOLS

Potters Mills clay paleosol

Diagnosis. Thin (42 cm in compacted paleosol), clayey to silty, dark reddish brown (2.5YR3/4) to weak red (2.5YR4/2) paleosol, containing numerous subhorizontal and vertical burrows (Fig. 4), half of which are encased or closely associated with caliche nodules (Fig. 5).

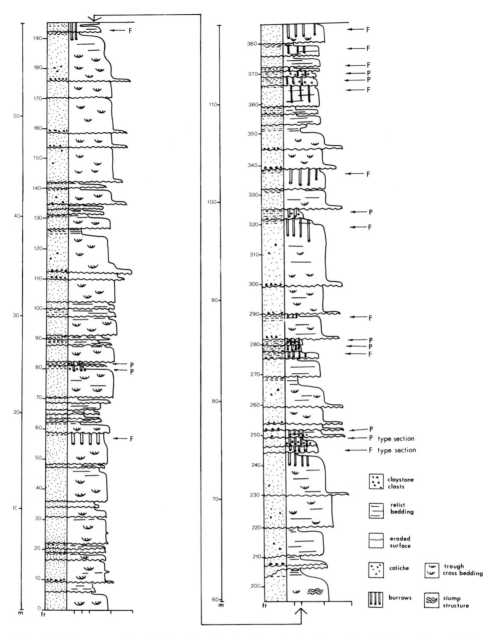

Figure 3. Columnar section of paleosols within the Upper Juniata Formation. P indicates Potter Mills Series paleosols; F indicates Faust Flat Series paleosols.

Derivation. Potters Mills is a small village in Pennsylvania, 4.2 km northwest of the type profile.

Description. In the following descriptions, measurements are from the top of the profile to the top of the described horizon, and the letters are their interpretation as a soil horizon, following the labeling scheme of Birkeland (1984). Unlike earlier schemes of nomenclature (used by Retallack, 1985), this scheme treats calcic horizons as B rather than C horizons. The micromorphological terminology is that of Brewer (1976).

+24 cm Bk of overlying paleosol and base of overlying

sedimentary unit; silty claystone; dark reddish brown (2.5YR3/4); weakly calcareous; prominent relict bedding; few, medium (3 to 15 mm) diffuse burrow-sheathing and fine, tubular calcareous nodules of reddish yellow (7.5YR7/2) with reddish brown (5YR5/4) neosequans; microtexture unistrial, agglomeroplasmic skelinsepic, mainly clay and quartz, with conspicuous mica, rare calcite, and rock fragments; common medium diffuse irregular sesquioxidic nodules and stain, locally isotic abrupt wavy contact to

0 cm, A, claystone; dark reddish brown (2.5YR3/4); cal-

Figure 4. Subhorizontal burrows from A horizon of Potters Mills clay. Scale is 1 inch.

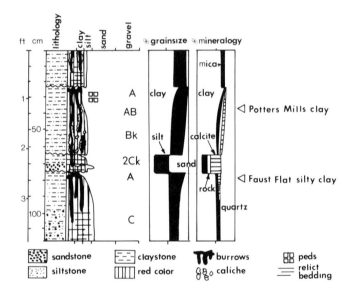

Figure 5. Columnar section (measured in field) and petrographic composition (from point counting of thin sections) of Potters Mills clay paleosol and Faust Flat silty clay paleosol, Late Ordovocian, central Pennsylvania. Letters indicate soil horizons.

careous; medium to coarse (3 to 4 cm) subangular blocky peds defined by abundant subhorizontal and vertical, 1 to 15 mm diameter para-aggrotubules, and in some areas by few, very dark grayish brown (10YR3/2) neomangans; these structures impart a hackly appearance to the rock except for relict bedding (presumably cumulic) nearest the surface; few medium, irregular, diffuse mottles of greenish gray (5GY5/1) claystone, presumably around relict organic matter; microtexture unistrial, agglomeroplasmic,

skelmosepic, mainly clay with conspicuous quartz, lesser mica and rare calcite; common diffuse sesquioxidic nodules, especially along relict clayey laminae; gradual smooth contact to

–8 cm, AB, silty claystone; weak red (2.5YR4/2); calcareous; weak structure of medium (3 to 4 cm) subangular, blocky peds, defined by abundant vertical, dark reddish brown (2.5YR3/4), 2 to 15 mm diameter para-aggrotubules, some of which are sheathed with a thin inner reddish brown (7.5YR7/6) neosesquan and thicker (1 to 2 mm) outer quasi-calcitan which imparts a light color to the surface of the trace; structure also defined in places by few, very dark grayish brown (10YR3/2) neomangans; microtexture unistrial, agglomeroplasmic, skelinsepic to inundulic; mainly clay with common quartz, little mica and calcite, rare feldspar and rock fragments; microstructure of the para-aggrotubules skelinsepic; common diffuse irregular sesquioxidic nodules, isotic in places; gradual smooth contact to

–19 cm, Bk; silty claystone; weak red (2.5YR4/2); calcareous; faint relict bedding; common dark reddish brown (2.5YR3/4), vertical para-aggrotubules, sheathed with inner reddish brown (5RY5/4) neosesquan and outer reddish yellow (7.5YR7/6) quasicalcitan; few, small (1 to 3 mm in diameter), calcareous crystal tubes; calcareous aggregations confined largely to this horizon, but patchily distributed on the scale of tens of centimeters over the 100 m of lateral exposure examined; one burrow found retains some clayey fill as a neoargillan around a central orthogranotubule; a few vertical parastriotubules exhibit spreiten texture; few medium, drab, greenish gray (5GY5/1), subhorizontal mottles near the base of this horizon, presumably after relict organic matter; microstructure unistrial, agglomeroplasmic, argillasepic to skelinsepic; mainly clay with abundant quartz, common calcite and mica, rare rock fragments and feldspar; few irregular diffuse sesquioxide nodules and stain; abrupt planar contact to

–32 cm; 2Ck; silty claystone; with shale laminae in upper part; weak red (2.5YR4/2); calcareous; a disrupted, 2 cm thick, medium-grained sandstone bed in the central part of this horizon is light yellowish brown (2.5Y6/4) with some drab mottles of greenish gray (5GY5/1) along its upper surface; much relict bedding and few para-aggrotubules like those in overlying horizons; microtexture intertextic silasepic and crystic, with laminae and clots (after clasts or rock fragments) of more clayey, porphyroskelic argillasepic texture; mainly quartz in a matrix of calcareous or chloritic clay and clear carbonate, common rock fragments and mica; few diffuse irregular isotic sesquioxidic nodules; locally abrupt wavy contact to A horizon of underlying Faust Flat silty clay paleosol.

Reconstructed soil. This paleosol is most similar to alluvial bottomland soils of the seasonally dry tropics, and has been identified as an Oxic Ustropept (USDA classification), Calcic Cambisol (FAO) and Calcareous Red Earth (CSIRO): with some trepidation considering likely differences in degree and kind of soil-forming processes during Late Ordovician time (Retallack, 1985).

The present paleosol is stained red by hematite, but the

original soil color may have been orange or brown from more hydrated ferric oxyhydrate minerals (Walker, 1967). The degree of calcification and ferruginization indicates alkaline and oxidizing conditions following general models of Retallack (1984). In modern strongly seasonal climates, carbonate accumulations may form during dry periods and ferruginization during wet seasons (Duchafour, 1982). These two processes and the mild alignment of the clay minerals (skelinsepic and skelmosepic agglomeroplasmic fabric) are indicators of a well-drained soil. Using Arkley's (1963) and Jenny's (1980) studies of soils in modern arid climates, the depth of caliche indicates that the soil received less than 40 cm of rainfall annually. The degree of calcification is analogous to Stage I of Gile and others (1966), which formed in roughly 3,000 to 4,000 yr. Presumably, most of this carbonate was derived from windborne dust, as appears to be the case for calcareous soils today (McFadden and Tinsley, 1985). The calcareous cement in horizon 2Ck is distinct from the caliche, however, and most similar to ground-water calcretes as described elsewhere by Netterberg (1969) and Mann and Horowitz (1979). Thus the water table may have been intermittently at 50 cm below the compacted paleosol surface. Permanent waterlogging within the soil is unlikely, considering the absence of gley features, apart from a few drab mottles similar to those formed in other paleosols around buried organic matter (Retallack, 1983).

Abundant burrows provide evidence that soil fauna played a significant role in aerating the soil, clay production, and enhancing soil structure. The exact nature of these organisms is poorly known. Presumably they were arthropods and were sustained by some kind of nonvascular vegetation (Retallack, 1985).

Other examples. In addition to other Potters Mills Series paleosols seen in the roadcuts southeast of Potters Mills, similar paleosols have been seen in the Juniata Formation elsewhere in Pennsylvania (Retallack, 1985).

Faust Flat Silty Clay Paleosol (new name)

Diagnosis. Very thin (22 cm in compacted paleosol) dark reddish brown (2.5YR3/4) to weak red (2.5YR4/2) profile with thin clayey surface horizon, very weakly calcareous to noncalcareous, containing abundant burrows varying greatly in width (2 to 21 mm), and a sandy burrowed subsurface horizon (Fig. 5).

Derivation. Faust Flat is a broad valley immediately west of the roadcut containing the type profile.

Description. Conventions for this account are as for the preceding paleosol description.

0 cm, A, siltstone; weak red (2.5YR4/2); weakly calcareous; abundant subhorizontal and vertical, 1 to 21 mm diameter, dark reddish brown (2.5YR3/4) para-aggrotubules; microtexture unistrial agglomeroplasmic skelinsepic; mainly clay and quartz, common calcite and mica, some feldspar; few wispy irregular diffuse sesquioxidic nodules; gradual smooth contact to

–18 cm C; sandy siltstone; weak red (2.5YR4/2); noncalcareous; conspicuous relict bedding and few vertical para-aggrotubules as in overlying horizon; microtexture unistrial

agglomeroplasmic skelinsepic; mainly clay and quartz, with common mica, feldspar, and calcite, but few rock fragments; few diffuse irregular sesquioxidic nodules, with isotic texture in places.

Reconstructed soil. This paleosol may be identified as a Fluvent (USDA: Soil Survey Staff, 1975), Eutric Fluvisol (FAO: Fitzpatrick, 1980) or Alluvial Soil (CSIRO: Stace and others, 1968). Although very weakly calcareous, the base status of this soil is presumed to have been within the range of Eutric Fluvisols because amounts of MgO, CaO, Na_2O, and K_2O (Table 1) are comparable to those in the overlying calcareous Potters Mills clay paleosol.

As with the Potters Mills clay, its original color may have been less red. The degree of calcification is greatly reduced in this soil, probably because of a shorter time for formation (probably less than 1,000 yr, judging from data of Gile and others, 1966). The conspicuous relict bedding, very mild orientation of the clays (agglomeroplasmic skelinsepic fabric), slightly reduced density of burrows, and small amount of clay in the A horizon also support the interpretation that this was a young soil. The burrows range from 2 to 21 mm in diameter, a much wider size range than observed in the Potters Mills clay. The biological significance of this difference is unclear, but we are continuing our investigation.

Other examples. Numerous other examples of Faust Flat Series paleosols were found in the roadcut southeast of Potters Mills (Fig. 2), as well as in association with Potters Mills Series paleosols in roadcuts on old highway 322 east of Reedsville (Retallack, 1985). Elsewhere in the Juniata Formation in Pennsylvania, especially in old roadcuts in which claystones are now heavily vegetated—for example, near Matternville, Waggoners Gap, Doubling Gap, and Pleasant Gap—Faust Flat Series paleosols are much more obvious than those of the Potters Mills Series. Several examples of Faust Flat Series paleosols can also been seen in the Late Silurian (Ludlovian) Bloomsburg Formation, near Palmerton, Pennsylvania. One of these, partly overprinted with caliche from an overlying paleosol, has been figured by Retallack (1985, Figs. 9, 15).

CHEMICAL COMPOSITION OF THE PALEOSOLS

In our attempt to assess quantitatively the amount of weathering these soil profiles have undergone, we have employed three approaches: (1) calculating the weight loss of the constituents from the profile, (2) comparing the variation in molecular ratios of selected oxides, and (3) normalizing each chemical component to a stable constituent to calculate concentration ratios. None of these methods is without drawbacks.

Concentration ratios are calculated on the assumption that a specific oxide—usually either TiO_2, SiO_2, or Al_2O_3—remains stable as weathering proceeds. Apparent gains and losses of other oxides can be compared with the presumed inert oxide. This method generally requires that the composition of the unweathered parent material is known and uniform: this is a serious problem for the Juniata paleosols because each paleosol devel-

TABLE 1. CHEMICAL COMPOSITION AND BULK DENSITY OF LATE ORDOVICIAN PALEOSOLS FROM THE JUNIATA FORMATION

Major Elements (weight percent)

Sample No.	Depth (cm)	SiO_2	TiO_2	Al_2O_3	Fe_2O_3	FeO	MgO	CaO	Na_2O	K_2O	MnO	P_2O_5	LOI	Totals
169	P+11	62.59	1.05	16.17	4.79	2.76	3.00	0.54	0.09	4.46	0.19	0.046	3.68	99.37
170	P-1	62.14	1.07	16.39	6.49	1.69	2.82	0.49	<0.04	4.68	0.19	0.040	3.87	99.91
171	P-14	66.70	1.00	14.19	3.55	2.48	2.80	1.01	0.45	3.81	0.20	0.063	3.90	100.15
172	P-30	67.10	1.01	14.83	3.98	2.21	2.54	0.50	0.44	4.04	0.20	0.085	3.37	100.31
173	P-34	64.68	1.06	15.43	4.09	2.54	2.73	0.57	0.41	4.31	0.20	0.057	3.34	99.42
174	P-37	62.76	1.04	15.00	4.39	2.28	3.14	1.26	0.29	4.11	0.21	0.087	4.60	99.17
175	P-48	60.18	0.73	10.30	2.63	1.74	4.44	5.91	0.34	2.63	0.13	0.28	9.72	99.03
176	F-5	67.21	0.98	14.43	3.91	2.29	2.58	0.55	0.50	3.81	0.21	0.040	3.27	99.78
177	F-47	69.72	0.96	13.79	3.70	2.07	2.29	0.43	0.50	3.62	0.20	0.037	3.06	100.38

Trace Elements (ppm)

Sample No.	Depth (cm)	Ba	Co	Cu	Cr	Li	Nb	Ni	Sc	V	G	Zn	Zr	Bulk Density (gcm⁻³)
169	P+11	355	21	<5	67	37	7	41	14.8	113	20	75	89	2.68
170	P-1	384	19	<5	67	25	<5	32	14.3	115	25	74	112	2.67
171	P-14	318	32	<5	58	33	11	35	12.8	92	28	64	112	2.70
172	P-30	358	34	<5	58	31	7	35	13.1	93	24	67	113	2.69
173	P-34	352	26	<5	60	32	6	33	13.4	97	27	67	119	2.66
174	P-37	361	20	<5	62	32	10	35	13.8	101	38	68	129	2.71
175	P-48	320	37	<5	42	28	15	25	10.7	66	44	---	87	2.64
176	F-5	316	29	5	59	37	16	38	12.7	94	29	66	186	2.71
177	F-47	306	20	13	54	36	17	36	11.9	85	30	61	247	2.65

Note: Depths are given in cm above (+) and below (-) the top of the type Potters Mills clay (P) and type Faust Flat silty clay (F) paleosols. Major and trace elements determined on a Baird PSI ICP and FeO from titration by Dr. A. J. Irving, University of Washington, Seattle; bulk density determined by weight difference in and out of water by C. F. Feakes, University of Oregon, Eugene.

oped on fining-upward sequences. This makes identification of a specific parent composition difficult. Well-developed paleosols can, however, be compared to the range of compositions seen in less well-developed paleosols.

For direct examination of the chemical variation within the soils, molecular ratios are more applicable to the Juniata paleosols. Using this approach, various combinations of oxides considered pedogenically significant are compared, and composition of the parent material is not a consideration.

Finally, calculation of weight gains and losses of constituents from the profile is based on the assumption of constant volume, which assumes minimal compaction of the profile due to the weight of the overlying sediment. In some paleosol soil studies (Retallack, 1986b), clastic dikes have been used to quantify the degree of compaction. In the Juniata paleosols, some compaction has occurred, as evidenced by partial flattening of the subhorizontal burrows. Assuming that these burrows were originally cylindrical, a crude compaction factor of 10 to 20 percent was calculated. The deformation of the horizontal burrows, however, varies greatly, and could have begun before burial of the paleosol, thus making quantitative estimates of compaction suspect. Compaction was not severe enough to affect noticeably the vertical and carbonate encrusted burrows. The ensuing calculations assume that compaction was negligible.

A suite of nine samples from the Juniata paleosols was analyzed for major and trace elements by ICP (inductively coupled argon plasma spectrometry) techniques at the University of Washington by Dr. A. Irving, who also determined values of FeO from potassium dichromate titration (Table 1). Bulk densities of the same samples were determined using standard methods. The range in density of these rocks was from 2.64 to 2.71 gm/cc (Table 1); the average density was 2.68 gm/cc. In general, the sandy C horizons are less dense than the clayey A horizons, which is probably because of the greater compaction of the A horizons.

Chemical variation

The variation of major oxides and of other elements has been plotted against columnar sections of the two paleosols (Figs. 6, 7). Disconformities at about 64 and 75 cm (Figs. 3, 4) represent abrupt changes in the composition of sediment originally deposited.

Sesquioxides and silica. The Potters Mills clay shows the most dramatic changes in sesquioxides and silica (Fig. 6). Iron and aluminum oxide increase by about 0.6 and 0.1 gm/cc, respectively, toward the top of the Potters Mills clay, whereas silica shows a corresponding decrease of about 0.2 gm/cc in the A

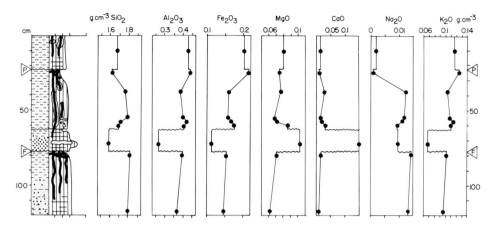

Figure 6. Variation in major oxides in Potters Mills clay (below upper triangle) and Faust Flat silty clay (below lower triangle) paleosols.

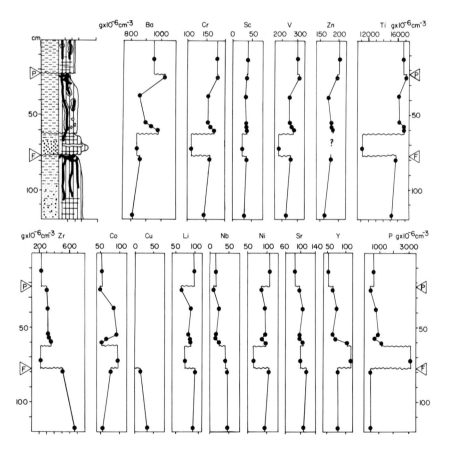

Figure 7. Variation in minor and trace elements in Potters Mills clay (below upper triangle) and Faust Flat silty clay (below lower triangle) paleosols.

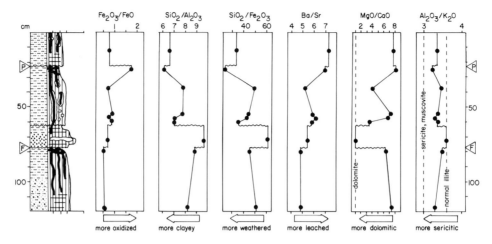

Figure 8. Selected molecular ratios (calculated in grams per cubic centimeter) chosen to illustrate degree of weathering and mineralogy of Potters Mills clay (below upper triangle) and Faust Flat silty clay (below lower triangle) paleosols.

horizon. The decrease in silica is attributable to two factors: an increase in the amount of clay in the A horizon, and desilication due to destruction of silicates. The increase in Fe_2O_3 toward the top of the paleosol is probably the result of oxidization of iron on exposure to atmospheric oxygen. The iron is now mostly present within hematite, but originally may have been within a variety of oxides or oxyhydrates (Walker, 1967). The Potters Mills clay also shows an increase in alumina in its A horizon, which corresponds to the increase in clay toward the top of the paleosol. The Faust Flat silty clay does not show so clearly the pedogenic trends evident in the Potters Mills clay. There is a slight increase in Al_2O_3 toward the A horizon of the Faust Flat silty clay, which is largely due to originally deposited clays. The variation in these three oxides is compatible with the field evidence that the Potters Mills clay is a more strongly developed paleosol than is the Faust Flat silty clay.

Alkaline earths. The sandy layer between the paleosols has a striking increase in alkaline earth oxides (Fig. 6). In this sample, these oxides are in equimolar proportions (Fig. 8) in support of petrographic observations that this rock is cemented by dolomite, which was also found to be the main carbonate mineral of the Juniata Formation by Horowitz (1965). Dolomitic nodules and cement correspond in abundance to the complementary variation in MgO and CaO through the entire profile, although the molar excess of MgO outside the intervening sandy layer (Fig. 8) means that much MgO is within chlorite, as noted for these rocks by Horowitz (1965) and Thompson (1970b). Of the two paleosols, the Potters Mills clay shows the most significant variations in these oxides. About 15 cm below the surface of the Potters Mills clay there is an increase in CaO of approximately 0.03 gm/cc, and the MgO content of the paleosol is 0.08 gm/cc. This finding has been interpreted as the depth to the calcic horizon. The Faust Flat silty clay, which is devoid of caliche nodules, has low values

of both oxides (<0.02 for CaO and <0.075 for MgO) throughout.

Alkalis. Of the alkali elements, there is a surficial depletion of soda in the Potters Mills clay, but an enrichment of potash (Fig. 6). This surficial accumulation is anomalous because the other bases (MgO, CaO, and Na₂) have all been leached from the upper portions of the Potters Mills clay. In modern soils, potassium enrichment may be the result of dry evaporitic conditions that cause accumulation of alkalis in the soil (Duchafour, 1982). As no corresponding enrichment in sodium is seen, this is an unlikely explanation. Potassium enrichments have been documented in many early Paleozoic and Precambrian paleosols (Gay and Grandstaff, 1980; Retallack, 1986a). Why potassium enrichment is so widespread in paleosols of early Paleozoic age and older has sparked some controversy. Studies on modern vegetation have shown that vascular plants have a remarkable ability to extract potassium from soil (Mehlich and Drake, 1955). Thus it is possible that, prior to the development of vascular plants, potassium was not removed from the soil in such great quantities (Weaver, 1967).

Another explanation for the K_2O enrichment is that it is a diagenetic phenomenon. Illitization of clays with depth has been documented in several studies (Hower and others, 1976). Morton (1985) has studied diagenetic illitization in Oligocene shales. His isotopic data indicate that the illitization of smectite has been punctuated. At depths of about 2 to 3 km, smectites were converted to illite with potassium liberated from the dissolution of potassium feldspar. This process was terminated by a local dewatering event. The degree to which potash enrichment is original or late diagenetic must be considered on a case-by-case basis.

The linear relationship between moles of K_2O and Al_2O_3 in the Juniata paleosols (Fig. 9) is an indication that the amount of potash is close to monomineralically controlled. The composition of illite usually varies between $K_2Al_4(Si_6Al_2O_{20})(OH)_4$ and $K_{1.5}Al_4(Si_{6.5}Al_{1.5}O_{20})(OH)_4$ (Deer and others, 1966), with 5:1 to 11:3 ratios of aluminum to potassium. The composition of the paleosols from the Juniata Formation is at or above this usual range, and approaches the molar proportions found in sericite and muscovite (Figs. 8, 9). All three minerals appear to be present. The main clay mineral revealed by X-ray diffraction studies is illite (Horowitz, 1965; Thompson, 1970b). Some of the recrystallized clay in the surface horizon of the Potters Mills clay could be sericite. Muscovite is rare toward the base of both paleosols. Within sandy lower horizons of the paleosols, K-feldspar also is more common. Dissolution of some of these grains could have contributed to illitization and sericitization of whatever clay minerals were once present at the surface of the Potters Mills clay. On the other hand, the Al_2O_3/K_2O ratios of the Faust Flat silty clay and the base of the Potters Mills clay are compatible with the presence of less weathered muscovite and K-feldspar there. The upper part of the Faust Flat silty clay and the sandy bed between the paleosols are now stoichiometrically illitic, and there are other reasons for supposing that some illite was originally present. The degree of weathering of the Potters Mills clay is mild by comparison with modern tropical kaolinitic soils, and there are no soil structures present which could be interpreted as evidence of large amounts of strongly swelling clays (smectites). Thus it is likely that both illite and potash were present in more than trace amounts throughout this soil, although it is difficult to be certain whether they were sufficiently abundant so that, like clay in this profile, they also increased in amount toward the surface. Some of this surficial clay may originally have been smectitic, mixed layer, or other kinds of clay.

Trace elements. Each trace element within these sedimentary rocks is present in amounts (Table 1) compatible with their derivation from a source terrain of sedimentary and metamorphic rocks of granitic to intermediate overall composition, as also determined by Krynine (1940) and Krynine and Tuttle (1941), from examination of heavy minerals. The enrichment of almost all the trace elements (excepting Co) toward the base of the Potters Mills clay paleosol (Fig. 7) can be related to the greater abundance of unweathered heavy and mafic minerals there. The distribution of Zr most clearly illustrates an original concentration of heavy minerals toward the base of the fining-upward sequence of sediment on which the paleosol formed. This element is present primarily in the extremely weather-resistant mineral zircon, which in these rocks is quite coarse-grained (Krynine, 1940). Zirconium also is much less abundant toward the top of the Faust Flat silty clay paleosol, probably for much the same reason. All other trace elements within the Faust Flat paleosol show different and much less variation than in the Potters Mills paleosol, thus confirming its lesser degree of development on a different sedimentary unit.

Apart from these patterns reflecting original sedimentation, there are two pedogenic patterns of trace elements in the Potters Mills clay paleosol: greater abundance at the surface (in Ba, Cr, Sc, V, Zn) and lesser abundance at the surface (Co, Li, Ni, Nb,

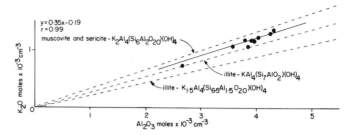

Figure 9. Molar proportions of K_2O and Al_2O_3 for both Potters Mills clay and Faust Flat silty clay paleosols (indicated by points and regression line); they fall between the usual stoichometries for illite and sericite.

Sr, Y). There is so little Cu that not much should be made of its distribution. The upward-increasing pattern is also seen in Ti. If these data were all normalized to Ti, as is sometimes done for aridland soils when their parent material is known, those elements that appear to be surficially enriched would be seen to have remained more or less steady in abundance. Like Ti, each of these trace elements (Ba, Cr, Sc, V, and Zn) tends to accumulate in clays of soils and others residual materials (Aubert and Pinta, 1977; Wedepohl, 1978). Their distribution in the Potters Mills clay can be related to the greater abundance of clay at its surface (Fig. 5). Surficial weathering of the original sediment, together with later fine-grained additions of windblown dust and flood-borne clay, presumably enriched these weather-resistant elements.

Of the trace elements that are depleted at the surface, only Co shows a pattern completely consistent with its incorporation within carbonate (compare Fig. 5). The other surficially depleted trace elements (Li, Nb, Ni, Sr, and Y), like P, appear to have been depleted from the surface of the paleosol by destruction of rock fragments and weatherable minerals during soil formation. There is no suggestion in this paleosol of surficial enrichment of P, Ni, or Y often associated with the accumulation of well-humified organic matter within modern soils. Zinc usually follows these elements in modern soils (Kovda and others, 1964; Aubert and Pinta, 1977) and is more abundant at the surface of the paleosol, but its pattern can be related to the distribution of clay in the paleosol. Thus, the distribution of phosphorus and organic matter in the original soil was probably unlike that of modern grassland and swampy soils, and more like tropical or forested soils. In these, most of the organic matter is loose litter and living organisms, rather than incorporated within the soil (Stevenson, 1969; Smeck, 1973). As another alternative, it could be that most of the biomass of the soil was well below the surface, sheltered from a harsh external environment. Considering the profound weathering of the uppermost sample, we believe the hypothesis of subterranean communities is less likely than that of a surficial carpet of loose vegetation and litter.

Molecular ratios

Molecular ratios provide a simple index for weathering in paleosols. The ratios are determined by dividing the weight percent of each oxide involved by its molecular weight, and then dividing the oxides as specified by the particular ratio. These ratios are expressed as a single value, thereby easily allowing comparisons to be drawn between various profiles. Different ratios of oxides have been developed to assess desilication, ferruginization, leaching, waterlogging, and other effects of weathering from one horizon to the next. We also calculated two additional molecular ratios (MgO/CaO and Al_2O_3/K_2O) in order to investigate the mineralogy of carbonate and clay within the profile, as already discussed.

The ratios of Fe_2O_3:FeO, SiO_2:Al_2O_3, and SiO_2:Fe_2O_3 exhibit typical pedogenic trends (Fig. 8) that are indicative of ferruginization and desilication in the Juniata paleosols. The bounding unconformities that separate the individual sedimentary units on which paleosols formed are represented in our figures by undulating connecting lines. Two paleosols—Potters Mills clay and Faust Flat silty clay—are present in this profile. The intervening horizon is a sandy depositional unit that shows no soil development and is compositionally distinct from the two paleosols.

The Fe_2O_3:FeO ratio shows a strong increase in oxidized iron toward the top of the Potters Mills clay paleosol. This ferruginization is marked in the Potters Mills clay, compared to the Faust Flat silty clay, which shows virtually no change in Fe_2O_3:FeO with depth. The intervening sandy bed has a Fe_2O_3:FeO ratio similar to the Faust Flat silty clay and the C horizon of the Potters Mills clay.

The SiO_2:Al_2O_3 values reflect clay content. A typical sodic feldspar, $NaAlSi_3O_8$, has a 3:1 ratio of silica to aluminum, whereas clays such as illite, $KAl_4(Si_7AlO_{20})(OH)_4$, have a 7:5 ratio. A decreasing ratio of silica to alumina indicates an increased proportion of clay minerals produced by either original sedimentation or by hydrolysis of the original silicates. Both the Potters Mills clay and the Faust Flat silty clay were developed within similar fining-upward cycles, but the Potters Mills clay has markedly increased Al_2O_3 relative to SiO_2 at the top of the paleosol. No such trend is evident in the Faust Flat silty clay. We interpret this difference in compositional variation to be largely the result of pedogenic clay formation. This is to be expected, since the Potters Mills clay is the better developed of the two paleosols. The intervening sandy layer has an extremely high ratio of SiO_2:Al_2O_3, reflecting its quartz-rich composition.

As with the other ratios, the Faust Flat silty clay exhibits little variation in SiO_2:Fe_2O_3 with depth. The uppermost portion of the Potters Mills clay, on the other hand, is depleted in SiO_2 relative to Fe_2O_3, presumably because of fixation of iron by oxidation after desilication due to weathering (Birkeland, 1984). Krauskopf (1979) has shown that the solubility of quartz increases exponentially under conditions of pH > 9. A pH of at least 7 is indicated by the presence of caliche nodules, but no psuedomorphs or other evidence of highly alkaline evaporite

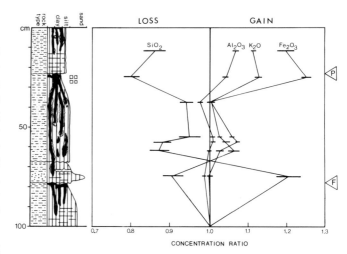

Figure 10. Concentration ratios showing gains and losses of major oxides relative to TiO_2 in Potters Mills clay (below upper triangle) and Faust Flat silty clay (below lower triangle) paleosols.

minerals have been seen. The depletion of silica from the A horizon of the Potters Mills clay is more likely due to destruction of other silicate minerals during weathering. Both rock fragments and micas become very scarce toward the top of the Potters Mills clay.

Since strontium is more soluble than the otherwise chemically similar barium, the ratio Ba/Sr is an indicator of leaching. This ratio increases with degree of drainage and with intensity and time of weathering, from near 2 in most rocks to 10 or more in strongly leached sandy soils such as Spodosols (Vinogradov, 1959). These ratios for paleosols of the Juniata Formation confirm that the Potters Mills clay, especially its surface, was much better drained and weathered longer than the Faust Flat silty clay.

Concentration ratios

To better assess the nature and degree of pedogenesis, concentration ratios were calculated for the major oxides (Fig. 10). For these calculations we have assumed that TiO_2 was stable throughout the profile. Minerals containing TiO_2 are virtually insoluble when soil conditions are moderately alkaline (Birkeland, 1984). Within the Juniata paleosols, alkaline conditions are indicated by the presence of caliche nodules. Conservation of TiO_2 is further supported by the virtually constant values of TiO_2 throughout the profile (Table 1). To establish actual concentrations or depletions, it is also necessary to know the original composition. Characterizing parent material has often been a problem for soil chemists (Krauskopf, 1979; Birkeland, 1984). Unaltered, uniform parent material is seldom encountered. This is especially a problem in fluvial sediments that include original sedimentary layering and fining-upward sequences. No single homogeneous parent material is available for the Potters Mills clay paleosol. In light of this, a different approach for approximating a reasonable parent material composition was employed.

Field examination and the chemical variation both provide evidence that the Faust Flat silty clay is much less pedogenically developed than the Potters Mills clay. Yet both developed on similar alluvial deposits. Based on this genetic similarity, the sandy through clayey horizons of the Faust Flat silty clay may be taken to approximate the compositional range of the parent materials for the Potters Mills clay. Thus the concentration ratios calculated for the Potters Mills clay represents the result of soil formation beyond that seen in the Faust Flat silty clay. A range of concentration ratios is gained, depending on whether clayey or sandy parts of the Faust Flat silty clay were used in the calculations as a parent material. This range can be envisaged as a kind of systematic error (represented by the heavily ruled horizontal bars in Fig. 10). The concentration ratio values for the individual oxides were calculated using the following equation (after Gay and Grandstaff, 1980):

$$CR = (M_w/M_p)/(TiO_{2\,w}/TiO_{2\,p}),$$

assuming TiO_2 is stable and, where CR = concentration ratio, M_w = concentration of the oxide in paleosol, M_p = concentration of the oxide in the parent material, $TiO_{2\,w}$ = TiO_2 in paleosol, and $TiO_{2\,p}$ = TiO_2 in parent material.

The concentration ratios demonstrate significant soil development of the Potters Mills clay beyond the compositional range of the Faust Flat silty clay. This is encouraging confirmation of surficial desilication, clay formation, and destruction of weatherable silicates such as mica and rock fragments, of subsurface calcification, and of ferruginization, already discussed. This degree of soil formation is slight by modern standards, but nevertheless significant.

DISCUSSION

As might be surmised, these Late Ordovician paleosols do not fit comfortably into modern soil classification schemes. The Juniata paleosols can be compared to modern grassland soils of regions with mild topographic relief and subhumid to semiarid climates. Some grassland soils have a mild degree of plant-soil interaction, somewhat similar to Late Ordovician soil formation. The presumed high degree of base saturation of the Juniata paleosols is also typical of grassland soils. Closer examination of this analogy reveals discrepancies. True grassland soils, Mollisols, have a distinct mollic epipedon (surface horizon) consisting of granular peds and masses of fine root traces. No evidence of such structures was seen in the Juniata paleosols. Also, the Juniata paleosols lack the thickness and degree of humification usually associated with Mollisols.

The red color and weak textural differentiation of the Juniata paleosols more closely allies them with Oxisols, which form in tropical to subtropical climates. These soils, however, are al-

most completely leached of cations and are generally much thicker and have a microstructure distinct from that of the Potters Mills clay or the Faust Flat silty clay paleosols. The red color of the paleosols could be in large part due to diagenetic dehydration of brown and yellow minerals.

The mild degree of weathering in the Juniata paleosols requires that they be classified as USDA Inceptisols (Potters Mills clay) and Entisols (Faust Flat silty clay). Entisols and Inceptisols are generally considered to form under short periods of weathering. Unfortunately, we have little knowledge of early Paleozoic weathering rates. Thus, it may be misleading to assume that the Potters Mills clay and Faust Flat silty clay formed in the same amount of time as a comparable modern Inceptisol or Entisol.

We can place the following constraints on Ordovician weathering regimes in alluvial settings. Surficial desilication, calcification, clay formation, and ferruginization, common to modern subtropical conditions, were effective processes in early Paleozoic soils. Despite the lack of vascular plants, large (1–21 mm diameter) animals were available to promote soil formation (by aeration and bioturbation, among other processes) by Late Ordovician time. Potassium enrichments, so widespread in other early Paleozoic and Precambrian paleosols, are also present in paleosols formed on alluvial parent materials. Both pedogenic and late diagenetic contributions to potash content seem likely, but the relative importance of these different processes remains difficult to disentangle.

CONCLUSIONS

We have identified and interpreted two Late Ordovician paleosols developed on alluvium. The weakly developed Potter Mills clay is distinguished from the very weakly developed Faust Flat silty clay by several processes: (1) the development of soil structure, soil horizons, and obliteration of bedding; (2) the presence of a caliche (Bk) horizon; (3) the degree of desilication, ferruginization, and leaching of base cations; and (4) the development of potash enrichment in the A horizon.

Three separate reductions of the chemical data were employed to assess the nature and degree of soil formation. Initial assessments of desilication, ferruginization, and other effects of weathering were provided by molecular ratios. Chemical variation diagrams illustrate the variation of the major oxides. A concentration ratio diagram was constructed on the assumption that TiO_2 was immobile during weathering. Since no homogeneous parent material was available, the range in composition of the very weakly developed Faust Flat silty clay paleosol was used to approximate a parent material composition for the Potters Mills clay paleosol. The concentration ratios show significant soil development in the Potters Mills clay beyond any soil formation in the Faust Flat silty clay. The degree of soil development is slight by modern standards, making these soils most similar to modern USDA Inceptisols and Entisols.

From our observation of the Juniata Formation at several localities in Pennsylvania, the Potters Mills clay and Faust Flat

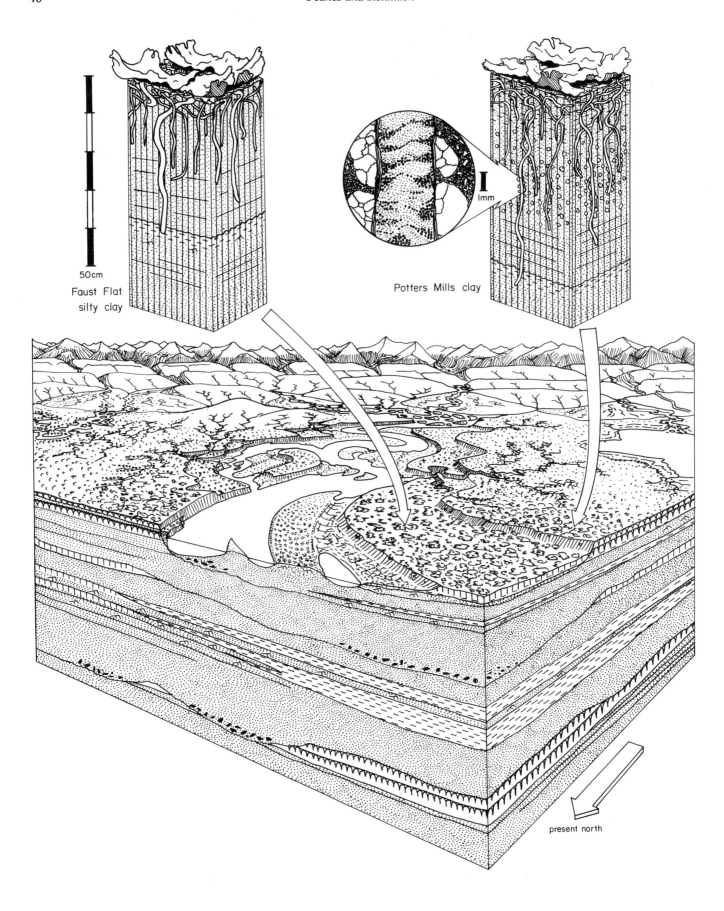

50cm

Faust Flat
silty clay

Potters Mills clay

1mm

present north

◄───────────────────────────────────────

Figure 11. Late Ordovician paleoenvironmental reconstruction showing flood-plain settings for Potters Mills clay and Faust Flat silty clay paleosols. Our fluvial reconstruction is based on measurements of asymmetric paleochannels in the roadcut southeast of Potters Mills. The nature of vegetation remains unknown; maximum conceivable biomass compatible with chemical and structural features of the paleosols is shown. Nature of animals that excavated burrows with w-shaped backfill layers (shown in enlargement) is also under further investigation.

silty clay are representative of two widespread kinds of paleosols formed on inland portions of coastal plains flanking the ancestral Appalachian Mountains (Fig. 11). We envisage these soils forming on streamsides (Faust Flat Series) and low terraces (Potters Mills Series) in a landscape that would have appeared barren, yet not quite desertlike. The exact nature of vegetation in this landscape is not known. It was probably nonvascular, and much more low-growing and monotonous than modern vegetation of comparable seasonally dry subtropical climates. Traces of a low-

diversity fauna, presumably arthropods as large as 2 cm across, appear to have been considerably more uniform between the limited range of ecosystems preserved (represented by the two paleosol series) than is the case in modern subtropical landscapes. The chemical studies reported here strengthen our impression of the Juniata Formation as an important record of an early stage in the evolution of multicellular soil fauna and flora and of soil-forming processes.

ACKNOWLEDGMENTS

We thank J. D. Lawson (University of Glasgow) and W. G. Chaloner (Royal Holloway and Bedford Colleges, England) for organizing an especially stimulating discussion at a meeting of the Royal Society, where some of these views were first aired, and for helpful comments made by P. V. Wright (University of Bristol) and J. A. Catt (Soil Survey of England and Wales). Chemical analyses were performed by A. J. Irving (University of Washington), and point counting of thin sections was done by R. W. Goodfellow (University of Oregon). The research was funded by a grant to C.R.F. from the Society of Sigma XI.

REFERENCES CITED

Arkley, R. J., 1963, Calculation of carbonate and water movement in soils from climatic data: Soil Science, v. 96, p. 239–248.

Aubert, H., and Pinta, M., 1977, Trace elements in soils: Amsterdam, Elsevier, 395 p.

Birkeland, P. W., 1984, Soils and geomorphology: Fair Lawn, New Jersey, Oxford University Press, 372 p.

Brewer, R., 1976, Fabric and mineral analysis of soil (2nd ed.): New York, Wiley, 470 p.

Deer, W. A., Howie, R. A., and Zussman, J., 1966, An introduction to the rock-forming minerals: London, Longman, 528 p.

Duchafour, P., 1982, Pedology; Pedogenesis and classification: London, Allen and Unwin, 448 p.

Fitzpatrick, E. A., 1980, Soils: London, Longman, 353 p.

Gay, A. L., and Grandstaff, D. E., 1980, Chemistry and mineralogy of Precambrian paleosols at Elliot Lake, Ontario, Canada: Precambrian Research, v. 12, p. 349–373.

Gile, L. H., Peterson, F. F., and Grossman, R. B., 1966, Morphologic and genetic sequences of carbonate accumulation in desert soils: Soil Science, v. 101, p. 347–360.

Holland, H. D., 1984, The chemical evolution of the atmosphere and oceans: Princeton, New Jersey, Princeton University Press, 582 p.

Horowitz, D. H., 1965, Petrology of the Upper Ordovician and Lower Silurian rocks in the central Appalachians [Ph.D. thesis]: State College, Pennsylvania State University, 221 p.

Hower, J., Eslinger, E. V., Hower, M. E., and Perry, E. A., 1979, Mechanisms of burial metamorphism of argillaceous sediment. 1. Mineralogical and chemical evidence: Geological Society of America Bulletin, v. 87, p. 725–737.

Jenny, H., 1980, The soil resource: New York, Springer, 377 p.

Kovda, V. A., Lakushevskaya, I. V., and Tyuryakov, A. N., 1964, Microelements in the soils of the U.S.S.R.; Jerusalem, Israel Program for Scientific Translations, 50 p.

Krauskopf, K. B., 1979, Introduction to geochemistry: Hightstown, New Jersey, McGraw-Hill, 617 p.

Krynine, P. D., 1940, Paleozoic heavy minerals from central Pennsylvania and their relation to Appalachian structure: Proceedings of the Pennsylvania Academy of Science, v. 14, p. 60–64.

Krynine, P. D., and Tuttle, O. F., 1941, Petrology of the Ordovician-Silurian boundary in Pennsylvania: Geological Society of America Bulletin, v. 52, p. 1917–1918.

Mann, A. W., and Horowitz, R. D., 1979, Groundwater calcrete deposits in Australia; Some observations from western Australia: Journal of the Geological Society of Australia, v. 26, p. 293–303.

McFadden, L. D., and Tinsley, J. C., 1985, Rate and depth of pedogenic carbonate accumulation in soils; Formation and testing of a compartment model, *in* Weide, D. L., ed., Soils and Quaternary geology of the southwestern United States: Geological Society of America Special Paper 203, p. 23–41.

Meckel, L. D., 1970, Paleozoic alluvial sedimentation in the central Appalachians; A summary, *in* Fisher, G. W., Reed, J. C., and Weaver, K. N., eds., Studies in Appalachian geology; Central and southern: New York, Interscience, p. 49–67.

Mehlich, A., and Drake, M., 1955, Soil chemistry and plant nutrition, *in* Bear, F. E., ed., Chemistry of the soil: New York, Reinhold, p. 395–444.

Morton, J. P., 1985, Rb-Sr evidence for punctuated illite/smectite diagenesis in the Oligocene, Frio Formation, Texas Gulf Coast: Geological Society of America Bulletin, v. 96, p. 114–122.

Netterberg, F., 1969, The interpretation of some basic calcrete types: South African Archaeological Bulletin, v. 24, p. 117–122.

Retallack, G. J., 1983, Late Eocene and Oligocene paleosols from Badlands National Park, South Dakota: Geological Society of America Special Paper 193, 89 p.

—— , 1984, Completeness of the rock and fossil record; Some estimates using fossil soils: Paleobiology, v. 10, p. 59–78.

—— , 1985, Fossil soils as grounds for interpreting the advent of large plants and animals on land: Philosophical Transactions of the Royal Society of London, B309, p. 105–142.

—— , 1986a, The fossil record of soils, *in* Wright, P. V., ed., Palaeosols; Their recognition and interpretation: Oxford, Blackwells, p. 1–57.

——, 1986b, Reappraisal of a 2200 Ma paleosol from near Waterval Onder, South Africa: Precambrian Research, v. 32, p. 195–232.

Retallack, G. J., Grandstaff, D. E., and Kimberly, M. M., 1984, The promise and problems of Precambrian paleosols: Episodes, v. 7, no. 2, p. 8–12.

Ross, R. J., 1982, The Ordovician system in the United States: Publishers International Union Geological Science, v. 12, 13 p.

Smeck, N. E., 1973, Phosphorus; An indicator of pedogenetic weathering processes: Soil Science, v. 115, p. 199–206.

Soil Survey Staff, 1975, Soil taxonomy; Handbook of the U.S. Department of Agriculture, v. 436, 754 p.

Stace, H.C.T., Hubble, G. D., Brewer, R., Northcote, K. H., Sleeman, J. R., Mulcahy, M. J., and Hallsworth, E. G., 1968, A handbook of Australian soils: Adelaide, Relim, 435 p.

Stevenson, F. J., 1969, Pedohumus; accumulation and diagenesis during the Quaternary: Soil Science, v. 107, p. 470–479.

Thompson, A. M., 1970a, Lithofacies and formation nomenclature in Upper Ordovician stratigraphy, central Appalachians: Geological Society of America Bulletin, v. 81, p. 1255–1260.

——, 1970b, Geochemistry of color genesis in red bed sequence, Juniata and Bald Eagle Formations, Pennsylvania: Journal of Sedimentary Petrology, v. 40, p. 599–615.

Vinogradov, A. P., 1959, The geochemistry of rare and dispersed elements in soils: New York, Consultants Bureau, 209 p.

Walker, T. R., 1967, Formation of red beds in modern and ancient deserts: Geological Society of America Bulletin, v. 78, p. 353–368.

Weaver, C. E., 1967, Potassium, illite, and the ocean: Geochimica Cosmochimica Acta, v. 31, p. 2181–2196.

Wedepohl, K. H., 1978, Handbook of geochemistry: Berlin, Springer-Verlag.

Yeakel, L. S., 1962, Tuscarora, Juniata, and Bald Eagle paleocurrents and paleogeography in the central Appalachians: Geological Society of America Bulletin, v. 73, p. 1515–1540.

MANUSCRIPT ACCEPTED BY THE SOCIETY JULY 1, 1987

Geological Society of America
Special Paper 216
1988

A paleosol interpretation for profiles exhibiting subaerial exposure "crusts" from the Mississippian of the Appalachian Basin

Frank R. Ettensohn
Department of Geological Sciences
University of Kentucky
Lexington, Kentucky 40506

Garland R. Dever, Jr.
Kentucky Geological Survey
University of Kentucky
Lexington, Kentucky 40506

Jeffrey S. Grow
Chevron, U.S.A.
New Orleans, Louisiana 70112

ABSTRACT

Subaerial exposure surfaces in the Middle and Upper Mississippian Slade Formation of northeastern Kentucky are largely composed of cutanic concentrations of micritic calcite within the former Ccam horizons of caliche soils. The association of this material with soil horizons and structures, as well as with abundant root traces, strongly indicates a pedogenic origin. In fact, the contribution of plants and small soil organisms was far greater than has been previously recognized.

The caliches occur as "interformational" profiles on disconformities separating lower Slade members and as "intraformational" profiles within three lower Slade units. Paleoexposure was related to position on a structurally active margin of the Appalachian Basin and to episodes of regional and local regression.

The caliches resulted from soil and ground-water conditions in a semi-arid climate characterized by seasonal rain and drought and an overall net moisture deficit. Growth of roots, desiccation, and displacive crystallization broke up parent limestones, allowing access of vadose waters and creating framework (skeleton) grains that were easily transformed into a mobile plasma fraction by solution. Solution of carbonate grains and eluviation of carbonate-bearing solutions primarily occurred during the moist rainy season, whereas illuviation rapidly followed the onset of drought. The calcium carbonate was deposited largely as internal, laminar plasma concentrations called cutans, which have been incorrectly referred to as "crusts" in previous work on the Slade. Accumulation of these cutanic laminae formed indurated laminar calcrete deposits near the bases of the caliche profiles. These calcretes may be of physicochemical or rhizocretionary origin, depending on conditions of exposure. More diffuse, irregular calcretes apparently developed along avenues of porosity and were formed by plasma separation, the in situ micritization of other limestone textures.

Although climate in the Meramecian and earliest Chesterian epochs was the major factor responsible for caliche formation, the length of exposure and the type of carbonate lithology controlled the nature and thickness of caliche profiles. "Intraformational" profiles are always thin and immature, representing short-lived exposure on porous lithologies like calcarenite. Conversely, "interformational" profiles are always mature or composite and represent longer periods of exposure on more impermeable lithologies such as calcilutite. Impermeable lithologies were important, because they prevented migration of soil waters and plasma below the soil profile.

By late Early Chesterian time, the climate had become more humid, and the latest formed caliches were partially destroyed by solution, creating a leached, clayey residual soil on top of earlier caliche soils. On structurally elevated areas, where exposure was long and drainage was good, this period of humid pedogenesis resulted in composite terra rossa paleosols produced from the humid weathering of older caliche profiles.

INTRODUCTION

Among the most common pedogenic features formed in carbonate rocks are subaerial exposure crusts, which are calcareous, crust-like structures that commonly coat or replace strata in the upper meter or so of many limestone sequences in subtropical to semi-arid areas. Today crusts are present in the Florida Keys, Bermuda, the Bahamas, the Yucatan Peninsula, Libya, Morocco, South Africa, Aldebra, Spain, the West Indies, Israel, and Australia (Rutte, 1958; Ruhe and others, 1961; Moseley, 1965; Ruellan, 1967; Krumbein, 1968; Multer and Hoffmeister, 1968, 1971; Ward and others, 1970; James, 1972; Read, 1974; Braithwaite, 1975; Choquette, 1976; Harrison, 1977; Watts, 1980; Warren, 1983; Hale and Ettensohn, 1984). Although crusts have been known for some time (e.g., Rutte, 1958; Ruhe and others, 1961), it was not until the work of Multer and Hoffmeister (1968, 1971) in the Florida Keys that their origin was understood. Those studies were the springboard that enabled interpretation of many other crust sequences, particularly in Quaternary and a few Paleozoic rocks. Among the first Paleozoic crust sequences so interpreted were those in the Middle and Upper Mississippian Slade Formation of northeastern Kentucky, formerly the Newman Limestone (Ettensohn and others, 1984b). Although the subaerial, vadose diagenetic aspects of the crusts were readily apparent, the pedogenic aspects were hardly recognized, perhaps because of the general unfamiliarity of most geologists with pedogenesis and pedogenic features. In recent years, however, increased awareness of pedogenesis has greatly facilitated interpretation of features ascribed, sometimes inadequately, to diagenesis or vadose diagenesis. It was the presence of so many pedogenic features associated with crusts in parts of the Slade that suggested to us that a pedogenic interpretation probably was more warranted than a wholly diagenetic one. This chapter describes the pedogenic features associated with crusts in the Slade, the pedogenic processes that produced them, and the environmental and structural framework in which they developed. We believe that the framework and processes discussed here are probably applicable to many other Paleozoic carbonate sequences.

Previous work

The so-called crusts in the Slade Formation were first suggested to be products of subaerial exposure and vadose diagenesis by Ferm and others (1971), Inden and Horne (1973), and Horne and others (1974). Subsequent studies by Dever (1973, 1977, 1980a,b), Ettensohn (1975, 1979, 1980, 1981), and Ettensohn and Dever (1979a,b,c) provided additional evidence for this origin. Walls and others (1975) and Harrison and Steinen (1978) first documented the microscopic aspects of the Kentucky crust profiles and noted their similarity to modern counterparts in the West Indies. Since their work, the Slade crusts and associated features have become almost the classic example of Paleozoic subaerial exposure and vadose diagenesis (e.g., Assereto and Kendall, 1977, p. 187, 189–190; Inden and Moore, 1983, p. 229; James and Choquette, 1984, p. 168). Inden and Horne (1973) first suggested that the crust profiles were actually "fossil soils," and Walls and others (1975) indicated that they were partially related to soil development, but not until the work of Grow (1982) and Ettensohn and others (1984a) were the pedogenic aspects of these "crusts" described and interpreted.

Study area

Exposure crusts and related features were examined on the western flank of the Appalachian Basin in northeastern and east-central Kentucky from Greenup County southward to Estill County (Fig. 1). The Slade outcrop belt (Fig. 1) is present along the Cumberland Escarpment of the Appalachian (Cumberland) Plateau (Ettensohn and others, 1984b). We have examined more than 100 exposures containing subaerial exposure features during the past 15 yr. These exposures are briefly described and located in Dever (1973, 1980a), Ettensohn (1975), and Grow (1982). The most accessible and spectacular examples of these exposure features are present along Interstate 64 in northeastern Kentucky (Ettensohn, 1986); the interstate cuts are described and located in Ettensohn and Dever (1979a,b,c) and in Ettensohn (1980, 1981). Other significant exposures containing these features in east-central Kentucky are present along Kentucky 1274 and in a few

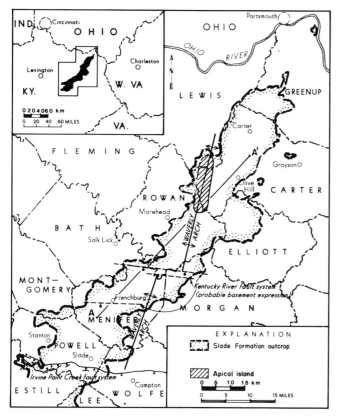

Figure 1. Map of study area showing outcrop belt of Slade Formation and structural features active during development of lower Slade pedocomplex. Apical Island was part of the Waverly Arch that was positive during most of Carboniferous time. A-A' indicates section line shown in Figure 5 (after Ettensohn, 1980).

quarries to the south (Dever and others, 1977; Ettensohn and others, 1984a) and along Interstate 75 (Dever and others, 1979).

Structural framework

The study area is underlain by two major structures (Figs. 1, 2) that were active during the Carboniferous: (1) a broad, east-west basement fault system with some surface expression in the Kentucky River and Irvine–Paint Creek Fault systems, and (2) a north-trending uplift, named the Waverly Arch by Woodward (1961). Both structures were active during the early Paleozoic (Woodward, 1961) and again in the late Paleozoic (Dever and others, 1977). Uplift on the fault zone was dominantly to the north, and much of the movement apparently was accommodated along recurrent growth faults (Dever and others, 1977). The Waverly Arch was a broad, linear uplift with slight migration of the axis of uplift during the Paleozoic. One part of the arch, called the Apical Island (Fig. 1) by Ettensohn (1975, 1977, 1980), underwent greater uplift than other parts of the structure and was a positive area during much of the Carboniferous.

Both structures apparently acted in concert, and Mississippian uplift on them is reflected by variations in thickness of deposits, distribution of strata, the location and nature of disconformities, and facies distribution (Dever and others, 1977; Ettensohn and Dever, 1979a,b,c; Ettensohn, 1980, 1981). A common manifestation of uplift near the structures is progressive thinning of strata due to erosion; at least five episodes of uplift have been identified by erosional disconformities (Ettensohn, 1981). Crust profiles on three of these disconformities are examined in this study; the profiles generally are thicker, better developed, and exhibit a greater variety of pedogenic features on and near the uplifted structural elements.

Stratigraphy

Subaerial exposure features in eastern Kentucky are developed in parts of three Mississippian formations: the Borden, Slade, and Paragon (formerly the Pennington Formation) (Fig. 3). The best development of these features occurs in four of the five members that form the lower part of the Slade Formation: the St. Louis, Ste. Genevieve, Warix Run, and Mill Knob (Fig. 3). The underlying Borden and overlying Paragon Formations are largely composed of siliciclastic sedimentary rocks. The Slade Formation is a newly designated unit for rocks that in large part were formerly included in the Newman Limestone (Fig. 3; Ettensohn and others, 1984b).

The St. Louis Member is composed of fossiliferous calcarenites and calcilutites; it represents a transgressive sequence upon which subaerial exposure features were superimposed with no intervening regressive sequence (Ettensohn and Dever, 1979c). Alteration of these subtidal carbonates by pedogenesis and erosion, which is more pronounced near regional structures, suggests that St. Louis deposition was interrupted by uplift. The St. Louis was deposited before any major Mississippian uplift, because it has a widespread distribution except for local areas where it was removed by later intra-Mississippian erosion (Figs. 4A, 5). Subaerial exposure features on the St. Louis are found only in parts of northeastern and east-central Kentucky near regional structures. To the south and southwest away from these structures, the disconformity atop the St. Louis and associated exposure features are less well developed and eventually disappear.

The Ste. Genevieve consists of massive oolitic calcarenites and locally interbedded calcilutites deposited in an extensive tidal sandbelt environment. Breccias and crusts at the top of the unit were equated by McFarlan and Walker (1956) to the Bryantsville Breccia at the top of the Ste. Genevieve Limestone in western Kentucky. The member is restricted to either side of the Waverly Arch, occurs mainly south of the fault zone, and thins depositionally and erosionally near these structures (Figs. 4B, 5). Exposure features are common on top of the Ste. Genevieve nearly everywhere it crops out in Kentucky, but are better developed near structural highs.

Ste. Genevieve deposition apparently was interrupted by uplift on regional structures late in Meramecian (Genevievian)

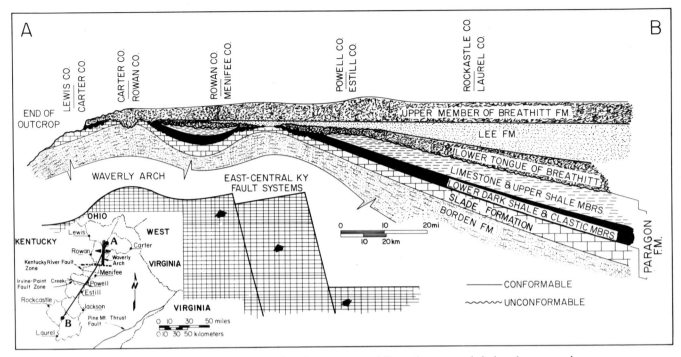

Figure 2. Schematic north-south section along east-central Kentucky outcrop belt, based on approximately 90 measured sections. Inferred relationships between major Carboniferous formations, unconformities, and underlying structure shown (after Ettensohn, 1980).

time (Dever, 1973, 1977, 1980a,b; Ettensohn and Dever, 1979a). Uplift must have been abrupt, for no regressive sequence is present unless subsequent erosion removed the evidence. During this period of exposure, deep erosion penetrated through the Ste. Genevieve into the St. Louis and Borden (Fig. 5). The few exposure features present in the Borden (Fig. 5) were formed during this period of erosion and exposure.

Following Genevievian exposure, a new marine advance in the Early Chesterian, represented by the Warix Run Member, invaded erosional lows on the northern uplifted block and extended out over large parts of the southern downdropped block (Fig. 4C). Hence, the Warix Run disconformably overlies eroded parts of the Ste. Genevieve, St. Louis, and Borden in the lows (Fig. 5) and has a characteristic disjunct distribution that reflects the presence of the Waverly Arch and the erosional lows (Fig. 4C).

The Warix Run is a massively bedded arenaceous calcarenite with large, high-angle cross-stratification. Upper parts of the Warix Run locally intertongue with the Mill Knob Member of the Slade. The Warix Run and Mill Knob are part of a fining-upward, regressive tidal channel–tidal flat complex, and the Warix Run is interpreted to represent a series of superimposed tidal-channel and tidal-bar deposits that occupied the erosion lows (Klekamp, 1971; Horne and others, 1974; Lierman, 1984). Subaerial exposure features generally are only moderately devel-

oped and occur locally at various horizons. Exposure during Warix Run deposition apparently was related to ephemeral periods of tidal-bar aggradation above mean sea level and tidal-channel migration.

With continued regression, shallow subtidal deposition in channels and on bars represented by the Warix Run gave way to dominantly tidal-flat deposition in the Mill Knob Member. Bioclastic and oolitic calcarenites, bird's-eye calcilutites, and laminated dolostones are most abundant. These lithologies may occur in the Mill Knob as distinct subunits or as parts of shoaling-upward sequences, any of which may be capped with crust zones. One to three crust zones commonly are present, but the upper crust zone is everywhere best developed. The Mill Knob is presently restricted to the flanks of the Waverly Arch (Figs. 4D, 5), but thin erosional remnants found on top of the arch suggest that the unit at one time overlapped it. This unit completed the filling of erosional lows begun in Warix Run time and subsequently lapped onto adjacent highs (Figs. 4D, 5).

Exposure features in the St. Louis, Ste. Genevieve, Warix Run, and Mill Knob members of the Slade commonly are associated with disconformities that are related to uplift on structures or regional regression. Uplift and regression apparently were significant during lower Slade deposition, such that they ended deposition of the units involved and ushered in exposure and disconformity development with accompanying paleosols. We

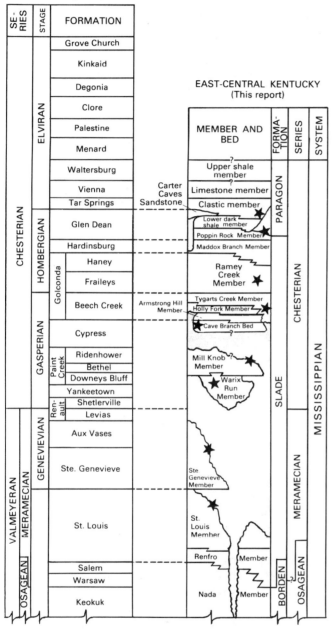

Figure 3. Stratigraphy of Slade Formation showing tentative correlations between members of Slade and Paragon Formations and formations of Mississippian type section. Mill Knob and underlying four members are informally included in lower part of Slade Formation. Stars indicate pedogenic horizons; most are associated with disconformities. Only those shown in the lower Slade are discussed herein (after Ettensohn and others, 1984b).

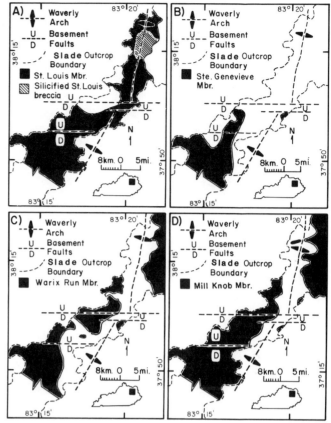

Figure 4. Distribution of four lower Slade members, reflecting control by structural features. Mapping based on 125 exposures throughout area (after Ettensohn, 1980).

have designated such paleosols and profiles as interformational (Fig. 6). The interformational profiles on top of the St. Louis, Ste. Genevieve, and Mill Knob are widespread and distinct enough to be mapped as pedoderms (Brewer and others, 1970) or geosols (Morrison, 1967; North American Commission on Stratigraphic Nomenclature, 1983). Because these lower Slade paleosols occur in close vertical succession, they form a pedocomplex (see Fink, 1976) (Fig. 5). Local regressions and shoal–sand bar aggradation produced ephemeral exposure and resulted in localized and commonly immature profiles. Because these profiles always occur within the given member, we designate them as intraformational (Ste. Genevieve, Warix Run, Mill Knob) (Fig. 6). Although exposure features also occur in younger Slade and Paragon members (Fig. 3), the effects of synsedimentary tectonism and regression were most intense during deposition of the four lower Slade members, and the tops of these members exhibit the best evidence of pedogenesis. The relative thickness and distribution of these members (Fig. 5) is in large part structurally controlled (Dever, 1973, 1977, 1980a,b).

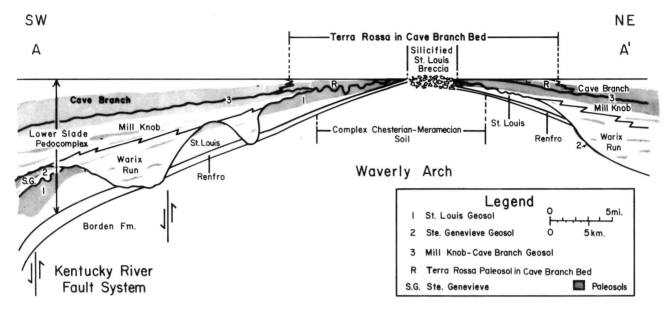

Figure 5. Schematic northeast-southwest section along line A-A′ in Figure 1, showing relative position of disconformities and associated geosols in relation to Waverly Arch and Kentucky River Fault Zone. Note location of terrae rossae and complex soils relative to the arch. Vertical scale is exaggerated.

The Cave Branch Bed (Fig. 3), which overlies various lower Slade members, is a gray to reddish brown claystone and shale. It is included in the upper part of the Slade, but we will show later that it is a clayey residual soil derived from the humid weathering of lower Slade carbonates, especially the Mill Knob Member. The bed is present throughout the study area, but is red only near structurally high features (Fig. 7). The clayey soils were partly reworked into tidal-flat muds during a late Early Chesterian transgression (Ettensohn, 1975, 1977, 1980, 1981).

Other horizons in the Slade and Paragon where subaerial exposure features are known include localized occurrences in the Tygarts Creek and Ramey Creek members (crusts, breccias, and microkarst; Ettensohn, 1977, 1980, 1981), on top of the Slade (Poppin Rock Member: ferricrete? and microkarst; Phalen, 1906, Ettensohn, 1975, 1977), and within the Paragon (brecciation and caliche pseudo-anticlines; Ettensohn and Chesnut, 1979; Fig. 3). Ferricretes and clayey soil profiles have also been noted atop the Mississippian-Pennsylvanian unconformity and within the Pennsylvanian strata of eastern Kentucky.

CALCIUM CARBONATE-RICH SOILS

Characterization

Subaerial exposure of carbonate rock may produce two types of end-member alterations and various intermediate phases, depending on the amount of moisture available (Harrison, 1977; Esteban and Klappa, 1983; James and Choquette, 1984). Where precipitation exceeds evapotranspiration, as in rainy, humid areas, carbonate is leached from soils and bedrock and transported to streams; karstic alterations dominate in these areas. However, in semi-arid and arid regions, precipitation, and hence leaching, are inadequate to remove carbonate from the system, so that local translocation and accumulation processes dominate (Goudie, 1983), forming caliche. Caliche is the end member that best describes the Slade profiles, but in many instances minor karstic features also are present.

The term caliche has several meanings, both pedogenic and nonpedogenic, and similar calcium carbonate-rich soil accumulations are known by numerous terms including calcareous duricrust, calcrete, cornstone, croute calcaire, hardpan, kankar, nari, petrocalcic layers, calcons, sabach, subaerial exposure crusts, and tosca (Carlisle, 1983; Goudie, 1983). Following the usage of Gonzalez-Bonorino and Terruggi (1952), we define a pedogenic caliche as "a strataform to irregular deposit, formed primarily by calcium carbonate, with earthy, concretional, pisolitic, banded or massive structure that is formed in the soil or subsoil of arid and semi-arid regions. The carbonate is deposited by capillary action or eluviation." Caliche very commonly forms in the C horizon, but is not restricted to that horizon alone. If the horizon has more carbonate than the parent material presumably had, which is commonly the case in caliches, the suffix "ca" is added to the horizon designation; the additional suffix "m" indicates strong cementation or induration (Buol and others, 1980).

The term calcrete is used here to describe highly indurated parts of caliche profiles, whether laminar or nonlaminar (Lam-

UNIT	LITHOLOGY	CLIMATE	CIRCUMSTANCES OF EXPOSURE (TIME)	RESULTS
Cave Branch and underlying carbonates	Mudstone and carbonates	Moist, subtropical	Uplift on apical island (long)	Composite or complex paleosols, terrae rossae; root traces; paleokarst; well-developed clayey soil profile; calcrete destruction; multi-unit profiles.
Mill Knob	calcilutite calcarenite	semi-arid	Regional and local regression (short - moderate)	Incomplete profiles; poorly developed Ccam horizon; thin laminar calcretes; desiccation breccias; "inter-" and "intraformational" profiles.
Warix Run	calcarenite	semi-arid	shoal accretion; channel migration (very short)	No profile; little or no Ccam horizon; diffuse and "vertical" calcretes rhizobreccias; azonal soils' "intraformational" profiles.
Ste. Genevieve	calcarenite calcilutite	semi-arid	shoal accretion and regional regression local uplift (very short-moderate)	"Interformational" profile on top like on top of Mill Knob and St. Louis; "intraformational" profiles within like those in Warix Run.
St. Louis	calcilutite	semi-arid	Uplift on local structures (long)	Thick well-developed Ccam horizon and profiles; well-developed pseudo-anticlines; thick calcretes and Rock House breccias; abundant root tubles; "interformational" profile.

Figure 6. Chart showing effects of lithology, climate, and circumstances of exposure (time) on development of soils in four lower Slade members. Approximate durations are suggested in text.

plugh, 1902; Gile, 1961). Most of the so-called subaerial exposure crusts found in the Slade are laminar calcretes. In fact, the term crust, which suggests a hard exterior coating, is largely inappropriate for the Slade calcretes. Although some calcretes form through the accumulation of exterior coating (e.g., Multer and Hoffmeister, 1968), most Slade calcretes were formed by alteration or coating of the interior surfaces of voids and cracks in parent carbonate rocks. An extensive soil terminology exists for describing the nature and origin of these coatings and related soil features, some of which have no equivalents in geologic terminology. Soil terminology used in this study is defined and compared with existing geologic terminology in Table 1.

Pedogenic caliches are interpreted to be the product of vertical concentration within the soil, primarily through the reorganization and translocation of existing carbonate. Such caliches may form through downward concentration (illuviation), upward concentration (capillary action), or in situ solution and reprecipitation (Goudie, 1983). In contrast, nonpedogenic calcretes are characterized by lateral transportation and introduction of wholly new carbonate solutions and resulting cements.

Controls on pedogenesis

The formation of any soil is complex, and the relative importance of agents considered by most workers to be most significant is still uncertain. Nonetheless, the agents have been identified and include climate, relief, vegetation, parent material, and time (Jenny, 1941; FitzPatrick, 1971; Hodgson, 1978).

Climate. The critical factor in caliche formation is the presence of a significant net annual moisture deficit in the soil environment. The necessary deficits have been estimated at between 500 and 1,000 mm (20 and 40 in) (Buol, 1965). Although such deficits are typical of semi-arid conditions with annual rainfalls between 100 and 500 mm (Reeves, 1976; Hubert, 1977; Buol,

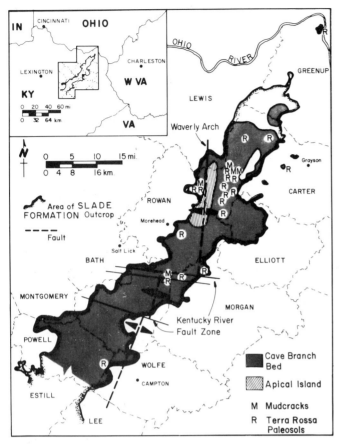

Figure 7. Distribution of Cave Branch Bed. Probable terrae rossae and reworked terrae rossae are present near structures. Mud cracks are present in upper reworked parts of Cave Branch near structures (after Ettensohn, 1980).

1965), caliche formation today also occurs in arid (Gile and others, 1966), temperate, subtropical (Multer and Hoffmeister, 1968; James, 1972), and tropical (Harrison, 1977) conditions. Even in areas of relatively high rainfall, caliches may form if the CaCO₃ source is large and readily available, especially if the area is hot (Goudie, 1973).

The ideal climate is Mediterranean, which is characterized by hot, dry summers, followed by cooler winters with moderate precipitation (Reeves, 1970; Arakel, 1982). Such conditions provide the wide temperature and moisture fluctuations necessary for caliche formation. In contrast, increased rainfall and decreased moisture deficits can build up vegetation and an organic-rich soil that will retain moisture and protect underlying carbonates from moisture and temperature fluctuations. When soil-moisture levels become stable and sufficiently large, net carbonate solution will occur, resulting in karst rather than caliche. Areas with Mediterranean climate also may have strong seasonal winds that are important for desiccation and evaporation, as well as for trans-

porting and depositing calcareous dust (Gile and others, 1966; James, 1972; Goudie, 1973, 1983) and salt spray (James, 1972; Walls and others, 1975), potentially important sources of calcium carbonate for soil profiles.

During Middle Mississippian time, eastern Kentucky was situated at approximately 5° to 10° S latitude (Ziegler and others, 1979) near the boundary of the wet equatorial belt and the dry trade-wind belt. With changing seasons, moist and dry belts would have alternately migrated toward the equator or South Pole (see Strahler and Strahler, 1973). This setting would have provided nearly equatorial levels of sunlight and alternation of moist and semi-arid condition necessary for accumulation of soil carbonate and caliche formation (Reeves, 1970, 1976; Buol, 1965; Gile and others, 1966). The presence of abundant caliche in the lower Slade supports this interpretation for the study area during the Meramecian. However, the absence of caliche and the presence of major paleokarst and terra rossa paleosols associated with the Cave Branch Bed (Figs. 5, 6, 7) suggest that the climate had changed to moister subtropical conditions by late Early Chesterian time (early Late Mississippian; Gasperian; Fig. 3).

Relief. The retention and reception of moisture in soil microenvironments are especially significant in soil formation. Desiccation by sun (Vageler, 1933) and wind (Harrison, 1977; James, 1972) directly counter the moistening effects of rainfall, whereas relief and vegetation influence soil-moisture levels in more indirect ways. Vageler (1933, p. 108) considered relief to be very important in the distribution of moisture in tropical soils. In semi-arid areas, surface runoff is typically very high, particularly in areas with relief, and soils in topographically low areas tend to be moister than those in surrounding high areas. Relief on the Slade exposure surfaces apparently was very low, generally no more than 0.6 m; most of this was related to a low, mammillated microkarst (see Walkden, 1974). Low gradient and relief are important for the formation of caliche, because net carbonate accumulation must exceed rate of removal (Klappa, 1983).

More important, however, in the Slade situation is the broad regional and local relief that exposed shallow-water, marine carbonates to pedogenic processes. On a regional scale, the position of the study area on the margin of the Appalachian Basin was significant. Paleosols tend to develop in areas of prolonged exposure and decreased subsidence, conditions more likely to occur near basin margins than toward basin centers. This pattern is borne out in the distribution of Mississippian caliches in Kentucky. From our study area on the basin margin, the thickness and number of exposure features decrease southeastwardly to Pine Mountain near the center of the Appalachian Basin, where such features are uncommon to rare.

Major local relief was a product of three processes in eastern Kentucky: uplift on structures, eustatic sea-level fall, and rates of shoal-sandbar aggradation that exceeded sea-level rise (Fig. 6). The significant effects of uplift on structures have already been mentioned, especially in the development of St. Louis and Ste. Genevieve caliches in east-central and northeastern Kentucky. However, exposure features atop the Ste. Genevieve throughout

TABLE 1. COMPARISON OF PEDOLOGIC AND GEOLOGIC TERMS FOR CALICHES*

Pedologic Term	Equivalent Geologic Term(s)
Plasma	Soluble calcium carbonate
Framework or skeleton grain	Lithoclast of parent rock, silt or larger
Lithorelict	Lithoclast of parent rock
Pedorelict	Clast of older caliche soil
Cutan (calcitan)	Micritic coating
Plane cutan	Micritic "crust" or lamina
Grain cutan	Vadose pisolite, diagenetic ooid, vadose ooid, diagenetic pisolite, coated allochem, vadoid
Glaebule	Nodule, concretion, vadoid
Crystallaria (crystic plasmic fabric)	Pore-fill calcite spar
Aseptic plasmic fabric	Structureless micrite
S-matrix	Matrix plus lithoclasts and voids
Plasma concentration	Feature formed by precipitation of $CaCO_3$ in one place
Plasma separation	In-situ modification of a surface (e.g., slickensides, neomorphism)
Stress cutan	Slickensides
Soil structure	Size, shape, and arrangement of soliod particles and voids
Ped	Natural soil aggregate separated from others by joints, voids, or other planes of weakness

*Terms may have slightly different meanings for soils other than caliches.

most of its distribution in eastern and western Kentucky must reflect a more regional control such as eustatic sea-level fall. In the Mill Knob, the presence of two or three thin regressive sequences capped by caliches, suggests cyclic episodes of sea-level rise and fall. The close association of subaerial-exposure features with intertidal and supratidal features in the Mill Knob reflects the lowering of sea level and the saline water table to the point that the sediments could support terrestrial plants. On the other hand, the poorly developed, sporadic nature of Warix Run calcrete zones on arenaceous, peloidal calcarenite bodies reflects short-lived exposure on shoals and tidal sand bars that accreted faster than sea-level rise.

Vegetation and other organisms. Organisms, particularly plants, are especially important agents of pedogenesis. Not only do they mechanically disaggregate parent material, they also may actively promote the dissolution or precipitation of calcium carbonate. The importance of lower plants, lichens, fungi, and bacteria in pedogenesis (Krumbein, 1968; Esteban, 1974; Kahle, 1977; Klappa, 1978, 1979a,b; Esteban and Klappa, 1983; Wilson and Jones, 1983), as well as of small soil animals (Wright, 1983), has also been noted.

Dense plant growth and accumulation of plant debris may have a detrimental effect on the formation of caliches. Plants provide shade that reduces soil temperature, retard surface runoff, and send out roots, promoting the buildup and development of an organic-rich, noncalcareous solum (A and B horizons). In turn, the accumulating soil that results can better retain moisture, which further enhances plant growth. Hence, vegetation has a masking effect that helps maintain moisture in sola despite significant external moisture deficits. Surfaces that are exposed or covered with only thin sola devoid of major vegetation do not exhibit this masking effect, and hence are subject to the wide temperature and moisture fluctuations that characterize semi-arid climates (Vageler, 1933, p. 104) and enhance caliche development.

Based on the abundance of crusts and the apparent rapidity with which they developed on some Slade carbonates, plant density is thought to have been sparse to moderate, and the organic-rich parts of most Mississippian soils probably were thin and poorly developed when present. Root tubules and casts are present, but rarely abundant.

Where rhizocretions and root tubules are abundant, the abundance is more likely related to extended periods of exposure and surface stability, which permitted more advanced stages of soil formation to develop. For example, caliche profiles are better developed and the influence of plants is more apparent in the St. Louis near the Apical Island area of the Waverly Arch and near the Kentucky River Fault System, where exposure was longer.

Time. Time and its effects are difficult to assess, and any time factor may be overridden by other parameters (Harrison, 1977). Nonetheless, given that other conditions are ideal, a positive correlation exists between time and the thickness of caliche profiles (Bretz and Horberg, 1979; Ruhe and others, 1961). Some idea of the time involved also can be gleaned from the circumstances of exposure, that is, the depositional and structural framework of the units (Fig. 6).

The interformational profile developed on the St. Louis near the Apical Island (Fig. 1) probably was the product of relatively long exposure; extrapolation from the chronology of Harland and others (1982) suggests a period of exposure from the middle Meramecian to nearly the end of the Early Chesterian, approximately 4 m.y. For interformational profiles atop the Ste. Genevieve and Mill Knob we suggest shorter periods of emergence, ranging from a few tens of thousands to a few hundred thousand years. For intraformational profiles that developed because of local regression (shoaling-upward Mill Knob sequences), we suspect that a few thousand to a few tens of thousands of years are involved. The shortest time frames must be represented by the poorly developed intraformational profiles in the Ste. Genevieve and Warix Run, which reflect exposure from ephemeral sand-bar accretion and channel migration; the time involved probably varied from a few hundred to a few thousand years.

Substrate. Harrison (1977) indicated that carbonate substrates play three important roles in caliche formation: (1) they are the major source of calcium carbonate dissolved and reprecipitated as caliche; (2) substrates can be directly incorporated into the caliche fabric in altered or unaltered form; and (3) their porosity and permeability may influence the nature and thickness of caliche profiles. The effects of all three roles are readily apparent in the Slade caliches, but porosity and permeability and the form of the Slade carbonate substrates (calcilutite vs. calcarenite) seem to have the most important aspects; they are discussed below.

DIAGNOSTIC PEDOLOGIC FEATURES IN THE LOWER PART OF THE SLADE FORMATION

The principal means of distinguishing paleosols is the recognition of diagnostic features known to occur in modern soils (Retallack, 1976). These features may be recognized by chemical analysis, mineral analysis, or by analysis of soil fabric and structure; of these, only analysis of soil fabric and structure is immediately available to the field geologist. In many instances, the fabric and structural aspects are so apparent to those with some pedogenic experience that mineral and chemical analysis is unnecessary or reduced to a secondary, corroborative role. Moreover, chemical and mineral analysis may even be impractical, as later diagenetic overprints may have destroyed original patterns.

Soil horizons

Typical ABC profiles apparently developed in places on the St. Louis, Ste. Genevieve, and Mill Knob, although the profiles are now truncated, revealing only parts of the C horizon (Figs. 8C, 9A, 10) or the C and basal parts of the B horizons (Figs. 8A,B, 11, 12). Truncated C horizons showing recognizable

parent material are the most commonly preserved profile relicts in the Slade, and even the C horizons display a vertical zonation of subhorizons (Figs. 10, 11).

The B horizon may be a "weathered B," characterized by the complete obliteration of parent-rock structures and textures and the formation of new soil structures, or an "illuvial B," characterized by a new accumulation of illuvial clays or iron and aluminum oxides (Duchaufour, 1982). The B horizons in the Slade are dominantly weathered Bs, but some evidence of illuvial clay, calcium carbonate, and silica is present. In terrae rossae described later, evidence of illuvial clay and iron oxide is even more abundant.

Preserved A horizons, indicated by accumulation of organics and loss of solubles, are extremely rare in the Slade, and only one example has been found. In this example from the Ste. Genevieve, a dark, organic-rich carbonate (A horizon) overlies little-altered parent material (C horizon) (Figs. 8H, 13). Because time was insufficient for a B horizon to develop, such AC soils are said to be immature profiles.

In some of the intraformational profiles from the Ste. Genevieve, Warix Run, and Mill Knob, probable azonal soils consisting largely of weathered parent material (C horizon) with some evidence of former plant activity (Figs. 8D–E, 14) apparently were all that ever developed.

Pedologic constituents

The basic pedologic constituents are framework or skeleton grains and plasma (Table 1). The most common framework grains in the Slade caliches are lithoclasts or lithorelicts (Brewer, 1976), which are silt-sized or larger (Figs. 15A,C, 16B,O). Some

Figure 8. Megascopic features from lower Slade caliches. Member abbreviation key for this and other photographic figures: Mssl = St. Louis, Msm = Mill Knob, Mscb = Cave Branch, Mshf = Holly Fork, Msah = Armstrong Hill, Mstc = Tygarts Creek. A, Truncated profile on St. Louis. B = B horizon; C = C horizon. Black line = base of melanization and of profile; white dotted line = disconformity. B, Truncated interformational profile with subtle pseudo-anticlines (T) and breccias (Br). B = B horizon; C = C horizon. Dashed line = boundary between B and C horizons and base of Cave Branch Bed. C, Truncated profile (C horizon) on St. Louis showing lows (black dashed lines) between planed pseudo-anticlines filled with calcrete and breccia. White dashed line = disconformity atop the St. Louis. D, Large root cast from an intraformational Warix Run azonal profile filled with rhizocretionary calcrete (solid arrows). Open arrows point to subtle lateral root branchings. E, Pocket of rhizobreccia and rhizocretionary calcrete from probable intraformational, azonal Ste. Genevieve profile. Radiating fractures probably related to root activity. Open arrows point to patches of diffuse calcrete. F, Dark laminae of diffuse calcrete following cross-laminae in the Ste. Genevieve. G, Dark, subparallel nodules (glaebules) of diffuse calcrete in siltstone from Nada Member of Borden. H, Thin A-C profile from the Ste. Genevieve. Dark, organic-rich carbonates (A horizon = A) overlie brecciated parent material (C horizon = C). Dark spots in white parent material are root casts.

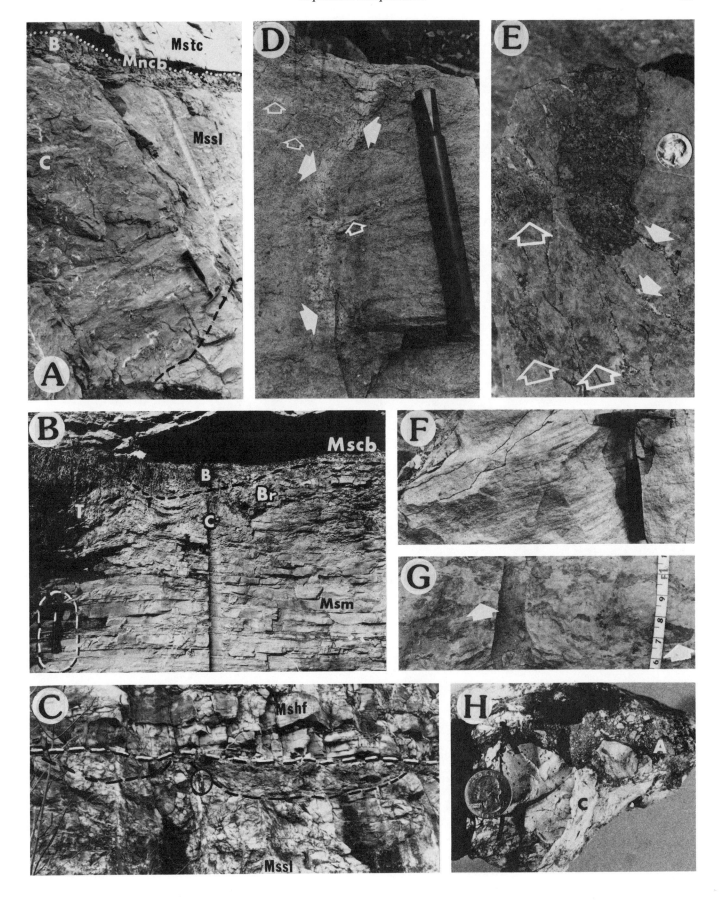

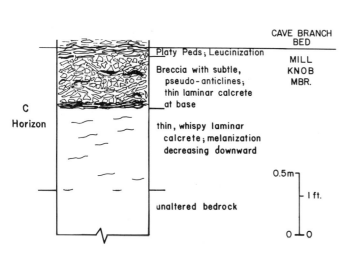

Figure 10. Schematic diagram of truncated interformational profile on Mill Knob in western Carter County. This type of profile, characterized mostly by breccia, very thin laminar calcretes, or the absence of calcretes, is typical of Mill Knob.

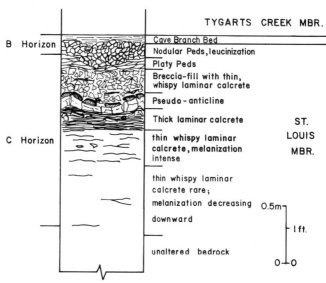

Figure 11. Schematic diagram of truncated paleosol on the St. Louis (see Fig. 8A) in northern Menifee County near Kentucky River Fault Zone. Zonation of features in C horizon is typical of well-developed caliches in the lower Slade.

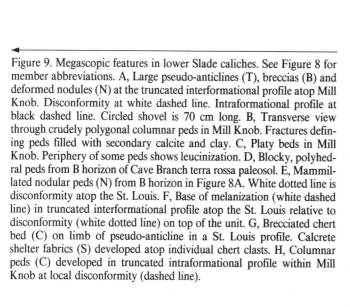

Figure 9. Megascopic features in lower Slade caliches. See Figure 8 for member abbreviations. A, Large pseudo-anticlines (T), breccias (B) and deformed nodules (N) at the truncated interformational profile atop Mill Knob. Disconformity at white dashed line. Intraformational profile at black dashed line. Circled shovel is 70 cm long. B, Transverse view through crudely polygonal columnar peds in Mill Knob. Fractures defining peds filled with secondary calcite and clay. C, Platy beds in Mill Knob. Periphery of some peds shows leucinization. D, Blocky, polyhedral peds from B horizon of Cave Branch terra rossa paleosol. E, Mammillated nodular peds (N) from B horizon in Figure 8A. White dotted line is disconformity atop the St. Louis. F, Base of melanization (white dashed line) in truncated interformational profile atop the St. Louis relative to disconformity (white dotted line) on top of the unit. G, Brecciated chert bed (C) on limb of pseudo-anticline in a St. Louis profile. Calcrete shelter fabrics (S) developed atop individual chert clasts. H, Columnar peds (C) developed in truncated intraformational profile within Mill Knob at local disconformity (dashed line).

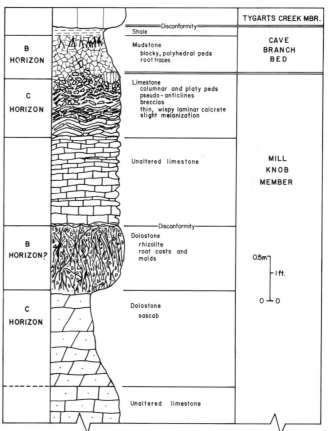

Figure 12. Schematic diagram showing two truncated paleosols in Mill Knob of northern Menifee County. Lower is intraformational profile developed on shoal complex; upper profile includes Cave Branch and is interformational profile developed on intertidal muds.

of the lithoclasts are pedorelicts (Brewer, 1976) because they were reworked from older caliches. Allochems within lithoclasts or parent material are not framework grains, because they were not distinct grains within the soil.

Plasma, on the other hand, is the relatively unstable, soluble fraction, no greater than colloidal size, that is not bound up in framework grains (Brewer, 1976). The plasma can be moved or concentrated easily throughout the soil profile, and its physical and chemical properties can be modified by subtle changes in the environment. In the Slade caliches, the plasma was most commonly soluble calcium carbonate, but colloidal organic matter, iron oxides, and silica, as well as clays, also were parts of the plasma fraction at various times and places. Where the framework grains are soluble, as was the case in the Slade, weathering of the grains probably provided most of the plasma.

All plasma, framework grains, and voids that compose the simplest soil structures or peds make up the s-matrix of the soil. Because of the solubility of the plasma in Slade caliches, much of it was concentrated in pedologic features distinct from the s-matrix; hence, a well-defined s-matrix generally is absent. Only in the Cave Branch terrae rossae is an s-matrix clearly present (Fig. 16P).

Pedologic features

Pedologic features include inherited features (pedorelicts and lithorelicts that compose most Slade framework grains) and features caused by plasma concentration (most cutans, glaebules), plasma separation ("diffuse calcrete," stress cutans), differences in particle arrangement (grading), and biological activity (root tubules). Such pedologic features are very common in the lower Slade caliches. However, only the most common features are described here; more detailed descriptions of these and other features are presented in Kubiena (1938), Brewer (1976), and Freytet and Plaziat (1982).

Precipitation of the calcium-carbonate plasma forms plasma concentrations, of which cutans—surface coatings within a soil (see Table 1)—are the most common type in the Slade. The so-called crusts or laminar calcretes of the Slade are merely accumulations of cutans. Brewer (1976) classified cutans based on the nature of the surfaces coated, composition, and process of formation. As for the surfaces, cutans enclosing framework grains are grain cutans (e.g., pisolites, vadoids: Fig. 16K,Q); cutans coating the walls of tubular channels are channel cutans (Figs. 17D and 16A,O); and cutans coating the walls, floors, and ceilings of planar voids are called plane cutans (e.g., rinds or crusts: Figs. 15A,D,G).

Based on their mineralogy, cutans may be argillans (clays: Fig. 16A,Q), ferrans (iron oxides and hydroxides: Fig. 16P), calcitans (calcite: Figs. 17R, 16A,K,O) and silans (silica: Fig. 17F). Calcitans form the majority of cutanic materials in the Slade, although argillans, ferrans, and silans are important locally (Grow, 1982).

The process of formation also plays a role in classification.

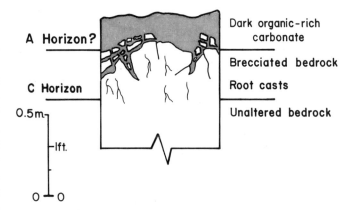

Figure 13. Schematic diagram of probable A-C soil profile (rendzina) from intraformational Ste. Genevieve profile in Rockcastle County (see Fig. 8H).

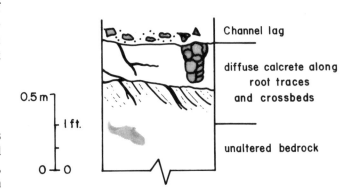

Figure 14. Schematic diagram showing features characteristic of probable azonal soils developed on Warix Run calcarenitic shoal complexes. Many of these profiles have been truncated by overlying shoal or channel complexes, which exhibit basal lags containing eroded calcrete fragments.

Figure 15. Megascopic features from lower Slade caliches. A, "Jig-saw" rhizobreccia with floating texture from the St. Louis. Lithorelicts or lithoclasts are separated by plane cutans of rhizocretionary calcrete with alveolar structure. Brecciation was probably caused by displacive crystallization of rhizocretionary calcrete. Scale 1 cm. B, Mat of root tubules on a bedding plane in the Ste. Genevieve. Tubules radiate outward from centers (tap roots?) shown at arrows. Scale = 5 cm. C, Rhizobreccia with lithorelicts and rhizocretionary calcrete (r) from Mill Knob. Note halo (arrow) and fracture emanating from root cast. Scale 4 cm. D, Plane cutans of rhizocretionary calcrete along thin recurring horizons in Warix Run, probably reflecting former cross-laminae. Scale = 5 cm. E, Large sink developed on St. Louis near Apical Island and formerly filled with Cave Branch claystone (terra rossa). Disconformity shown by dotted line. F, Microkarst (k) developed on axis of pseudo-anticline. G, Rhizocretionary (r) and physicochemical (p) calcrete (plane cutans), shelter fabrics (s), and black pebbles (b) from St. Louis profile. H, Root casts and molds in rhizolite from Mill Knob (see Fig. 12). Scale given in centimeters. I, Alveolar structure (a) and rhizobreccia from Mill Knob. Scale = 5 cm.

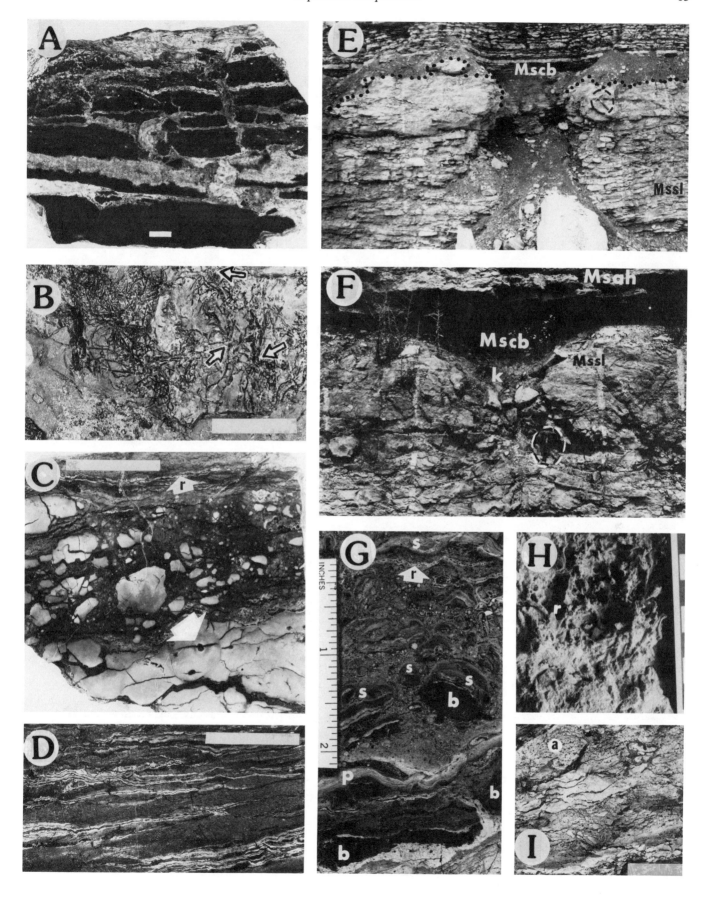

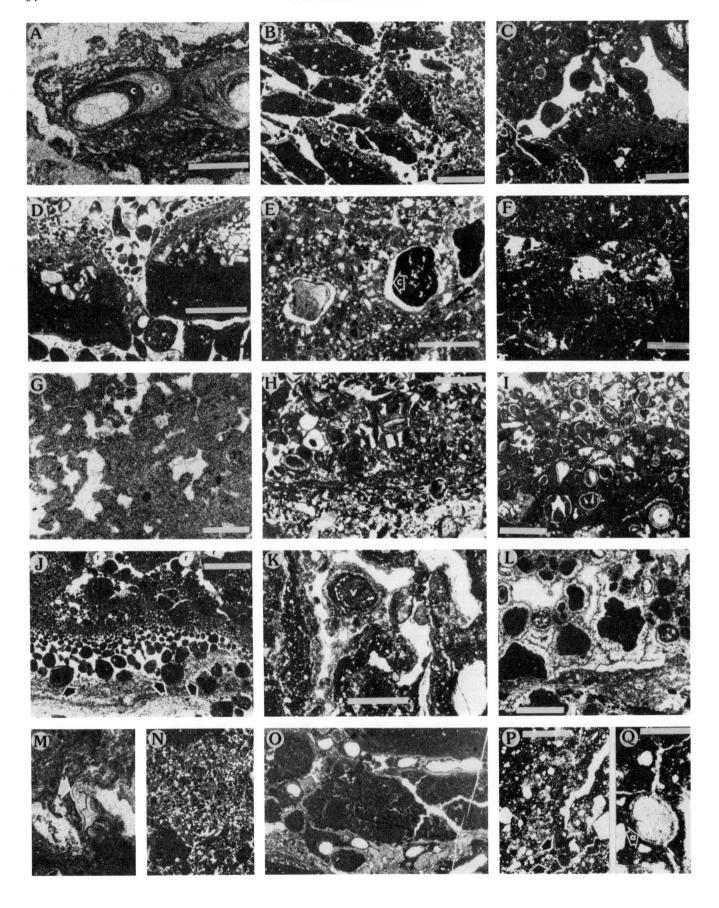

The most relevant process is illuviation, and illuviation cutans form through movement of cutanic material in solution and suspension and subsequent deposition (Brewer, 1976). Most of the micritic coatings in the Slade calcretes are sequential illuviation cutans, formed by precipitation of successive calcium-carbonate laminae from supersaturated solutions in a soil environment, commonly with biological mediation.

Glaebules are globular plasma concentrations present on both megascopic and microscopic levels (Figs. 8G, 16E,K, 17A–B). In the Slade, two types of glaebules are present: nodules with an undifferentiated internal fabric, and vadoids (Peryt, 1983) with a concentric internal fabric. Nodules are found only in more massive argillaceous siltstones from parts of the Borden exposed during Genevievian erosion. They are irregular, but crudely rounded and subhorizontal (Fig. 8G), having apparently

◄───────────────────────────────

Figure 16. Micromorphologic features from lower Slade caliches. Unless otherwise stated, scale = 1 mm. A, Crystal tubes and channel cutans (calcitans = c, argillans = a). Smaller tubes above and below large central tubes may reflect root hairs or fungal hyphae growing in association with roots. Scale = 0.5 mm. St. Louis. B, Subangular blocky structure caused by brecciation. Individual clasts or lithorelicts form shelter fabrics for vadose silt. Ste. Genevieve. C, Crude inverse grading in vadose silt, apparently derived from fracture above. Ste. Genevieve. D, Vadose silt moving down fracture between silt-covered clasts. Mill Knob. E, Circumgranular cracks around two nodules and fossil fragment in largely micritized groundmass from Warix Run. Scale = 0.5 mm. F, Agglomeritic structure, or filling of voids between larger peloids with smaller ones. Note partially backfilled burrow or pedotubule (b) that was once connected to irregular galleried chamber (to left). St. Louis. G, Thin-section of nodular ped in B horizon of St. Louis paleosol, showing complete alteration of parent material through solution (spar-filled voids) and neomorphism to microspar. H, Micritization of Warix Run calcarenite proceeding along linear fronts that emanated from silty, quartzose cross-lamina at bottom of photo. I, Micritization of oolitic calcarenite in Ste. Genevieve along linear horizon not apparent in photo. Micritization here appears to have radiated outward somewhat selectively from small coalescing centers. This kind of apparent plasma segregation, or in situ alteration, is principal factor in forming diffuse calcrete. J, Normally graded vadose sediment in part derived from two now-closed fractures above. Fractures were apparently closed by roots (root cast = r). "Pebble dents" (arrows) below three larger peloids indicate that vadose silt below graded sequence was unconsolidated when sequence was deposited. St. Louis. K, Vadoid (v), apparently formed through concentric lamination of vadose silt and rhizocretionary calcrete in root tube complex. St. Louis. L, Lacy structure produced through dissolution of individual clasts except for outer rim and infilling with spar. Ste. Genevieve. M, Fibrous calcite, now being micritized, filling void in Ste. Genevieve caliche. Scale = 0.5 mm. N, Dropping structure of probable fecal pellets from A horizon of A-C soil. Ste. Genevieve. O, Displacive calcitans (rhizocretinary calcrete) around root tubules. Chain-like arrangement of root tubules is typical of alveolar structure. Formation of calcitans and root tubules were instrumental in generating breccia clasts or lithorelicts in this rhizobreccia. P, S-matrix of Cave Branch terra rossa. A plane cutan or ferran (arrows) fills lower part of fracture on ped margin. Q, Grain cutan (iron-rich argillan) coating quartz grain along fracture in Cave Branch terra rossa. Scale = 0.5 mm.

formed along poorly developed bedding. Nodules do not occur in well-bedded Slade carbonates.

Vadoids are essentially sequential grain cutans (Fig. 16K). Little or no movement of the grain or clast is required for vadoid development, as it is possible for films of water to enclose a grain partially or completely. It is also possible for nearly complete encapsulation of grains by roots to result in concentric lamination (Fig. 16K).

Pore-fill calcite cement (crystallaria) is another type of plasma concentration; it is classified on the basis of the shape of the void it fills (Brewer, 1976). Hence, crystallaria may be classified as crystal tubes (Fig. 17D), crystal chambers (Fig. 16L,M), or crystal sheets (see Table 1).

Plasma separations result from the in situ modification of plasma (Brewer, 1976). Surface modification of peds from shear, for example, produces stress cutans or slickensides. Aggrading and degrading neomorphism, or alteration of various cements and allochems to micrite, microspar, or pseudospar, is another form of plasma separation. The degrational recrystallization of allochems and cements to micrite is the most prevalent form of plasma separation in the Slade. The exact mechanism of micritization is unknown, but micritization appears to have moved outward from porous horizons (e.g., cross-bed laminae) along linear fronts (Fig. 16H) or to have moved outward from individual points in diffuse circular fronts. As these diffuse fronts met, they produced the clotted texture noted by James (1972) (Fig. 16I). In our samples, sparry cements are micritized first, followed by various allochems, particularly ooids, ooid nuclei, and echinoderm grains. Seiser (1973) suggested that similar micrites in South African calcretes were a product of dissolution and rapid precipitation of micrite cement because of evaporation. This type of micritization probably occurs in our calcretes, but the finely diffuse nature of the micrite and the fact that it may "cross-cut" various cement and grain types (Fig. 16I) suggests degrading neomorphism. This kind of micritization may be quite common in vadose environments (James, 1972), and should not be confused with cutans.

Other pedologic features result from differences in the arrangement of framework grains. Some of these differences result from processes of physical sedimentation in the soil. A very notable result is graded and inversely graded vadose sediment (Fig. 16C,J). Such grading reveals the influence of gravity or downward-moving vadose waters in the soil profile and control by the size and shape of vertical passages through which the vadose sediment passed (Fig. 16C,D,J).

Finally, pedologic features may be generated through pedoturbation, the reorganization of soil materials by wetting and drying, or by the activity of plants and/or animals (Hole, 1961). Evidence for activity by both plants and animals is present. Very small peloids, averaging 0.04 mm in diameter, may occur in large masses (Fig. 16N) as fillings between larger compound peloids (Fig. 16F), or as coatings and bridges within tubular fenestrae. These small peloids are nearly identical to those that Wright (1983) suggested were the calcified fecal material of small soil

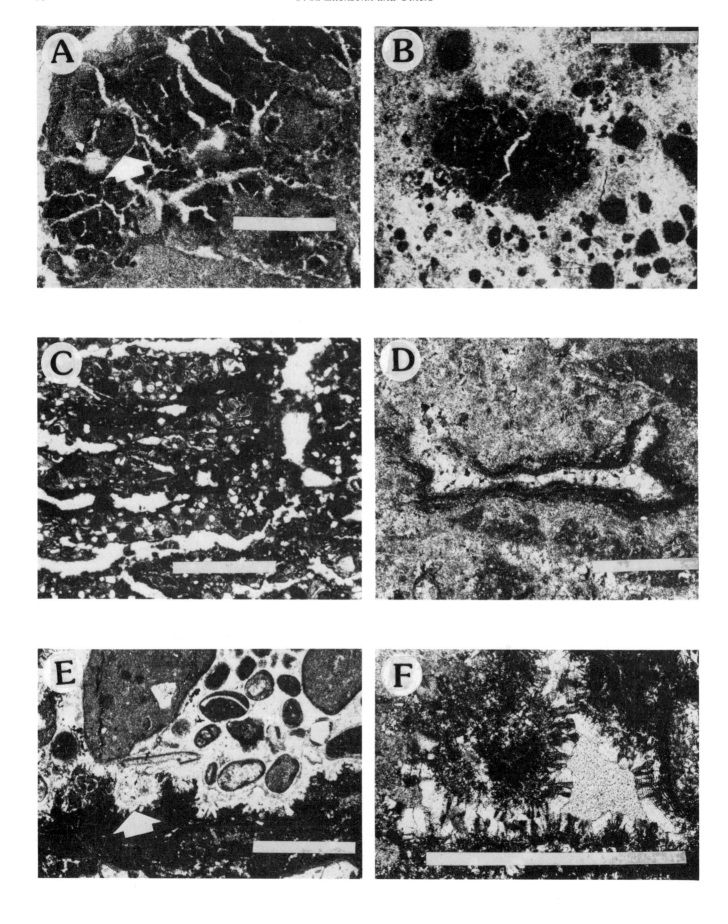

arthropods and worms. Backfilling of some tubular voids with these peloids (Fig. 16F) indicates that some of the organisms probably were soil ingesters (Wright, 1983).

Tubular fenestrae produced by plants are generally smooth-walled, circular, and bifurcate (Fig. 16K); channel cutans commonly encase the tubes (Figs. 16A, 17D). Animal burrows, on the other hand, do not bifurcate, are not smooth-walled, are galleried with irregular roofs, and generally lack cutanic coatings (Fig. 16F) (see Klappa, 1980; Wright, 1983).

In addition, probable lichen or algal bores have been tentatively identified (Fig. 17E), suggesting possible surface calcrete alteration or actual calcrete formation by lichens (lichen stromatolite: Klappa, 1979a).

Soil structure

In the lower Slade, soil structures exist on both megascopic and microscopic scales. The most common megascopic structures are platy peds, which divide parent rock into irregularly lenticular, subparallel units (Figs. 9C, 10) that may be mistaken for crude bedding. Columnar or prismatic peds (Fig. 9B,H), mammilated, nodular peds (Figs. 9F, 11), and blocky, polyhedral peds (Figs. 9D, 12, 18) also occur.

Peds in the Slade are commonly separated from each other by voids, slickensided surfaces (stress cutans), or surface coatings of clay or secondary calcium carbonate (ped cutans). Development of fractures or voids between peds (Fig. 9B–E,H) is largely controlled by wetting and drying history (Yaalon and Kalmar, 1972), and to a lesser extent by roots. Most megascopic soil structures form in the B horizon (FitzPatrick, 1971), providing a way to identify that horizon in the Slade (Figs. 11, 12, 18). Moreover, peds in the Slade show the complete alteration of parent material characteristic of that horizon (Figs. 16G, 17A). Large peds are typically compound or tertiary peds, formed of smaller secondary peds. Secondary peds, in turn, are formed of very small primary peds, ordinarily microscopic in scale. Typical primary soil microstructures or peds from the Slade include subangular blocky (produced by wetting and drying: Fig. 16B), granular (produced by wetting and drying and fecal material?: Fig. 17B), alveolar (produced by rooting: Fig. 16), labyrinthine (produced by animal activity: Fig. 17C), dropping (fecal material: Fig. 16); agglomeritic (produced by animal activity and compaction: Fig. 16), lacy (produced by solution: Fig. 16), and wedge (produced by wetting and drying: Fig. 17A).

Root traces

Root systems sent out by drought-resistant plants in semiarid areas are extremely important, because physical and chemical processes related to them are fundamental to pedogenesis (Klappa, 1983; FitzPatrick, 1971; Buol and others, 1980). The most important of these processes include physical disintegration of rocks, control of soil-water levels, and the control of pCO_2 in soils through plant respiration, photosynthesis, and decay. Moreover, because plant roots excrete various substances on which microorganisms thrive, roots greatly enhance microbial soil activity in parts of the soil near the root systems, called the rhizosphere (FitzPatrick, 1971).

One of the most common features associated with root growth in soils are tubular structures produced by plants and animals (Figs. 16K,O, 17D). In calcareous soils, these tubes may be generated by dissolution through secretion of organic acids and chelating compounds or through other environmentally or organically mediated processes, such as increased pCO_2, decreased temperature, and decreased pH; on the other hand, decreased pCO_2, high temperatures, increased pH, increased evapotranspiration, and microbial activities may result in a calcium-carbonate precipitation that fills the tubes (Multer and Hoffmeister, 1971; Read, 1976; Klappa, 1983). Moreover, penetration and growth of roots in calcretes may produce extensive fracture systems (Figs. 8E, 15C), as well as abundant rhizoliths and locally extensive rihzobreccias.

Based on the classification of Klappa (1980), two types of rhizoliths are common in the Slade caliches: root casts and root tubules. Root casts are sediment- or cement-filled molds or borings left after root decay. Root casts are present in the Ste. Genevieve, Warix Run, and Mill Knob members of the Slade. They are generally 2 to 4 mm in diameter and most commonly filled with sparry calcite (Figs. 16J–K,O, 17I); fillings of micritic cement and vadose sediment are present locally. At one locality in the Warix Run, a root cast 20 cm long and 2 cm wide at its greatest diameter was filled with laminar calcrete and interlaminated root tubules (Fig. 8I). The calcrete apparently was generated by successive growths of smaller root nets occupying a larger root mold. Some root casts exhibit oxidation halos in the surrounding matrix; most are associated with fractures and incipient breccias (Fig. 15C), suggesting that the fractures were created by boring roots or that the roots sought paths of weakness along fractures. In upper parts of some caliche profiles, root casts are so dense that they make up nearly the entire calcrete (Figs. 12, 15H); Klappa (1980) called such rocks "rhizolites."

Root tubules are commonly submillimeter-size cemented cylinders around root molds. Commonly, they exhibit a spar-filled cylindrical void surrounded by concentrically laminated

---

Figure 17. Micromorphologic features from lower Slade caliches. Scales = 1 mm. A, Wedge structure from a columnar ped from Ste. Genevieve interformational profile. Note complete alteration of parent material characteristic of B horizon and presence of glaebular nodule (arrow). B, Granular structure. Diffuse glaebular nodules. St. Louis. C, Labyrinthine structure. Branching crystal tubes partially lined with micritic channel cutans. Warix Run. D, Channel cutan (calcitan) and branching crystal tube. St. Louis. E, Laminar calcrete or lichen stromatolite (?) from interformational profile whose upper surface was bored by probable algae or lichens before burial by unaltered oolite. Ste. Genevieve. F, Siliceous cutans or mamillary silans under crossed nicols. St. Louis.

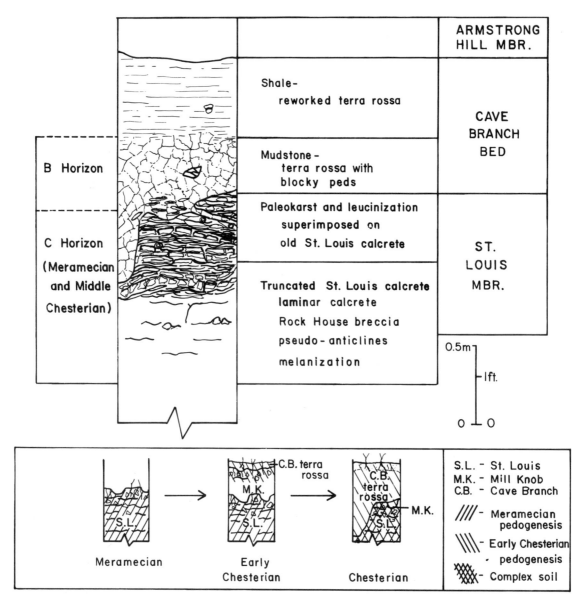

Figure 18. Schematic diagram of the composite or complex soil developed on the St. Louis in eastern Rowan County near Waverly Arch Apical Island. Bottom panel shows schematic history of development of this soil.

micrite (Fig. 16A). They are present in all lower Slade members but are widest (nearly 2 cm) in the St. Louis. The small voids may occur as discrete tubules (Fig. 17I), chain-like, linear series of voids (Figs. 15A,G,I, 16O), or random concentrations (Harrison, 1977). The structure created by the small voids and anastomosing micrite walls that separate them has been called "alveolar texture" (Esteban, 1974) (Fig. 15I). Similar textures have been described by Steinen (1974), Harrison and Steinen (1978), and Arakel (1982).

In most places, root tubules are seen only in section view. However, Ste. Genevieve exposures in three localities exhibit

two-dimensional, bedding-plane views of entire root systems, preserved as small micrite-enclosed root tubules (Fig. 15B). These bedding-plane surfaces show what was probably a root mat, formed by the overlapping and intersection of many root systems. The preserved Ste. Genevieve systems apparently were small lateral root systems radiating outward from large central roots. Individual radiating root systems had diameters ranging from 10 to 16 cm. The root systems apparently sought out planes of weakness and porous areas like bedding planes, fractures, and cross-laminae along which to grow. Hence, in some areas, tubules and casts are concentrated in thin, recurring horizons (Fig. 16O).

Root molds are known only from one locality in the Mill Knob. Here, they are the product of secondary dissolution of calcite cement from a dolomitic matrix containing the molds.

Rhizobreccias are in situ breccias generated largely through root activity (Klappa, 1980). The brecciation may involve parent rock, bedded cherts, or calcrete itself in the Slade. The breccias may show root casts associated with fractures, and angular fragments with minimal calcrete development (Fig. 15C), or may exhibit an "exploded jig-saw" or floating texture with alveolar calcrete filling interstices (Fig. 15A). In the latter type of rhizobreccia, clasts are usually oriented subparallel to bedding. On a microscopic scale, clasts were formed by entrainment of areas of parent material within networks of small rootlets, now represented by spar-filled clasts or tubules (Fig. 16O). Root-related alteration of clasts and their coating with micrite laminae may give many breccia clasts a rounded appearance (Fig. 16K).

Calcrete

As previously mentioned, we use the term calcrete to refer to caliche that was indurated in the ancient soil environment. Admittedly, it is difficult to determine what was indurated at the time of soil formation, but comparison of Slade calcretes with analogous features in modern caliches leads us to conclude that they probably were indurated during or shortly after formation. Second only to breccias in frequency of occurrence throughout the Slade, calcretes are among the most distinctive features in both recent and ancient caliche profiles (Bretz and Horberg, 1949; Ruhe and others, 1961; Gile and others, 1966; Multer and Hoffmeister, 1968, 1971; James, 1972; Walkden, 1974; Read, 1974, 1976; Walls and others, 1975; Choquette, 1976; Hubert, 1978; Harrison and others, 1978; Adams, 1980; Arakel, 1982; Warren, 1983; James and Choquette, 1984). They include the "subaerial exposure crusts" and "calcareous crusts" commonly described in North American geologic literature.

We recognize four types of calcrete in the Slade: (1) physicochemical calcrete; (2) calcrete rinds (microcrystalline rinds of Multer and Hoffmeister, 1968); (3) rhizocretionary calcrete (root tubules and alveolar calcrete); and (4) a rather diffuse, "patchy" calcrete. Because of their laminar nature, physicochemical and rhizocretionary calcretes are commonly grouped together as laminar calcrete.

Physicochemical calcretes exhibit abundant laminae, most of which are less than 3 mm in thickness. Thin sections show, however, that each lamina is actually composed of many smaller, indistinctly bounded laminae. The thicker visible laminae may built up deposits nearly 30 cm thick in the Slade, especially in surface lows. Individual laminae, however, have little lateral extent and pinch and swell over irregularities; microscale unconformities are present. The boundaries between individual laminae appear to be sharp, and alveolar texture is absent (Fig. 15G). The pronounced banding reflects different degrees of staining by organic matter (Multer and Hoffmeister, 1968; Ward and others, 1969; Walkden, 1974; Warren, 1983) and perhaps by iron com-

pounds (Brown, 1956; Read, 1976). Both dark- (dark gray, brown, black) and light-colored (white, tan, light gray) laminae are present, but lighter colored laminae are more commonly associated with rhizocretionary laminae. Most laminae are subhorizontal, probably reflecting the influence of bedding, but some also occur at oblique and vertical angles, reflecting the influence of cross-stratification, pseudo-anticline limbs, or joints. The calcrete laminae now generally occur near the very tops of lower Slade stratigraphic units, but we believe that this position is the product of later erosion. In the more complete paleosol profiles, the laminar calcretes are thickest and best developed 40 cm to 1 m below the surface (Fig. 11). Above and below this level, calcretes become sparse, and those present have a thin (only a few laminae), indistinct character (Figs. 10, 11). Physicochemical calcretes in the Slade are best developed in calcilutites; with few exceptions, they are poorly developed in calcarenites and calcareous sandstones.

Calcrete rinds are thin (a few millimeters thick), generally dark, nonlaminated crusts that usually form immediately on exposed bedrock (Multer and Hoffmeister, 1968). They are probably the only real crusts in the Slade and are very rare, known only from one exposure where they coat the surfaces of paleokarst. Because the karst vertically truncates older laminar calcrete, the rinds are discordant to older laminae (Fig. 19B).

Rhizocretionary calcrete also exhibits laminae, but the laminae are associated with root tubules and alveolar texture (Fig. 15I), indicating the involvement of roots in its formation. The generally light-colored laminae may occur in any orientation and may completely fill or concentrically coat root molds (Figs. 8D, 16A, 17D). Rhizocretionary calcrete may occur by itself (Figs. 7A,C,D,I) or be complexly intercalated within dark physicochemical calcrete (Fig. 15G). Although occurring in all lithologies, rhizocretionary calcrete composes most of the calcretes found in calcarenites.

Diffuse, "patchy" calcrete is found only in calcarenites, sandstones, and siltstones of the Slade and Borden; it is nearly everywhere brownish gray (5 YR 4/1; Goddard and others, 1963) in color. This calcrete occurs as "bodies" that vary from rounded, globular, or amoeboid shaped to crudely laminar (Figs. 8E,G, 19). The longest dimension of these bodies ranges from a few millimeters to a few tens of centimeters. The boundaries of the calcrete with adjacent country rock are always diffuse to gradational. Weathering of siltstones containing this type of calcrete commonly produces nodule-like bodies of the diffuse calcrete (Fig. 8G). The position of the bodies appears to be random or related to indistinct bedding. Where diffuse calcrete develops, laminar calcretes generally are rare, and the laminar calcretes that do develop are subvertical rhizocretionary calcretes.

Caliche pseudo-anticlines

Caliche pseudo-anticlines are one type of antiformal structure that occurs under a range of conditions, varying from subtidal to arid subaerial (Assereto and Kendall, 1977). These

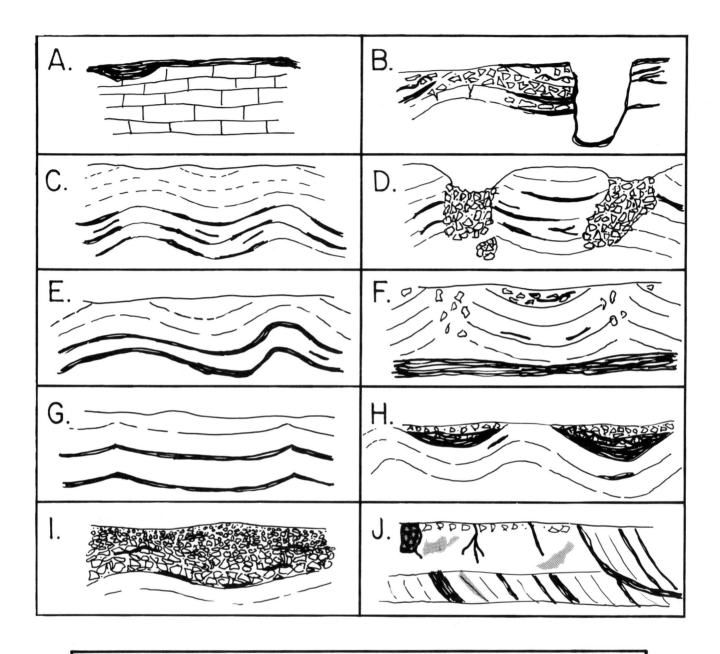

Legend

 Breccia

 Laminar calcrete

 Pseudo-Anticline

 "Diffuse" calcrete

structures are commonly called "tepees," because of their resemblance to Indian tents in cross section, but Assereto and Kendall (1977) recommended that the term caliche pseudo-anticline, first used by Price (1925), be restricted to the "dry end members" formed in fresh-water soil profiles.

In most Slade profiles, pseudo-anticlines are rather inconspicuous features, but are almost always found to be present on close inspection (Figs. 8B–C, 9A, 15F). In many examples, the pseudo-anticlines are highlighted by secondary chert infillings along separated beds or axial fractures. Amplitudes of the pseudo-anticlines range from 20 to 76 cm, and the periodicity ranges from 30 cm to 7 m. In some extremely large examples, the amplitude may reach two meters with periodicities of nearly 36 m. At one locality, an anticlinal feature in the St. Louis was nearly 70 m across. The largest pseudo-anticlines were found in the St. Louis near the Waverly Arch and Kentucky River Fault Zone, where the duration of uplift and exposure was greatest. Multiple tiers of pseudo-anticlines may occur in the same exposure, but the periodicity of successive tiers rarely coincides. Most of the pseudo-anticlines in any given horizon are irregularly developed and do not exhibit uniform amplitude or periodicity, conditions that support a subaerial origin (Assereto and Kendall, 1977). The few examples in the Mill Knob that exhibit sharp, regular and uniform patterns probably are peritidal tepees. In some areas, only a single limb or series of limbs appears to be present; these isolated limbs may represent small, imbricate caliche thrusts. If present at the top of a unit, pseudo-anticlines are generally truncated (Figs. 8C, 9A). Slade pseudo-anticlines display the typically splayed-out, upturned bedding; most of the upward expansion is taken up by separation along bedding planes and along fractures subparallel to bedding. In some cases, upwarped beds are brecciated, and fragments "float" in a calcrete "matrix" (Fig. 9A). Brecciation may be so intense in places that the former presence of pseudo-anticlines may be difficult to discern (Fig. 8B). Locally, compaction generated by pseudo-anticline formation was great enough to

deform underlying layers, and compression generated in areas of shortening ("downfolds") was great enough to break underlying layers and move the fragments so that they accumulated as large nodules in areas of distension under the pseudo-anticlines (Fig. 9A). Apical fractures and brecciation (Smith, 1974), however, are uncommon in Slade pseudo-anticlines (e.g., Fig. 9A) indicating that brittle deformation was not dominant. The general absence of vertical fractures, the irregular nature of pseudo-anticline layers, and the apparent ease with which underlying layers were deformed into nodules suggest that sediments were not completely lithified, thereby permitting pseudo-anticline formation through plastic deformation.

The formation of pseudo-anticlines and laminar calcretes in the Slade apparently were closely related. Laminar calcretes commonly infill many of the subhorizontal fractures associated with pseudo-anticlines, but are best developed below the surface at or near the base of the pseudo-anticline horizon (Figs. 11, 19C,E–G). Laminar calcrete and breccias also commonly accumulated in the troughs between pseudo-anticlines (Figs. 8C, 19H). Some of the common relationships between laminar calcrete and pseudo-anticlines are shown in Fig. 19.

In all pseudo-anticlines exposed at the surface, the apical and axial portions were most subject to breakdown and weathering, because formative compression and deformation were concentrated there. Hence, in those parts of the St. Louis exposed for long periods of time, the axial portions of planed pseudo-anticlines exhibit intense alteration (Fig. 15F, 19D). In these pseudo-anticlines, most evidence of laminar calcrete has been destroyed; solution-modified, largely uncemented breccias dominate. Individual clasts have been leached and bleached, and interstices are filled with shale from overlying units. If karst is present, sinks have preferentially formed on the apical regions of pseudo-anticlines (Fig. 15F, 19D).

Breccias

Breecias are the most nearly ubiquitous features of the Slade caliches. They occur even where laminar calcrete is absent and may be superimposed on any of the other features described herein. Breccia fragments may display a complete range of angularity and sphericity, both on a megascopic and microscopic scale. The fragments may show some rotation from their original orientation or occur nearly in situ, fitting well with adjacent fragments and continuing parallel to stratification (Figs. 15A, 16O; Harrison and Steinen, 1978). Many of the breccias appear to be multi-cyclical, exhibiting multiple episodes of fracturing and recementation; Bretz and Horberg (1949) referred to such breccias as "Rock House breccias," after a locality in New Mexico where they were first noted.

Layers in the limbs of pseudo-anticlines may undergo brecciation soon after formation, and in some senile pseudo-anticlines (Assereto and Kendall, 1977), brecciation nearly obscures their former presence (Figs. 8B, 10). Many small-scale (a few centimeters) pseudo-anticlinal structures, called "buckle cracks" by

Figure 19. Chart showing schematically some possible relationships between calcretes, pseudo-anticlines, breccias, and paleokarst. A, Calcrete crusts coating surface of unbroken bedrock. B, Calcrete rinds (very thin crusts) coating paleokarst and discordant with older laminar calcretes. C, Thin laminar calcretes concentrated in lows between pseudo-anticlines low in former profile (see Fig. 15F). D, Microkarst and solution breccias concentrated at apical portions of pseudo-anticlines. E, Laminar calcretes completely coating ruptured bedding planes in irregular pseudo-anticlines low in former profile. F, Thick laminar calcretes concentrated below pseudo-anticline horizon low in former profile. G, Like "E" above, but pseudo-anticlines are regular and chevron-shaped. H, Concentration of laminar calcrete and breccia in lows between pseudo-anticlines at eroded surface (see Fig. 8C). I, Senile pseudo-anticlines so brecciated they are barely observable. Note crude grading of breccias and near-absence of calcrete (see Fig. 8B). J. Probable azonal soil showing pocket of rhizobreccia, diffuse calcrete, and rhizocretionary and diffuse calcrete concentrated along root traces, scours, and cross-stratification (see Fig. 8D–F).

Reeves (1970), also contribute to brecciation. In the upper part of some Slade profiles, the breccias exhibit a crude grading, in which angular pebble-size clasts grade upward to rounded, granule- and coarse sand-size fragments. The upward decrease in size and the rounding are attributed to the increased influence of mechanical weathering and solution near the exposed surface. Rounding of clasts elsewhere in the caliches may be related to circumgranular fracturing (Fig. 16E).

Locally, black pebbles (cailloux noirs) are common in the breccias (Fig. 15G). Black pebbles, common in both ancient and recent caliches, probably reflect the infusion of organic matter into carbonates; they are commonly used as evidence of terrestrial plants and subaerial exposure (Ward and others, 1970; Flügel, 1982; Warren, 1983). Many of the clasts essentially float in a micritic calcrete "matrix" (Fig. 15A,C,G) (Brown, 1956; Read, 1976; Watts, 1978; Harrison and Steinen, 1978).

Shelter fabrics

Descending vadose waters may encounter locally impermeable barriers like chert bands or clasts, micrite layers or clasts, black pebbles, or calcrete bands during eluviation. Such "plugged horizons" (Gile and others, 1966; Reeves, 1970; Hubert, 1978; Arakel, 1982) prevent further downward movement of soil water, resulting in the buildup of laminar calcrete and vadose sediment only on the upper surface. The extent and impermeability of the barrier prevents accumulation on the sheltered underside. Shelter fabrics occur on both megascopic (Figs. 9G, 15G) and microscopic (Fig. 16B) scale in the Slade, and clearly reflect the downward translocation of soil materials.

Sascab

"Sascab," or chalky caliche, is a term used to describe the soft, powdery carbonate that develops below a caliche caprock (Isphording, 1976; Esteban and Klappa, 1983). In the Slade, the light-colored sascab is mainly restricted to the more massive, finer grained lithologies in the Mill Knob, and, rarely, the Warix Run members. Most sascabs appear to have been secondarily dolomitized, and are moderately indurated but friable, like chalk; they typically form reentrants upon exposure and weathering (Fig. 12). As illustrated and discussed by others (Reeves, 1970; James, 1972; Esteban and Klappa, 1983; Klappa, 1983), sascabs apparently were not exposed to the atmosphere and always occur low in the profile below some type of crust, hardpan, or impermeable calcrete horizon. In the Slade, they occur at the base of the caliche profile (Fig. 12) and are transitional with the parent material. Thin sections of the sascab reveal nearly complete recrystallization to microspar and evidence of dissolution and brecciation on a micro-scale.

Blank and Tynes (1965), Reeves (1970), James (1972), and Klappa (1973) all indicated that sascab-like lithologies reflect the presence of fresh water and resulting dissolution and precipitation. We believe that the massive character of the lithologies involved and their presence below indurated, impermeable horizons would have prevented the downward migration of pedogenic processes, thereby explaining the absence of laminar calcretes and related features. The impermeable or plugged horizons also might have confined ground waters below so that, at least in Slade examples, sascab may have been a wholly phreatic development, but one clearly related to plugged horizons created by calcretes above. Contact with fresh water may have resulted in recrystallization to microspar (Folk, 1965), whereas a fluctuating water table may explain alternating episodes of dissolution and precipitation.

Melanization and leucinization

Most lower Slade profiles exhibit a pronounced darkening or melanization near the top of the caliche (Figs. 8A, 9F). The intensity of melanization increases with depth below a very light, thin surface layer to a point about 0.6 to 0.8 m below the surface; from this point downward, the intensity decreases for approximately 0.5 m, at which point the natural color of the parent rock returns (Figs. 8A, 11). The intensity and depth of melanization apparently increased with duration of exposure. The most intense and deepest melanization occurs in the St. Louis near local structures, where it may develop to depths of 3.5 m below the surface of the caliche. The melanized interval roughly parallels surface relief (Fig. 9), indicating that melanization is somehow related to the surface.

Melanization is caused by the eluviation of colloidal organic matter from the surface (Buol and others, 1980). Production and inclusion of organic matter apparently occurs in environments where the pH is high enough and the Eh low enough so that preservation of organic matter accompanies deposition of secondary calcite. Much of the organic matter is algal (Ward and others, 1970). The process may occur at the surface so that individual clasts or parts of clasts ("black pebbles") are affected (Warren, 1983).

Leucinization, or the paling of soil horizons, is brought about by the removal of dark organic material to lower horizons or its transformation to lighter colored forms (Buol and others, 1980). In the Slade, leucinization is restricted to the uppermost parts (0.3 m) of the profile (Figs. 10, 11) and to the margins of peds (Fig. 9C); it is very common in and near solution breccias. This paling in the Slade is apparently a near-surface phenomenon related to the leaching of carbonates; it progresses downward with lowering of the surface through weathering and erosion.

Paleokarst

Solution features are commonly associated with calcrete horizons (Walkden, 1974; Wright, 1982a,b), but they are generally poorly developed because of the dearth of moisture where calcretes form. Most of the karst found in the lower Slade is microkarstic in scale, generally with a maximum relief of 0.6 m. The presence of small solution holes lined with microcrystalline rinds and filled with breccias (Grow, 1982) suggests that the solution features formed contemporaneously with the calcretes. In fact, where visible, the mammillated paleokarstic surfaces may be coated with thin laminar calcrete. Similar surfaces, which are associated with alveolar texture and rhizocretionary calcrete, have been interpreted to have formed under vegetation cover and are called deckenkarren (Wright, 1982b).

Near the Waverly Arch Apical Island, small caves, solution-collapse features, and relatively large sink holes are present in the St. Louis (Fig. 15E–F); some sinks are nearly 4 m deep and 6 m wide. Solution breccias and irregular piping may be associated with the sinks, and they are filled with what is apparently a terra rossa paleosol. This large-scale karstic truncation of a calcrete horizon suggests that the karst and terra rossa represent later soil development, probably during a moister climatic regime.

Terra rossa

Near the Waverly Arch Apical Island, an interval 0.3 to 0.6 m of chunky, moderate reddish brown (10R 4/6), mottled claystones containing solution-rounded clasts of caliche eroded from below overlies the St. Louis and erosional remnants of the Mill Knob (Figs. 9D, 16). The claystone and overlying shale, apparently reworked from the underlying claystone during transgression, are included in the Cave Branch Bed of the Slade. Walls and others (1975) noted the similarity of these claystones to the paleosols of Bermuda, and Ettensohn (1975, 1980, 1981) and Ettensohn and others (1984a) suggested that they represent a terra rossa paleosol. They are very similar to terrae rossae described by Duchaufour (1982) in that they developed on limestones, are reddish brown, and exhibit polyhedral peds (Fig. 9D) bound by stress cutans (slickensides) and sesquioxide glaebules. The reddish brown color is a product of rubification, the release and progressive oxidation and hydration of iron (Buol and others, 1980; Duchaufour, 1982). Some secondary bluish green mottles in the claystones probably reflect gleization, the reduction of iron under subsequent waterlogged soil conditions (Buol and others, 1980).

The major accretionary aspect of terrae rossae results from the inclusion of wind-blown dust, and the presence of very fine sand- and silt-size quartz (more than 20 percent) in the Cave Branch (Fig. 16P) may reflect an eolian source. Reddish-colored claystones and shales in the Cave Branch are restricted to the axis of the Waverly Arch (Fig. 7) (Ettensohn, 1975, 1980, 1981), suggesting that uplift and extended exposure on the arch were significant in their formation.

Silica

Secondary silica is common in soil materials and is an important constituent of caliches (Reeves, 1976; Watts, 1980). In the Slade, secondary silica in the form of bedded and nodular cherts is common in the St. Louis, Ste. Genevieve, and Mill Knob members, but most of this chert is very early diagenetic in origin,

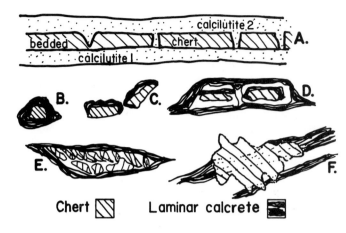

Figure 20. Schematic diagram showing some possible relationships between chert and calcrete in lower Slade. B-E involve reworking of nonpedogenic chert in soil profile. A, Early emplacement of nonpedogenic chert. Chert bed was emplaced, then brecciated, after calcilutite 1 was deposited but before deposition of calcilutite 2. B, Grain cutans (vadoid) formed around chert clast. C, Chert clasts forming shelter fabrics. D, Multicyclical deposition of cutans as shelter fabrics and grain cutans on and around chert clasts. E, Grain cutans around clast of reworked chert clasts. F, Probable pedogenic chert nodule replacing laminar calcretes low in profile.

having formed and in some cases undergone brecciation before overlying calcareous muds were deposited (Fig. 20A). In most cases, the cherts were brecciated during pseudo-anticline formation, and calcrete accumulated on and around chert clasts (Figs. 9G, 20B–E). Locally, in lower parts of St. Louis profiles near regional structures, rather diffusely shaped chert bodies replace calcrete (Fig. 20F). The dark color of the chert, unusual for St. Louis cherts in northeastern Kentucky, suggests that silicification probably was contemporaneous with melanization. On the Waverly Arch Apical Island, bodies of chertified St. Louis breccia (Fig. 5) up to a meter thick may represent silcretes that formed much later during the Mississippian-Pennsylvanian transition.

PROFILES AND PROCESSES IN LOWER PARTS OF THE SLADE FORMATION

Interpretation of pedogenic processes active during episodes of exposure of lower Slade carbonates requires consideration of some variables already discussed, namely, climate, relief, vegetation, parent material, and time. The relatively homogeneous nature of the Slade Formation, the relatively short time required for deposition of the lower Slade, and the even shorter time involved in soil formation, suggest to us that most of the above variables and their effects remained constant during lower Slade time. Locally and over short periods of time, some changes in the type of carbonate parent material and climate were important, but the only variable that could yield major changes during the short times involved was time itself, because pedogenic processes may become more intense and more varied with increased exposure time. Hence, we believe that variations in the length of exposure are largely responsible for the types of paleosol profiles present in the lower Slade. Fortunately, the stratigraphic, depositional, and structural frameworks previously established impose certain, albeit loose, time constraints on the development of the paleosols (Fig. 6), which allow us to follow the probable progression of profile development with increased time.

Immature profiles

The earliest stages of profile development are represented by immature, intraformational profiles in Ste. Genevieve and Warix Run calcarenites (Figs. 13, 14). Because these paleosols developed on ephemeral shoals and interchannel areas, they have very localized distributions and reflect short periods of weathering. Insufficient time was available for development of complete profiles and a good Ccam horizon. Desiccation breccias and caliche pseudo-anticlines are uncommon, apparently because most shrinkage and displacive crystallization, respectively, were accommodated by the porous nature of the calcarenites. Calcretes generally are thin and indistinct, and many are vertical or subvertical rhizocretionary calcretes associated with rooting (Fig. 8D) and rhizobreccias (Figs. 8E, 15A,C,I). Approximately 80 percent of the calcrete from these profiles is rhizocretionary. We believe that rhizocretionary calcretes dominated in these settings because biologically mediated deposition probably occurred faster than physicochemical deposition. On the ephemeral sand-bar and shoal complexes, time apparently was not adequate for thorough rock breakup, solution, and physicochemical precipitation. Desiccation and plants did most of the breakup, and most precipitation was biologically mediated by plants. Roots may concentrate calcium (Goudie, 1973; Hubert, 1978; Klappa, 1983), actively dissolve calcium carbonate (Read, 1976; Klappa, 1983), or cause rapid calcium-carbonate deposition (Klappa, 1979, 1983), and other soil organisms (e.g., fungi, algae, actinomycetes, and bacteria) may have similar effects. Moreover, if porous calcarenites, siltstones, and sandstones were involved, the retention time for water must have been greatly reduced. In such porous lithologies, it is difficult to develop the impermeable, plugged horizons on which physicochemical illuviation occurs.

Lacking plugged horizons, vadose waters apparently penetrated far into these lithologies along avenues of porosity. Accompanying micritization formed the diffuse calcretes, which characterize porous lithologies and occur at depths below preserved surfaces (as much as 3 m) far greater than most physicochemical calcretes occur. The occurrence of diffuse calcrete and nodules formed of diffuse calcrete along cross-stratification (Fig. 8F), channel scours, and bedding planes clearly indicates the significance of avenues of porosity.

Hence, most of the paleosols preserved on these short-lived shoals and bars appear to have been azonal soils formed from recently lithified sands, slightly modified by brecciation and the development of rhizocretionary and diffuse calcretes (Fig. 14). Locally, immature A-C soils or rendzinas (see Duchaufour, 1982; Wright, 1983), representing a greater degree of pedogenesis than that indicated by the azonal soils, are present in the Ste. Genevieve (Figs. 8H, 13). Most intraformational profiles in the Warix Run and Ste. Genevieve have been truncated by migrating tidal channels, so it is possible that A horizons may have been more common than the number actually preserved.

Local regressions during Mill Knob deposition gave rise to intraformational profiles that probably reflect somewhat longer time frames than those inferred for intraformational Warix Run and Ste. Genevieve profiles. These profiles are common in the Mill Knob and represent soils developed on shoaling-upward, intertidal-supratidal sequences. Profiles are generally immature, consisting only of a poorly developed Ccam horizon. Locally, B horizons are preserved (Fig. 12), and C horizons commonly show a well-developed zonation of platy peds, breccia and pseudo-anticlines, laminar calcrete, and melanization (Figs. 10, 12). Most of the preserved profiles contain both rhizobreccias and desiccation breccias. Sufficient time was available for initial pseudo-anticline formation, but those formed are either small or indistinguishable because of subsequent brecciation (Figs 8B, 10). Thin laminar calcretes, generally rhizocretionary in nature, are present at the base of the profile but are very thin and indistinct elsewhere in the paleosols (Fig. 10). In some profiles, however, laminar calcrete is totally absent (Fig. 12). At one peculiar locality, the calcrete is wholly a rhizolite, formed of secondarily calcified root tubules and root molds in completely altered parent material (Figs. 12, 15H).

The general absence of B horizons suggests that most of these paleosols were azonal or A-C soils, although we cannot preclude the possibility that the A and B horizons have been eroded. Nonetheless, even the preserved C horizons in these Mill Knob profiles reflect an increased complexity of form and apparent processes that make them intermediate between the intraformational profiles of the Ste. Genevieve and Warix Run and the interformational profiles on the St. Louis, Ste. Genevieve, and Mill Knob.

Mature profiles

Interformational profiles, on top of the Ste. Genevieve and Mill Knob, and locally on top of the St. Louis, formed during regional regression and/or structural uplift. These paleosols reflect longer periods of exposure and are generally thicker, commonly exhibit B horizons, and reflect a greater number and intensity of pedogenic processes. Profiles developed on the Ste. Genevieve and St. Louis commonly exhibit well-developed breccias, pseudo-anticlines, and moderately thick laminar calcretes (Fig. 11). In contrast, profiles formed on top of the Mill Knob exhibit poorly developed pseudo-anticlines, and laminar calcrete is usually absent except for thin, indistinct laminae (Fig. 12).

The differences between the two types of interformational

profiles are apparently related to climate. The Ste. Genevieve and simple St. Louis profiles are semi-arid profiles, whereas those on top of the Mill Knob probably formed in humid, subtropical conditions (Fig. 6). Dissolution of at least the upper parts of the Mill Knob has produced the chunky, claystone residuum that composes part of the Cave Branch (Fig. 9D). The claystone represents B-horizon material that contains traces of carbonized roots (Fig. 12). In better drained areas on top of the Waverly Arch, terrae rossae are present in the Cave Branch (Figs. 5, 7). In these settings, most of the carbonate was leached from the profile, leaving little available for illuviation as laminar calcrete.

Composite soils

On and near structural highs, the St. Louis exhibits well-developed profiles (Fig. 18), which are composite soils formed during at least two or three stages of erosion. Because deposition of the Ste. Genevieve, Warix Run, and Mill Knob did not occur or was very localized on the Waverly Arch (Ettensohn, 1975, 1977, 1979, 1980, 1981) (Fig. 4), the St. Louis was largely exposed for a period of approximately 4 m.y. On the Waverly Arch Apical Island, moreover, the St. Louis and all the Slade are absent except for a thin silicified breccia of St. Louis clasts (Figs. 4A, 5). High on the flanks of the arch near the Apical Island, however, St. Louis profiles have been severely truncated by major paleokarst development (Figs. 5, 15E–F) and are directly overlain by red claystones of the Cave Branch Bed, which we have interpreted to be a terra rossa paleosol. Farther down the flanks of the arch, the chunky Cave Branch claystones overlie and are gradational with the Mill Knob, but are no longer red (Fig. 5). The absence of the Mill Knob high on the arch coincides with major paleokarst on the St. Louis and red coloration in the Cave Branch (Fig. 5).

According to Duchaufour (1982), terrae rossae form through the dissolution of limestones in humid areas with rainfall in excess of 1 m. In contrast to calcretes, which are dominantly of accretionary or replacement origin, terrae rossae are dominantly degradational because limestones are broken down, commonly with considerable volumetric loss (Goldhammer and Elmore, 1984). Hence, we believe that the Cave Branch terrae rossae reflect the beginning of a more humid climatic regime in the Early Chesterian. Because these claystones are closely associated with the underlying Mill Knob, they apparently represent the B horizons of clayey soils developed on the Mill Knob during humid pedogenesis. As already indicated, the absence or poor development of laminar calcrete in the Mill Knob can also be explained by the advent of humid pedogenesis.

High on the flanks of the Waverly Arch near the Apical Island, where the Mill Knob was already thin or absent, humid pedogenesis destroyed what remained of the Mill Knob, and then exposed Meramecian caliche paleosols on the St. Louis to humid pedogenesis resulting in paleokarst and more terra rossa formation. Hence, the unusually thick and well-developed St. Louis paleosols in this area are actually the product of two periods of pedogenesis, making them composite or complex paleosols (Fig. 18). The restriction of terra rossa paleosols in the Cave Branch to areas near structural highs (Fig. 7) probably reflects prolonged exposure and better drainage.

Processes

Brecciation of parent carbonate material to form framework or skeleton grains was commonly the initial stage of Slade caliche formation. Desiccation and root growth seem to have been the most important agents of brecciation based on the dominance of desiccation breccias and rhizobreccias in our most immature profiles. Displacive crystallization, solution, diurnal heating and cooling, and persistent wetting and drying were probable secondary causes of brecciation.

Once the limestones were "opened" for at least partial penetration by vadose water, formation of caliche pseudo-anticlines by displacive crystallization (Smith, 1974; Assereto and Kendall, 1977; Watts, 1978) could have begun. Exposure in semi-arid conditions would have permitted rapid evaporation of vadose pore fluids and any remaining marine pore fluids, forming supersaturated solutions that are necessary for displacive crystallization (Watts, 1978). Displacive micritic (Fig. 15A,D) and fibrous calcite (Fig. 16M) cements (Watts, 1978) are extremely common microscopic features in Slade calcretes. Thermal expansion, moisture swelling, and growth of roots (Assereto and Kendall, 1978; Klappa, 1980) are other factors that no doubt also influenced pseudo-anticline formation. Pseudo-anticlines in the Slade are nearly everywhere better developed in calcilutites than in calcarenites, apparently because dense micrite did not accommodate displacive crystallization as well as the more porous, granular fabric of calcarenites. Hence, pseudo-anticline formation enhanced the mechanical breakup of the limestones and opened them more prominently for solution, eluviation, and illuviation.

Through solution, fragmented bedrock or framework grains were quickly transformed into plasma that was translocated, mainly downward. The abundance of shelter fabrics (Figs. 9G, 15G, 16B) and graded vadose sediments (Fig. 16C,J) clearly reflects this downward movement. Plants and other soil organisms also may have contributed to this movement.

The amount of solution apparently was governed by the climate. Semi-arid climates throughout most of Meramecian and earliest Chesterian time allowed only limited solution and subsequent rapid deposition; hence, most of the carbonate plasma was retained in the profile. In the latest Early Chesterian, however, increased moisture in a more humid climate did not permit much retention of plasma through illuviation, for most of the carbonate plasma was flushed out of the profile and into the drainage system. As a result, paleosols formed on the Mill Knob and St. Louis at this time exhibit a dearth of calcretes, major paleokarst, and terra rossa residua.

Illuviation of plasma material is related to physicochemical or biologically mediated precipitation of calcium carbonate. Both types of precipitation are merely examples of plasma concentration, and which type dominates, depends on length of exposure, type of bedrock, and position in the profile. When the length of exposure was short and the rocks especially porous, biologically mediated precipitation apparently dominated, because biologic agents are able to retain water and bring about rapid carbonate precipitation.

An increase in the amount of physicochemical calcretes to at least 50 percent of the calcretes present in interformational profiles atop the St. Louis and Ste. Genevieve, suggests that physicochemical illuviation was more prominent in longer exposed profiles. These calcretes apparently were best developed some distance below the surface in calcilutites deformed by pseudo-anticlines. The distance below the surface is important, because intense surface brecciation creates a more effective downward drainage and drier surface soils (Stirk, 1954), which have a negative impact on physicochemical calcrete formation near the surface. Though rhizocretionary calcretes may be common anywhere in a profile, physicochemical calcretes and related pedologic features are more common in lower, presumably moister, parts of the soil profiles, especially near the bases of pseudo-anticline horizons (Figs. 11, 19C,E–G). Pseudo-anticline formation creates large linear fractures at greater depth; these permit vadose waters and roots to penetrate and dissolve dense and largely impermeable calcilutites. The calcilutites are important because their relative impermeability restricts vadose water movement to fracture porosity. Vadose water with carbonate plasma will continue to move downward or laterally along fractures until an unbroken, impermeable calcilutite layer, or plugged horizon, is encountered. Commonly, this is the first undeformed calcilutite layer below the pseudo-anticline horizon, but layers unbroken by vertical fractures in the limbs of pseudo-anticline may form other plugged horizons. On these plugged horizons, calcretes slowly accreted upward, commonly created more fractures and larger pseudo-anticlines through displacive crystallization. Locally developed plugged horizons on individual micrite and chert clasts and beds may form lesser calcrete accumulations or shelter fabrics much higher in the profile. Most physicochemical calcretes are laminar simply because the impermeable planes on which they accreted were ruptured bedding planes and subhorizontal fractures. Lacking fracture porosity and permeability, any carbonate plasma from overlying soil materials could have only illuviated on bedrock surfaces forming thin crusts (Fig. 19B) or in the troughs between pseudo-anticlines (Fig. 19H).

The downward movement of soil water and eluviation of carbonate plasma probably was most common during wet seasons. During intervening dry periods, when the net loss of water from the soils far exceeded input, increased soil-suction pressure forced the illuviation or deposition of the carbonate plasma as caliche (Netterberg, 1971). Soil-suction pressures increase during dry seasons as the net effects of evaporation, transpiration, photosynthesis, and higher temperatures create a concomitant decline in pore-water pressure and pCO_2, which decreases the solubility of calcium carbonate to the point of saturation, and precipitation occurs. Purely biochemical reactions in soils may also cause precipitation, but apparently over shorter durations.

In more porous parent materials such as calcarenite, the above processes of plasma concentration apparently were subordinate to plasma separation or in situ recrystallization (neomorphism) because of short retention times for water. In these lithologies, the micritization of entire fabrics (degrading neomorphism) seemingly occurred along avenues of porosity.

Silification of calcretes is yet another process that occurred locally in the Slade profiles. Most of the silica in calcretes probably was released by replacement of silicates with calcite in an alkaline setting (Walker, 1960). Resulting silica solutions or gels apparently moved downward to zones lower in the caliche profile where silica precipitation (illuviation) was favored by the possibility of longer residence and slower reaction times (Reeves, 1970; Walls and others, 1975). Moreover, during very arid conditions, dehydration of silica saturated gels favors silica deposition.

Finally, biological activity may be superimposed on any of the above processes. Although pedoturbation by plants probably occurred in most profiles at every state of development, faunal pedoturbation seems to have been restricted to accumulations of organic debris in the Slade.

We belive that most of the above processes operated contemporaneously to a greater or lesser extent. However, the evolution of Slade profiles inferred in previous sections suggests that mechanical breakup processes dominated the early phases of profile development and set the stage for processes related to eluviation and illuviation, which predominated in later stages of development.

CONCLUSIONS

The subaerial exposure "crusts" associated with disconformities in lower parts of the Slade Formation are calcareous Mississippian paleosols related to episodes of structural uplift and marine regression. Two general types of profiles are present. The most abundant and easily recognized is the calcareous paleosol or caliche. Microscopic and megascopic examination of the caliches indicate that they are pedogenic accumulations of calcium carbonate formed in a semi-arid climate. These caliches are paleosols inasmuch as they supported plants and exhibited both horizon zonation and soil structure. Most of the profiles have been truncated so that only C horizons are ubiquitous, but B horizons, in which parent material is unrecognizable and organized into large peds, as well as organic-rich, calcareous A horizons, are preserved locally.

Most of the preserved caliche profiles are characterized in part by crust horizons. Most of what have been called crusts in the Slade are cutans, plasma concentrations consisting of laminae of micritic calcite illuviated on mechanically separated bedding planes or subparallel fractures that formed impermeable, plugged horizons low in the soil profile. Illuviation apparently resulted from either physicochemical (e.g., evaporation) biologically mediated (e.g., transpiration and photosynthesis) processes.

A moister, subtropical climate near the end of lower Slade deposition gave rise to more humid pedogenesis and a second type, or clayey soil profile, characterized by solution of underlying caliches and the formation of a clayey residuum. Elevation on structural highs intensified these processes to the point that surface carbonate units were completely reduced to a terra rossa residuum.

The major factor in the formation of the caliche soils was an evaporative, moisture-deficient climate, which effectively immobilized the carbonate plasma in the soil profile. In contrast, the clayey soils that developed later reflect a nearly complete leaching of carbonate plasma from the profile because of increased moisture. Though climate was apparently the chief control over the type of soil that developed, length of exposure and type of carbonate parent material significantly influenced the maturity and nature of the resulting profiles.

Past geological characterization of subaerial exposure crusts and caliches has emphasized vadose diagenesis and environmental significance, but pedogenic analysis offers yet another means for understanding their origin and significance.

ACKNOWLEDGMENTS

We thank W. R. Sigleo, J. Reinhardt, H. S. Chafetz, and W. L. Watney for their constructive criticism of early versions of the manuscript; their comments have greatly improved this paper. We also acknowledge the photographic and reproductive services of the Kentucky Geological Survey, the drafting skills of Beth M. Ettensohn, and the typing skills of Marjorie A. Palmer and Marilyn W. Wooten.

REFERENCES CITED

Adams, A. E., 1980, Calcrete profiles in the Eyam Limestone (Carboniferous) of Derbyshire; Petrology and regional significance: Sedimentology, v. 27, p. 651–660.

Arakel, A. V., 1982, Genesis of calcrete in Quaternary soil profiles, Hutt and Leeman lagoons, western Australia: Journal of Sedimentary Petrology, v. 52, p. 109–125.

Assereto, R. L., and Kendall, C. G. St. C., 1977, Nature, origin, and classification of peritidal tepee structures and related breccias: Sedimentology, v. 24, p. 153–210.

Blank, H. R., and Tynes, E. W., 1965, Formation of caliche in situ: Geological Society of America Bulletin, v. 76, p. 1387–1391.

Braithwaite, C.J.R., 1975, Petrology of paleosols and other terrestrial sediments on Aldebra, western Indian Ocean: Philosophical Transactions of the Royal Society of London, 13, v. 273, p. 1–32.

Bretz, J. H., and Horberg, L., 1949, Caliche in southeastern New Mexico: Journal of Geology, v. 57, p. 491–511.

Brewer, R., 1976, Fabric and mineral analysis of soils: Huntington, New York, Robert E. Krieger Publishing Co., 482 p.

Brewer, R., Cook, K.A.W., and Speight, J. G., 1970, Proposal for soil stratigraphic units in the Australian stratigraphic code: Journal of the Geological Society of Australia, v. 17, p. 103–109.

Brown, C. N., 1956, The origin of caliche on the northeastern Llano Estacado, Texas: Journal of Geology, v. 64, p. 1–15.

Buol, S. W., 1965, Present soil-forming factors and processes in arid and semi-arid regions: Soil Science, v. 99, p. 45–49.

Buol, S. W., Hole, F. D., and McCracken, R. J., 1980, Soil genesis and classification, second edition: Ames, Iowa State University Press, 406 p.

Carlisle, D., 1983, Concentration of uranium and vanadium in calcretes and gypcretes, *in* Wilson, R.C.L., ed., Residual deposits; Surface related weathering processes and materials: Oxford, Blackwell Scientific Publications, p. 185–195.

Choquette, P. W., 1976, Recent calcareous crusts (caliche) in Isla Mujeres, Quintana Roo, Mexico; Insights from isotopic composition, *in* Weidie, A. E., and Ward, W. C., eds., Carbonate rocks and hydrogeology of the Yucatan Peninsula, Mexico, Field Trip 5, 1976 AAPG/SEPM Annual Convention: New Orleans, Louisiana, New Orleans Geological Society, p. 139–158.

Dever, G. R., Jr., 1973, Stratigraphic relationships in the lower and middle Newman Limestone (Mississippian), east-central and northeastern Kentucky [M.S. thesis]: Lexington, University of Kentucky, 121 p.

——, 1977, The lower Newman Limestone; Stratigraphic evidence of Late Mississippian tectonic activity, *in* Dever, G. R., Jr., and others, Stratigraphic evidence for late Paleozoic tectonism in northeastern Kentucky, Field Trip Guidebook, 1976 AAPG Eastern Section: Kentucky Geological Survey, p. 8–18.

——, 1980a, Stratigraphic relationships in the lower and middle Newman Limestone (Mississippian), east-central and northeastern Kentucky: Kentucky Geological Survey, Series 11, Thesis Series 1, 49 p.

——, 1980b, The Newman Limestone; An indicator of Mississippian tectonic activity in northeastern Kentucky, *in* Luther, M. K., ed., Proceedings of the technical sessions, Kentucky Oil and Gas Association, 36th and 37th Annual Meetings, 1972 and 1973: Kentucky Geological Survey, Series 11, Special Publication 2, p. 42–54.

Dever, G. R., Jr., Hoge, H. P., Hester, N. C., and Ettensohn, F. R., 1977, Stratigraphic evidence for late Paleozoic tectonism in northeastern Kentucky, Field Trip Guidebook, 1976 AAPG Eastern Section: Kentucky Geological Survey, 80 p.

Dever, G. R., Jr., Hester, N. C., Ettensohn, F. R., and Moody, J. R., 1979, Newman Limestone (Mississippian) of east-central Kentucky and Lower Pennsylvanian slump structures, *in* Ettensohn, F. R., and Dever, G. R., Jr., eds., Carboniferous geology from the Appalachian Basin to the Illinois Basin through eastern Ohio and Kentucky, Field trip No. 4, 9th International Congress of Carboniferous Stratigraphy and Geology: Lexington, University of Kentucky, p. 175–181.

Duchaufour, P., 1982, Pedology (English ed.): London, George Allen and Unwin, 448 p.

Esteban, M., 1974, Caliche textures and "Microcodium:" Bollettino della Societa Geologica Italiano (suppl.), v. 92, p. 105–125.

Estaban, M., and Klappa, C. F., 1983, Subaerial exposure environment, *in* Scholle, P.A., Bebout, D. G., and Moore, C. H., eds., Carbonate depositional environments: American Association of Petroleum Geologists Memoir 33, p. 1–54.

Ettensohn, F. R., 1975, Stratigraphy and paleoenvironmental aspects of Upper Mississippian rocks, east-central Kentucky [Ph.D. thesis]: Urbana, University of Illinois, 320 p.

——, 1977, Effects of synsedimentary tectonic activity on the upper Newman Limestone and Pennington Formation, *in* Dever, G. R., Jr., and others, Stratigraphic evidence for late Paleozoic tectonism in northeastern Kentucky, Field Trip Guidebook, 1976 AAPG Eastern Section: Kentucky Geological Survey, p. 18–29.

——, 1979, Generalized description of Carboniferous stratigraphy, structure and depositional environments in east-central Kentucky, *in* Ettensohn, F. R., and Dever, G. R., Jr., eds., Carboniferous geology from the Appalachian Basin to the Illinois Basin through eastern Ohio and Kentucky, Field Trip No. 4, 9th International Congress of Carboniferous Stratigraphy and Geology: Lexington, University of Kentucky, p. 64–77.

——, 1980, An alternative to the barrier-shoreline model for deposition of Mississippian and Pennsylvanian rocks in northeastern Kentucky: Geological Society of America Bulletin, v. 91, pt. 1, p. 130–135; pt. II, p. 934–1056.

——, 1981, Mississippian–Pennsylvanian boundary in northeastern Kentucky, *in* Roberts, T. G., ed., G.S.A. Cincinnati '81 field trip guidebooks, v. 1, Stratigraphy, sedimentology: Falls Church, Virginia, American Geological Institute, p. 195–257.

——, 1986, The Mississippian-Pennsylvanian transition along Interstate 64, northeastern Kentucky, *in* Neathery, T. L., ed., Southeastern Section of the Geological Society of America: Boulder, Colorado, Geological Society of America, Centennial Field Guide Volume 6, p. 37–42.

Ettensohn, F. R., and Chesnut, D. R., 1979, Stratigraphy and depositional environments in the upper Hartselle, Bangor, and Pennington formations of south-central Kentucky, *in* Ettensohn, F. R., and Dever, G. R., Jr., eds., Carboniferous geology from the Appalachian Basin to the Illinois Basin through eastern Ohio and Kentucky, Field Trip No. 4, 9th International Congress of Carboniferous Stratigraphy and Geology: Lexington, University of Kentucky, p. 194–201.

Ettensohn, F. R., and Dever, G. R., Jr., 1979a, The Newman Limestone on the east side of the Waverly Arch, *in* Ettensohn, F. R., and Dever, G. R., Jr., eds., Carboniferous geology from the Appalachian Basin to the Illinois Basin through eastern Ohio and Kentucky, Field Trip No. 4, 9th International Congress of Carboniferous Stratigraphy and Geology: Lexington, University of Kentucky, p. 96–107.

—— , 1979b, The Waverly Arch apical island, *in* Ettensohn, F. R., and Dever, G. R., Jr., eds., Carboniferous geology from the Appalachian Basin to the Illinois Basin through eastern Ohio and Kentucky, Field Trip No. 4, 9th International Congress of Carboniferous Stratigraphy and Geology: Lexington, University of Kentucky, p. 108–112.

—— , 1979c, The Newman Limestone west of the Waverly Arch, *in* Ettensohn, F. R., and Dever, G. R., Jr., eds., Carboniferous geology from the Appalachian Basin through eastern Ohio and Kentucky, Field Trip No. 4, 9th International Congress of Carboniferous Stratigraphy and Geology: Lexington, University of Kentucky, p. 119–124.

Ettensohn, F. R., Dever, G. R., Jr. and Grow, J. S., 1984a, Fossil soils and subaerial exposure crusts in the Mississippian of eastern Kentucky, *in* Rast, N., and Hay, H. B., eds., Field Trip Guides for Geological Society of America Annual Meeting, Southeastern and North-Central Sections: Lexington, Department of Geology, University of Kentucky and Kentucky Geological Survey, p. 84–105.

Ettensohn, F. R., Rice, C. L., Dever, G. R., Jr., and Chesnut, D. R., 1984b, Slade and Paragon Formations; New stratigraphic nomenclature for Mississippian rocks along the Cumberland Escarpment in Kentucky: U.S. Geological Survey Bulletin 1605-B, 37 p.

Ferm, J. C., Horne, J. C., Swinchatt, J. P., and Whaley, P. W., 1971, Carboniferous depositional environments in northeastern Kentucky, Guidebook, Geological Society of Kentucky Annual Spring Field Conference: Kentucky Geological Survey, 30 p.

Fink, J., 1976, Mitteilungen der Kommission für Quatar: Forschung der Osterreichischen Akademie der Wissenschaften, v. 1, p. 65–71.

FitzPatrick, E. A., 1971, Pedology: Edinburgh, Oliver and Boyd, 306 p.

Flügel, E., 1982, Microfacies analysis of limestones: Berlin, Springer-Verlag, 633 p.

Folk, R. L., 1965, Some aspects of recrystallization in ancient limestones, *in* Pray, L. C., and Murray, R. C., Dolomitization and limestone diagenesis: Society of Economic Paleontologists and Mineralogists Special Publication 13, p. 14–48.

Freytet, P., and Plaziat, J. C., 1982, Continental carbonate sedimentation and pedogenesis; Late Cretaceous and Early Tertiary of southern France: Contributions to Sedimentology 12 (Stuttgart), 213 p.

Gile, L. H., 1961, A classification of ca horizons in soils of a desert region, Dona Ana County, New Mexico: Proceedings of the Soil Science Society of America, v. 25, p. 52–61.

Gile, L. H., Peterson, F. F., and Grossman, R. B., 1966, Morphological and genetic sequences of carbonate accumulation in desert soils: Soil Science, v. 101, p. 347–360.

Goddard, E. N., Trask, P. D., DeFord, R. K., Rove, O. N., Singewald, J. T., Jr., and Overbeck, R. M., 1963, Rock-color chart: Boulder, Colorado, Geological Society of America, 16 p.

Goldhammer, R. K., and Elmore, R. D., 1984, Paleosols capping regressive carbonate cycles in the Pennsylvanian Black Prince Limestone, Arizona: Journal of Sedimentary Petrology, v. 54, p. 1124–1137.

Gonzalez-Bonorino, F., and Terruggi, M. E., 1952, Lexico Sedimentologico: Instituto Nacional de Investigaciones de Ciencias Naturales, Buenos Aires, Publicaciones de extension cultural y didactica, no. 6, 164 p.

Goudie, A., 1973, Duricrusts in tropical and subtropical landscapes: Oxford, Clarendon Press, 174 p.

—— , 1983, Calcrete, *in* Goudie, A. S., and Pye, K., eds., Chemical sediments and geomorphology: London, Academic Press, p. 93–131.

Grow, J. S., 1982, Pedogenic carbonates (caliche) in the lower Newman Limestone (Mississippian) of northeastern and east-central Kentucky; Evidence for subaerial exposure, weathering, and soil formation [M.S. thesis]: Lexington, University of Kentucky, 145 p.

Hale, A. P., and Ettensohn, F. R., 1984, Micromorphological features observed in pedogenic carbonates (caliche) on San Salvador Island, Bahamas; Proceedings of the Second Symposium on the Geology of the Bahamas: San Salvador, Bahamas, College Center of the Finger Lakes Bahamian Field Station, p. 265–277.

Harland, W. B., Cox, A. V., Llewellyn, P. G., Pickton, C.A.G., Smith, A. G., and Walters, R., 1982, A geologic time scale: Cambridge, Cambridge University Press, 131 p.

Harrison, R. S., 1977, Caliche profiles; Indicators of near-surface subaerial diagenesis, Barbados, West Indies: Bulletin of Canadian Petroleum Geology, v. 25, p. 123–173.

Harrison, R. S., and Steinen, R. P., 1978, Subaerial crusts, caliche profiles, and breccia horizons; Comparison of some Holocene and Mississippian exposure surfaces, Barbados and Kentucky: Geological Society of America Bulletin, v. 89, p. 385–396.

Hodgson, J. M., 1978, Soil sampling and soil description: Oxford, Clarendon Press, 241 p.

Hole, F. D., 1961, A classification of pedoturbations and some other processes and factors of soil formation in relation to isotropism and anisotropism: Soil Science, v. 19, p. 375–377.

Horne, J. C., Ferm, J. C., and Swinchatt, J. P., 1974, Depositional model for the Mississippian-Pennsylvanian boundary in northeastern Kentucky, *in* Briggs, G., ed., Carboniferous of the southeastern United States: Geological Society of America Special Paper 148, p. 97–114.

Hubert, J. F., 1977, Paleosol caliche in the New Haven Arkose, Connecticut; Record of semiaridity in Late Triassic–Early Triassic time: Geology, v. 5, p. 302–304.

—— , 1978, Paleosol caliche in the New Haven arkose, Newark Group, Connecticut: Palaeogeography, Palaeoclimatology, Palaeoecology, v. 24, p. 151–168.

Inden, R. F., and Horne, J. C., 1973, Caliche soil horizons on oolitic shoals and carbonate mud mounds in Carboniferous (Newman Limestone) of eastern Kentucky [abs.]: American Association of Petroleum Geologists Bulletin, v. 57, p. 785–786.

Inden, R. F., and Moore, C. H., 1983, Beach environment, *in* Scholle, P. A., Bebout, D. G., and Moore, C. H., eds., Carbonate depositional environments: American Association of Petroleum Geologists Memoir 33, p. 211–265.

Isphording, W. C., 1976, Weathering of Yucatan limestone; The genesis of terra rossas, *in* Weidie, A. E., and Ward, W. C., Carbonate rocks and hydrogeology of the Yucatan Peninsula, Mexico, Field Trip 5, 1976 AAPG/SEPM Annual Convention: New Orleans, Louisiana, New Orleans Geological Society, p. 259–274.

James, N. P., 1972, Holocene and Pleistocene calcareous crust (caliche) profiles; Criteria for subaerial exposure: Journal of Sedimentary Petrology, v. 42, p. 817–836.

James, N. P., and Choquette, P. W., 1984, Limestones; The meteoric diagenetic environment: Geoscience Canada, v. 11, p. 161–194.

Jenny, H., 1941, Factors of soil formation: New York, McGraw-Hill, 281 p.

Kahle, C. F., 1977, Origin of subaerial Holocene calcareous crusts; Role of algae, fungi, and sparmicritization: Sedimentology, v. 24, p. 413–455.

Klappa, C. F., 1978, Biolithogenesis of Microdium; Elucidation: Sedimentology, v. 25, p. 489–522.

—— , 1979a, Lichen stromatolites; Criterion for subaerial exposure and a mechanism for the formation of laminar calcretes (caliche): Journal of Sedimentary Petrology, v. 43, p. 387–400.

——, 1979b, Calcified filaments in Quaternary calcretes; Organo-mineral interactions in the subaerial vadose environment: Journal of Sedimentary Petrology, v. 49, p. 955–968.

——, 1980, Brecciation textures and tepee structures in Quaternary calcrete (caliche) profiles from eastern Spain; The plant factor in their formation: Geological Journal, v. 15, p. 81–89.

——, 1983, A process-response model for the formation of pedogenic calcretes, *in* Wilson, R.C.L., ed., Residual deposits; Surface related weathering processes and materials: Oxford, Blackwell Scientific Publications, p. 211–220.

Klekamp, C. T., 1971, Petrology and paleocurrents of the Ste. Genevieve Member of the Newman Limestone (Mississippian) in Carter County, northeastern Kentucky [M.S. thesis]: Cincinnati, Ohio, University of Cincinnati, 38 p.

Krumbein, W. E., 1968, Geomicrobiology and geochemistry of the "nari-limecrust" (Israel), *in* Muller, G., and Friedman, G. M., eds., Recent developments in carbonate sedimentology in central Europe: Berlin, Springer-Verlag, p. 138–147.

Kubiena, W. L., 1938, Micropedology: Ames, Iowa, Collegiate Press, 243 p.

Lamplugh, G. W., 1902, Calcrete: Geological Magazine, v. 9, p. 575.

Lierman, R. T., 1984, A facies model for the Warix Run and Paoli–Beaver Bend Limestone Members of the Newman Limestone (Upper Mississippian) of east-central Kentucky: Geological Society of America Abstracts with Programs, v. 16, p. 152.

McFarlan, A. C., and Walker, F. H., 1956, Some old Chester problems; Correlations along the eastern belt of outcrop: Kentucky Geological Survey, Series 9, Bulletin 20, 36 p.

Morrison, R. B., 1967, Principles of Quaternary soil stratigraphy, *in* Morrison, R. B., and Wright, H. E., Jr., eds., Quaternary soils: Reno, Center for Water Resources Research, Desert Research Institute, University of Nevada, p. 1–69.

Moseley, F., 1965, Plateau calcretes, calcreted gravels, cemented dunes, and related deposits of the Mallegh-Bomba region of Libya: Zeitschrift für Geomorphologie (neue folge), Band 9, p. 166–185.

Multer, H. G., and Hoffmeister, J. E., 1968, Subaerial laminated crusts of the Florida Keys: Geological Society of America Bulletin, v. 79, p. 183–192.

——, 1971, Subaerial laminated crusts of the Florida Keys, *in* Multer, H. G., ed., Field guide to some carbonate rock environments: Madison, New Jersey, Fairleigh Dickinson University, 158 p.

Netterberg, F., 1971, Calcrete in road construction: Pretoria, South Africa, National Institute for Road Research Bulletin 10, p. 1–73.

North American Commission on Stratigraphic Nomenclature, 1983, North American stratigraphic code: American Association of Petroleum Geologists Bulletin, v. 67, p. 841–875.

Peryt, T. M., 1983, Classification of coated grains, *in* Peryt, T. M., ed., Coated grains: Berlin, Springer-Verlag, p. 3–6.

Phalen, W. C., 1906, Origin and occurrence of certain iron ores of northeastern Kentucky: Economic Geology, v. 1, p. 660–673.

Price, W. A., 1925, Caliche and pseudo-anticlines: American Association of Petroleum Geologists Bulletin, v. 9, p. 1009–1017.

Read, J. F., 1974, Calcrete deposits and Quaternary sediments, Edel Province, Shark Bay, western Australia: American Association of Petroleum Geologists Memoir 22, p. 250–282.

——, 1976, Calcretes and their distinction from stromatolites, *in* Walter, M. R., ed., Stromatolites; Developments in sedimentology 20: Amsterdam, Elsevier, p. 55–71.

Reeves, C.C., 1970, Origin, classification, and geologic history of caliche on the southern High Plains, Texas and eastern New Mexico: Journal of Geology, p. 352–362.

——, 1976, Caliche, origin, classification, morphology, uses: Lubbock, Texas, Estacado Books, 233 p.

Retallack, G. J., 1976, Triassic palaeosols in the Upper Narrabeen Group of New South Wales; Pt. I, Features of the palaeosols: Journal of the Geological Society of Australia, v. 23, p. 383–399.

Ruellan, A., 1967, Individualisation et accumutation du calcaire dans les sols et depots quaternaires du Maroc: Paris, Office de la Recherche Scientifique et Technique Outre-Mer, Cahiers, Serie Pedologie, v. 5, p. 421–460.

Ruhe, R. U., Cady, J. G., and Gornez, R. S., 1961, Palaeosols of Bermuda: Geological Society of America Bulletin, v. 72, p. 1121–1142.

Rutte, E., 1958, Kalkkrusten in Spanien: Neues Jahrbuch für Geologie und Paläontologie, v. 106, p. 52–138.

Seisser, W. G., 1973, Diagenetically formed ooids and intraclasts in South African calcretes: Sedimentology, v. 20, p. 539–551.

Smith, D. B., 1974, Origin of tepees in Upper Permian shelf carbonate rocks of Guadalupe Mountains, New Mexico: American Association of Petroleum Geologists Bulletin, v. 58, p. 63–70.

Steinen, R. P., 1974, Phreatic and vadose diagenetic modification of Pleistocene limestone; Petrographic observations from the subsurface of Barbados, West Indies: American Association of Petroleum Geologists Bulletin, v. 58, p. 1008–1024.

Stirk, G. B., 1954, Some aspects of soil shrinkage and the effect of cracking upon water entry into the soil: Australian Journal of Agricultural Research, v. 5, p. 279–290.

Strahler, A. N., and Strahler, A. H., 1973, Environmental geoscience; Interaction between natural systems and man: Santa Barbara, California, Hamilton Publishing Co., 511 p.

Vageler, R., 1933, An introduction to tropical soils: London, MacMillan and Co., 240 p.

Walkden, G. M., 1974, Paleokarstic surfaces in Upper Visean (Carboniferous) limestones of the Derbyshire block, England: Journal of Sedimentary Petrology, v. 44, p. 1232–1237.

Walker, T. R., 1960, Carbonate replacement of detrital crystalline silicate minerals as a source of authigenic minerals in sedimentary rocks: Geological Society of America Bulletin, v. 71, p. 145–152.

Walls, R. A., Harris, W. B., and Nunan, W. E., 1975, Calcareous crust (caliche) profiles and early subaerial exposure of Carboniferous carbonates, northeastern Kentucky: Sedimentology, v. 22, p. 417–440.

Ward, W. C., Folk, R. L., and Wilson, J. L., 1970, Blackening of eolianite and caliche adjacent to saline lakes, Iala Mujeres, Qunitana Roo, Mexico: Journal of Sedimentary Petrology, v. 40, p. 548–555.

Warren, J. K., 1983, On pedogenic calcrete as it occurs in the vadose zone of Quaternary calcareous dunes in coastal South Australia: Journal of Sedimentary Petrology, v. 53, p. 787–796.

Watts, N. L., 1978, Displacive calcite: Evidence from recent and ancient calcretes: Geology, v. 6, p. 699–703.

——, 1980, Quaternary pedogenic calcretes from the Kalahari (southern Africa); Mineralogy, genesis, and diagenesis: Sedimentology, v. 27, p. 661–686.

Wilson, M. J., and Jones, D., 1983, Lichen weathering of minerals; Implications for pedogenesis, *in* Wilson, R.C.L., ed., Residual deposits; Surface related weathering processes and materials: Oxford, Blackwell Scientific Publications, p. 5–12.

Woodward, H. B., 1961, Preliminary subsurface study of southeastern Appalachian Interior Plateau: American Association of Petroleum Geologists Bulletin, v. 45, p. 1643–1655.

Wright, V. P., 1982a, Calcrete palaeosols from the Lower Carboniferous Llanelly Formation, South Wales: Sedimentary Geology, v. 33, p. 1–33.

——, 1982b, The recognition and interpretation of paleokarsts; Two examples from the Lower Carboniferous of South Wales: Journal of Sedimentary Petrology, v. 52, p. 83–94.

——, 1983, A rendzina from the Lower Carboniferous of South Wales: Sedimentology, v. 30, p. 159–179.

Yaalon, D. H., and Kalmar, D., 1972, Vertical movement in an undisturbed soil; Continuous measurement of swelling and shrinkage with a sensitive apparatus: Geoderma, v. 8, p. 231–240.

Ziegler, A. M., Scotese, C. R., McKerrow, W. S., and others, 1979, Paleozoic paleogeography: Annual Review of Earth and Planetary Sciences, v. 7, p. 473–502.

MANUSCRIPT ACCEPTED BY THE SOCIETY JULY 1, 1987

Printed in U.S.A.

Geological Society of America
Special Paper 216
1988

Pedogenesis of some Pennsylvanian underclays; Ground-water, topographic, and tectonic controls

Thomas W. Gardner
E. G. Williams
Philip W. Holbrook
Department of Geosciences
The Pennsylvania State University
University Park, Pennsylvania 16802

ABSTRACT

Clay mineral analyses of underclays directly below the Upper Elkhorn Coals (eastern Kentucky) and the Lower Kittanning Coal (western Pennsylvania) demonstrate systematic lateral and vertical variations that include changes in the kaolinite-illite ratio, mica loss ratio, weathering ratio, apparent thickness of mica, and distribution of chlorite. Clay mineral analyses of associated, unweathered shales indicate that approximately 30 percent of the regional variation in Lower Kittanning underclay mineralogy is inherited from the parent material. The remaining variation is attributed to in situ pedogenesis.

Petrographic analysis of thin sections from a fluvial sandstone subjacent to the Upper Elkhorn underclay suggests that position of the ground-water table controlled pedogenesis. Two distinct alteration zones separated by a diffuse, subhorizontal boundary are present in the sandstone: an upper zone characterized by kaolinization of feldspars, dissolution of chlorite and detrital dolomite, and absence of siderite; and a lower zone characterized by ferron dolomite replacement of both detrital feldspar and detrital dolomite, and authigenic pore fillings of chlorite and siderite.

These systematic changes in sandstone and underclay mineralogy are consistent with a pedogenic model in which the process of podzolization was controlled by position of the ground-water table and topography. In this model, the main phase of organic material accumulation occurred above the underclay after water-table levels intersected the land surface as a result of compaction, subsidence, or marine transgression. Regional gravity and structure data in western Pennsylvania further suggest that syntectonic movements were the fundamental controls on regional topography and ground-water levels, and thus, pedogenesis.

INTRODUCTION

That Carboniferous underclays are of pedogenic origin is an old (Logan, 1842), but still controversial, hypothesis. Common definitions of underclays ranging from purely descriptive "an argillaceous, gray, non-bedded stratum found directly (but not always) under a coal" (Brownwell, p. 138, 1978) to genetic "a bed of clay rock, sometimes siliceous . . . without bedding . . . [with] carbonized roots of plants . . . represent(ing) the old soil on which grew the vegetation" (Challinor, p. 322–323, 1978), offer no real solution to the problem of origin.

Models of underclay genesis are numerous, but can be di-

vided generally into allochthonous and autochthonous classes (Fig. 1). Allochthonous models (Grim and Allen, 1938; Schultz, 1958) suggest that the mineralogy of underclays is inherited from either lithologic (bedrock or soil) or climatic change in the source area. Williams and others (1974) have effectively demonstrated that as much as 30 percent of the variation in underclay mineralogy can be attributed to initial variation in parent material mineralogy. More widely accepted autochthonous models (Fig. 1) suggest that underclay properties are generally acquired at the site of deposition, either during or after sedimentation. Because

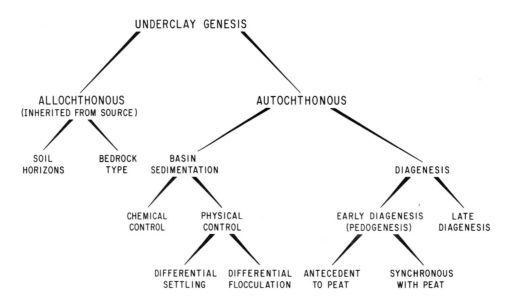

Figure 1. General diagram of underclay genesis models.

of variation in the possible depositional setting and the timing of underclay formation, numerous autochthonous models have been proposed for the origin of underclays (Fig. 1).

Within a sedimentary basin, variation in water salinity or alkalinity is inferred as a control on the reconstitution of degraded illite (Parham, 1964; Williams and others, 1968) and the alteration of illite to chlorite (Parham, 1964), or on the differential flocculation of kaolinite and illite (Parham, 1964; O'Brien, 1964; Williams and others, 1974). These models imply that some or all of the regional variation in illite/kaolinite ratios of underclays is controlled by regional variations in water chemistry of marine, brackish, fresh-water, and lacustrine environments.

Other autochthonous models suggest in situ underclay pedogenesis soon after sediment deposition under generally acidic conditions. Differences in these pedogenic models derive from inferred drainage characteristics and oxidation states of sediment during underclay genesis or the temporal relationship between underclay genesis and peat accumulation. One group of autochthonous models suggests that underclay genesis is antecedent to peat accumulation in an oxidizing, poorly to well-drained environment (Weller, 1930, 1931) above a paleo-water table (Williams and others, 1965; Smyth, 1984; Percival, 1986).

Another group of models suggests underclay genesis is nearly synchronous with peat accumulation. Small changes in water pH, rates of bacterial decomposition of organic material, and/or leaching produce either peat accumulation or the development of underclays (Stout, 1923; Patterson and Hosterman, 1960; Huddle and Patterson, 1961; Smith and O'Brien, 1965; Moore, 1968). The near-surface, "swampy" environments are inferred from the presence of organic matter to be both reducing

and acidic. Keller (1956, 1958) further suggested intense upward leaching in swamps by dialysis. A third group of autochthonous models suggests underclay genesis subsequent to peat deposition by intense organic acid leaching (Staub and Cohen, 1978) to produce a gleyed soil profile (McMillan, 1956). Rimmer and Eberl (1982) have offered the provocative suggestion that underclay diagenesis may be occurring today, given the existing pH of some underclays.

Diagnostic underclay properties, which have been the focus of numerous studies cited previously, are: (1) vertical variability in clay mineral composition, especially kaolinite, illite, chlorite-type clays, and mixed layered clays; (2) distribution of iron mineral species, mostly oxides and carbonates; (3) depletion of silica; and (4) texture, bedding, and clay mineral fabric. The problem of underclay genesis is essentially to determine the time of acquisition of those chemical and mineralogical properties, the physiochemical environment(s) that could generate the observed properties, and the depositional setting(s) most likely to produce those physiochemical constraints.

This chapter proposes that certain Pennsylvanian underclays owe most of their morphology and mineralogy directly to pedogenesis, which is determined to a large degree by the position of the ground-water table and paleotopography. It is further suggested that, for a given paleoclimate, syntectonic movements were the fundamental controls of regional topography and ground-water levels, and thus pedogenesis.

Data to support this thesis come from local, vertical variations in clays, iron minerals, and alteration zones in a fluvial sandstone and underclay subjacent to the Upper Elkhorn Coals in eastern Kentucky and regional horizontal and vertical variations in clay minerals from the Lower Kittanning underclay in western

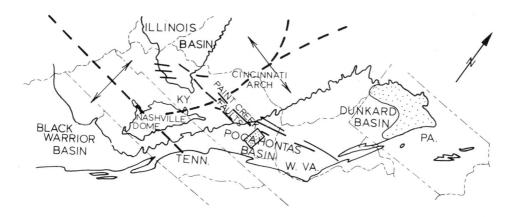

Figure 2. Location map of study areas (outlined in stippled pattern), which illustrates outcrop limit of Pennsylvanian sediments and major tectonic features.

Pennsylvania. Mineralogical evidence is based on x-ray analyses of approximately 500 samples from 78 profiles through the Lower Kittanning underclay and two profiles through the Upper Elkhorn underclay, as well as petrographic analysis of 42 thin sections from a sandstone subjacent to the Upper Elkhorn underclay.

REGIONAL SETTING

The underclays and sandstone from the Upper Elkhorn interval outcrop along the western edge of the Pocahontas Basin (Fig. 2) within a hinge zone of down-to-the-basin faults that separated the subsiding Appalachian Basin from the stable cratonic platform to the north (Horne and Ferm, 1976). Underclays from the Lower Kittanning interval outcrop extensively along the eastern and northern rim of the Dunkard Basin (Fig. 2) within a zone of northeast-trending folds and negative Bouguer gravity anomalies (Williams and Bragonier, 1974).

Middle Pennsylvanian cyclothems in the study areas consist of interbedded, lenticular deposits of shale, siltstone, sandstone, coal, and discontinuous limestones and calcareous marine zones (Fig. 3). Detailed stratigraphic sections and facies models have been described for the older Upper Elkhorn interval in the Breathitt Formation (Westphalian B) (Baganz and others, 1975; Gardner 1977, 1983) and for the younger Lower Kittanning interval in the Allegheny Group (Westphalian D) (Williams, 1960; Williams and Ferm, 1964; Williams and Bragonier, 1974). Paleoclimate during Westphalian B and D was probably warm and tropical, judging from the equatorial position of Kentucky and Pennsylvania (Phillips and Peppers, 1984). However, rainfall distribution may have changed from ever-wet tropical (high rainfall evenly distributed throughout the year) during Westphalian B to more seasonal and perhaps lower rainfall by Westphalian D (Cecil and others, 1985).

MINERALOGICAL VARIATION

Lower Kittanning Underclays

The Lower Kittanning underclays can be grouped into four categories (Fig. 4, A through D) as defined by their clay mineral properties. The diagram is entered by initially grouping underclay profiles into categories with or without chlorite in some part of the sampled profile. Because chlorite is very sensitive to leaching or oxidation, and because it is present in detrital rocks in the Lower Kittanning interval, its absence in some Lower Kittanning underclays and its presence in others of the same age, suggest varying degrees of the in situ removal of chlorite (Williams and Holbrook, 1985).

The two groups of underclays are further subdivided by the presence of a distinctive vertical sequence of clay minerals in the upper portion of the underclay profile. Four criteria are used to determine if in situ weathering of the underclay had occurred: namely, an absence of chlorite in the upper part of the profile, an increase in the kaolinite/mica ratio toward the top of the profile, an increase in vermiculite toward the top of the profile, and a decrease in mica basal spacing toward the top of the profile. For the Lower Kittanning underclay, the mica is a detrital $2M_1$ polymorph (Holbrook, 1973). Those underclay profiles that contain no chlorite and that exhibit well-defined vertical increases in the kaolinite/mica ratio and decreases in mica thickness are inferred to have undergone the greatest amount of weathering or alteration (Fig. 4, category A). In contrast, Lower Kittanning underclays that contain chlorite in all parts of the profile are inferred to have undergone little if any weathering (Fig. 4, category D). These profiles also exhibit no vertical changes in the kaolinite/mica ratio. Underclays believed to have undergone intermediate amounts of weathering have chlorite in the lower parts and show some vertical variation in the kaolinite/mica ratio (Fig. 4, cate-

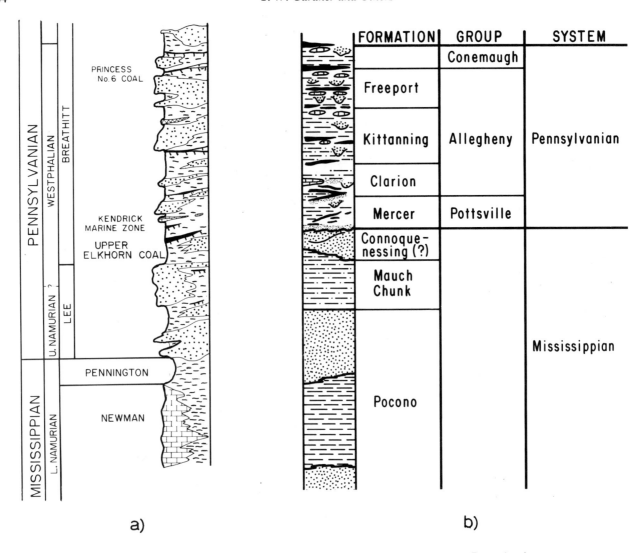

Figure 3. Generalized stratigraphic column: a, eastern Kentucky; b, western Pennsylvania.

gory B). A fourth type of underclay contains no chlorite and exhibits no vertical variation in the kaolinite/mica ratio (Fig. 4, category C). These are interpreted to be transported clays, eroded from adjacent topographic highs where weathered clays were forming.

In a typical, weathered, chloritic underclay (Fig. 4, category D), the upper 50 cm is plastic, light gray, rooted, and does not contain chlorite (Fig. 5). The lower portion of the profile is medium gray (N-4), hard, and bedded with no evidence of slickensides. Siderite nodules are present below 1.8 m. In most chloritic profiles, mica is better crystallized with sharper x-ray diffraction peaks and greater apparent mica thicknesses than in weathered samples (Figs. 6, 7) that contain no chlorite.

Vertical variation in clay mineral content (Fig. 6) and corresponding x-ray patterns (Fig. 7) illustrate a typical weathered underclay profile (Fig. 4, category A). The kaolinite-mica ratio

increases exponentially upward, and mica diminishes in thickness of basal spacing in the same direction. Vermiculite increases in the upper part of the profile; chlorite is absent through the entire section of underclay. In contrast, Figure 8 illustrates an underclay that shows no systematic variation in clay mineralogy and contains no chlorite (Fig. 4, category C), conditions interpreted to mean that the clay was transported from an adjacent, deeply weathered soil.

Table 1 summarizes the mineralogical properties of the four underclay categories (Fig. 4). The parameters describe the average clay mineralogy of each category as well as parameters sensitive to weathering within profiles. The weathering ratio is the kaolinite/mica ratio of the top 30 cm of a profile divided by the same ratio of the bottom 30 cm. The mica loss ratio is the cubed basal thickness of the mica in the bottom 30 cm divided by the same value in the top 30 cm. Both ratios are designed so that a value of 1.0 means no vertical mineralogical gradient and therefore no evidence for weathering, a conclusion that assumes the clay-rich sediments were deposited without a vertical mineralogical gradient.

Upper Elkhorn Underclays

Vertical variations of clay minerals in underclays from the Upper Elkhorn interval are similar to slighted weathered underclays in the Lower Kittanning interval (Fig. 4, class B). A representative example that—importantly—does not have an associated overlying coal comes from a sequence of interbedded crevasse-splay, swamp, and subaerial levee sediments (Fig. 9) within the Upper Elkhorn interval, which is well exposed in outcrops along U.S. 460 in eastern Kentucky (Baganz and others, 1975; Gardner, 1983). Facies within this interval (Fig. 9) are similar to modern crevasse-splay and subaerial levee environments (Arndorfer, 1973; Coleman, 1976).

An underclay occurs in a shale unit at the top of a fining-upward sequence (Fig. 9, 3.0 to 4.1 m). *Lepidodendron* and *Calamites* preserved in growth position mark the top of the paleosol (4.1 m) and overlie a 70-cm-thick, rooted, nonbedded, buff-colored plastic clay. Organic material is preserved along smooth, clay-coated ped surfaces. A narrow 10-cm-thick band containing sphaerosiderite nodules (Fig. 10) separates the overlying rooted, buff-colored plastic clay from a well-bedded, non-rooted, drab, gray-green shale with carbonized impressions of an unidentified delicate flora along bedding planes (3 to 3.4 m).

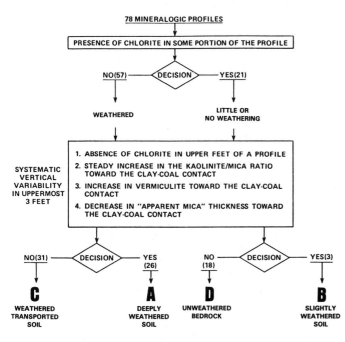

Figure 4. Flow diagram illustrating classification procedure for the 18 Lower Kittanning underclays.

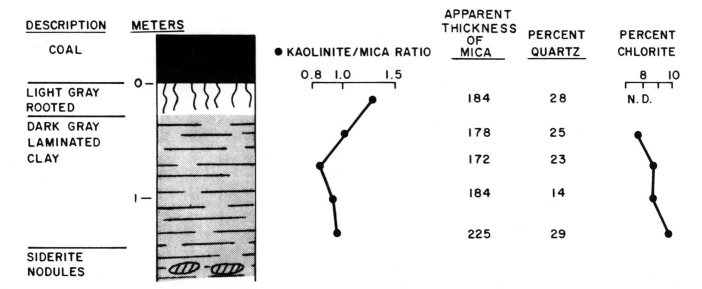

Figure 5. Vertical profile of a typical chloritic underclay showing megascopic appearance and mineralogical variability. Relative amounts of clay minerals were determined from x-ray peak heights (Holbrook, 1973). Apparent thickness of mica (given in Angstroms) is calculated from the standard Scherrer formula. Chemical compositions for clay mineral species are reported in Holbrook (1973).

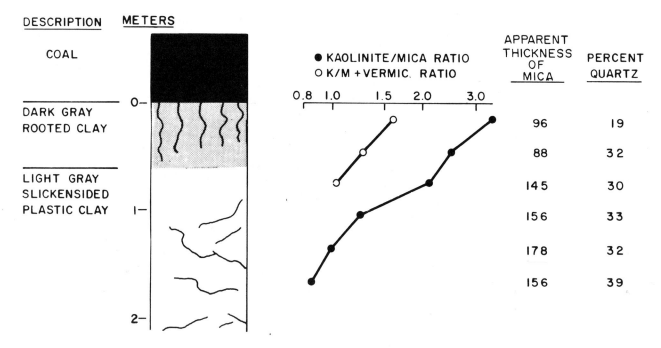

Figure 6. Vertical profile of typical weathered underclay showing megascopic appearance and mineralogical variability. Analytical techniques as in Figure 5. X-ray patterns are available in Holbrook (1973).

Similar occurrences of siderite have been reported from modern sediments in the Atchafalaya Basin (Ho and Coleman, 1969) Carboniferous underclays in England (Deans, 1934; Curtis and others, 1975), the Olive Hill Clay Bed in eastern Kentucky (Smyth, 1984), and Triassic paleosols in Australia (Retallack, 1976, 1981).

Systematic changes in the clay mineral composition of the rooted zone relative to the nonrooted zones indicate that pedogenesis has modified the clay mineral assemblage in the former. In the finely laminated, gray-green shales immediately above and below the rooted zone, kaolinite/illite ratios are constant (samples 0, 1, 5, and 6 in Fig. 9). Dominant basal reflections at 14.2, 10.2 and 7.15 Å are narrow, sharply defined peaks (Fig. 11). A nonexpandable or collapsable clay mineral with a peak of 14.2 Å represents a minor, but constant, chlorite component in the unweathered sediment (Fig. 11). Within the paleosol, samples 2 and 3 taken from intervals 10 and 30 cm below the top of the rooted zone have no detectable chlorite, but show an increasing kaolinite/illite ratio with depth to the siderite horizon (sample 4). A pronounced shoulder on the diffraction peak at 10.2 Å suggests illite degradation and transformation to a mixed layered clay. A broadened lower peak at 7.15 Å suggests a decrease in the amount, size, and/or crystallinity of kaolinite near the top of the soil profile. This zone of dominant illuviation and transformation in the underclay is probably transitional from a cambic to an argillic horizon (Soil Survey Staff, 1975). Sample 4 from the sphaerosiderite zone produces the sharpest peaks for kaolinite,

illite, and chlorite, as well as the highest kaolinite/illite ratio. The upward decrease in the kaolinite/illite ratio within the top 30 cm of the Upper Elkhorn underclay (Fig. 9, samples 2, 3, and 4) is not observed in any of the Lower Kittanning underclays (Figs. 5, 6, 8). This may be due to erosion of the uppermost part of the profile in the Lower Kittanning Kittanning, to slight differences in pedogenesis between the two locations that could be due to climate or paleotopography, or to a lack of samples in the Lower Kittanning underclays within 30 cm of the base of the coal.

Coal is not present above the underclay (Fig. 9, 4.1 m). Fossil plants are preserved in growth position, indicating rapid sedimentation. The contact between the underclay and overlying shale unit is horizontal and appears to be nonerosional. The paleosol grades laterally off the depositional high on the crevasse system into a burrowed siderite in the back marsh environment. Coal has not been observed at the underclay interval in laterally adjacent outcrops. Together, these data suggest that coal never occurred on top of the underclay and that an overlying peat is not a necessary condition for pedogenesis.

Upper Elkhorn Sandstone

Stratigraphically below and extending laterally beyond the crevasse-splay system (Fig. 9) is a fining-upward, fluvial, feldspathic litharenite (Fig. 12a, c). Gardner (1983) discussed the paleohydrology and paleomorphology of the fluvial system, informally named the Harold sandstone from outcrops near

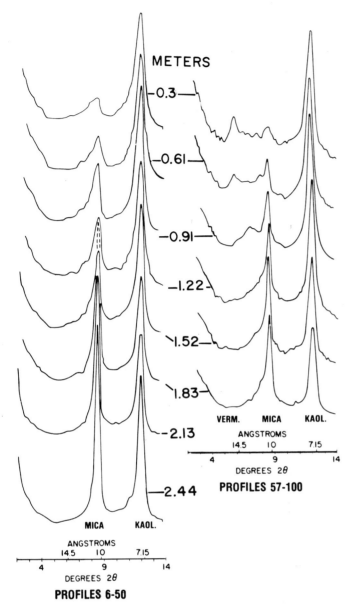

Figure 7. X-ray patterns of typical weathered underclay. Profile 57-100 is illustrated in Figure 6. Metric marker gives depth below coal.

Harold, Kentucky. The Harold sandstone is 10 ± 2.0 m thick with a wavy, erosional base. The basal unit consists of slumped bay-fill sediments and synsedimentary siderite clasts up to 4 cm in maximum diameter. Sedimentary structures range from large-scale, festoon cross-beds as much as 1 m thick at the base, through medium-scale trough cross-beds, 20 to 30 cm thick, and into parallel to ripple laminations near the top of the fining-upward cycle.

The top of the fining-upward cycle is capped by 0.7 m of clayey, rooted, nonbedded overbank sediment with an overlying

Upper Elkhorn Nos. 1,2 Coal bed. The underclay at the top of this fining-upward cycle (Fig. 12a) is similar to the crevasse-splay paleosol (Fig. 9). Organic material is preserved along smooth, clay-coated ped surfaces. The kaolinite/illite ratio increases to a maximum value, 70 cm below the top of the underclay, just above the lower boundary of root penetration (Fig. 12b). The kaolinite/illite ratio decreases downward into the fine, ripple-bedded sandstone that makes up the top of the channel sandstone 1 m below the underclay. Chlorite and siderite were not detected in this underclay by x-ray diffraction.

Petrographic analyses of thin sections from the sandstone subjacent to the Upper Elkhorn Nos. 1,2 Coal bed suggest both that the type of mineral variation observed in the underclays can be produced in situ, and that the alteration profiles are controlled to a large degree by the position of the ground-water table relative to the land surface.

Vertical variations in the distributions of authigenic minerals in the Harold sandstone were determined from 42 thin sections (200 counts per thin section). Two distinct alteration zones separated by a diffuse boundary are evident along the outcrop extent of the Harold sandstone; an upper kaolinite zone and a lower ferroan dolomite zone (Fig. 12d).

The ferroan dolomite zone extends, on average, to 5 m above the base of the sandstone and is characterized by ferroan dolomite replacement of both detrital feldspars (Fig. 13a) and detrital dolomite (Fig. 13b). Feldspar content ranges from 4 to 13 percent of each thin section, with potassium feldspars composing 60 to 90 percent of that total. Feldspar grains can be fresh and subangular or almost entirely replaced by ferron dolomite. Plagioclase is replaced preferentially by ferron dolomite. Chlorite and siderite are minor alteration products in the ferroan dolomite zone and occur as authigenic pore fillings (Fig. 13c). Detrital siderite can also occur as grains squashed around framework quartz grains and as a basal, pebble lag (Gardner, 1983). Detrital dolomite can represent up to 3 percent of total point counts on any thin section in the lower alteration zone. A detrital origin for dolomite is suggested by subrounded grains that usually touch adjacent grains and by the overall hydraulic equivalence of dolomite and adjacent quartz grains (Fig. 14). A suggested source for the carbonate grains was the adjacent interdistributary bay and marine units through which the fluvial system eroded (Gardner, 1977). Similar detrital dolomite has been reported from near-shore, marine rocks of Late Cretaceous age in Texas (Amsbury, 1962) and the Western Interior (Sabins, 1962), Miocene age in Spain (Freeman and others, 1983), and Devonian age in New York (Lindholm, 1969).

A 5-m-thick zone of kaolinite alteration occurs above the ferroan dolomite zone. It extends from an average of 5 m above the sandstone base into the underclay where the fine grain size makes petrographic identification difficult. Kaolinizaation of feldspar is the dominant alteration product (Fig. 13d). Approximately 70 percent of the feldspars show some evidence of kaolinization. Ferroan dolomite cement and small rhombs of siderite occur locally near fine-grained, organic-rich laminations, but total

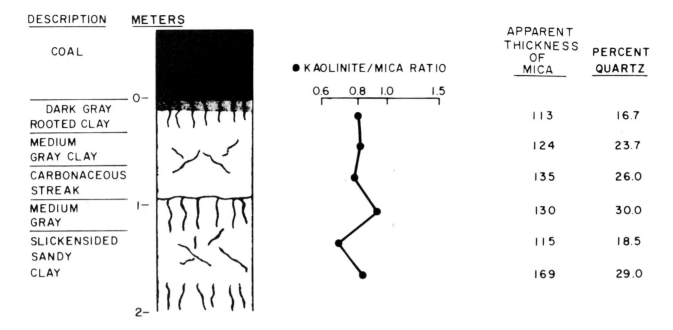

Figure 8. Vertical profile of a typical transported underclay. Analytical techniques as in Figure 5. X-ray patterns are available in Holbrook (1973).

TABLE 1. SUMMARY OF LOWER KITTANNING UNDERCLAY AND SHALE PROPERTIES

Profile Type*	Average Kaolinite/Mica Ratio	Average Chlorite (%)	Weathering Ratio $\frac{K_T}{M_T} / \frac{K_B}{M_B}$	Mica Loss Ratio $(TM_B)^3/(TM_T)^3$	Number of Profiles
Weathered Alluvial (A)	1.39	0.0	2.29	6.66	26
Unweathered Alluvial (B)	1.27	0.0	1.16	3.03	31
Weathered Marine (B)	0.97	2.0	3.92	9.30	3
Unweathered Marine (D)	0.61	7.5	1.41	4.28	18
Allegheny† Shales	0.56	8.3	----	----	9

*Capital letter designations refer to classification in Figure 4.

†Average values for nine Allegheny shales described in Holbrook (1973).

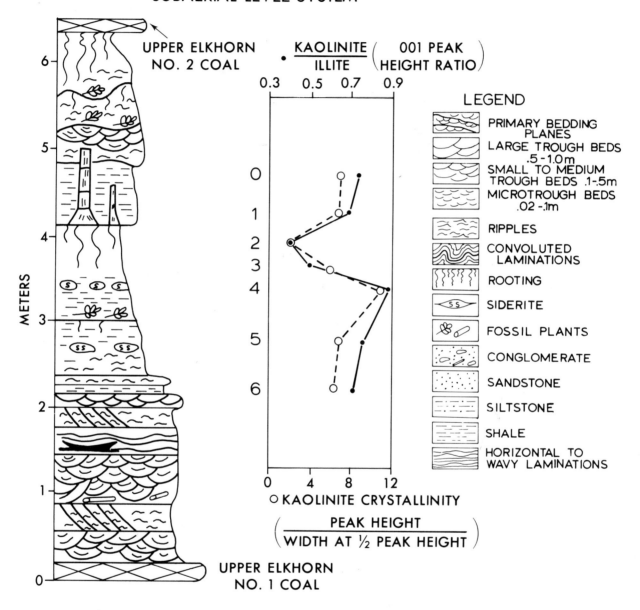

Figure 9. Stratigraphic column of crevasse-splay and subaerial levee system within the Upper Elkhorn Coal interval and the corresponding vertical clay mineral profile. Numbers adjacent to profile indicate corresponding x-ray patterns in Figure 11.

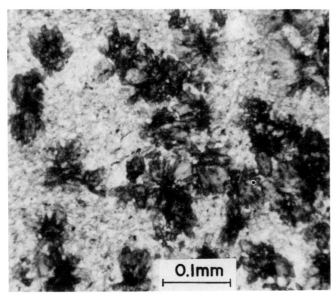

Figure 10. Photomicrograph of sphaerosiderite zone at 3.4 m (Fig. 9). Radiating sphaerosiderite nodules appear to have nucleated around dark, organic centers in a silt-clay matrix. (Plane, transmitted light.)

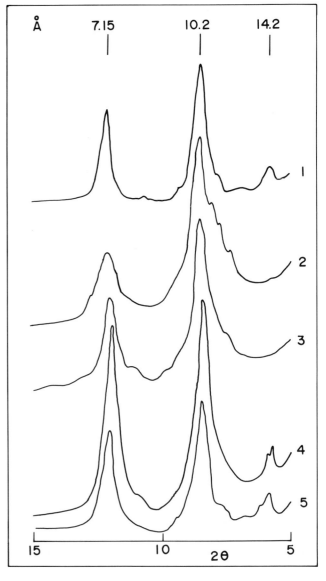

Figure 11. X-ray diffraction patterns of clay (<2 μm) smears. Diffraction patterns from the uppermost and lowermost samples are not shown but are nearly identical to samples 1 and 5, respectively. (Ni-filtered CuKα radiation.)

less than 1 percent of thin section point counts. Detrital dolomite generally is absent, but a few dolomite grains with red (iron oxide) rims do occur in the kaolinite zone. Authigenic chlorite is not observed in the kaolinite zone.

PEDOGENIC MODEL

Vertical Variations

Clay mineral profiles from Upper Elkhorn and Lower Kittanning underclays and petrographic variations in the Harold sandstone can best be explained by a two-stage pedogenic model (Fig. 15). In the initial stage, kaolinization took place on topographic highs above and within a near-surface, seasonally(?) fluctuating ground-water table. The amount of seasonal fluctuation in the ground-water table would probably have increased during the change from ever-wet tropical to season tropical from Westphalian B to D (Cecil and others, 1985; Donaldson and others, 1985). There was generally downward movement of acidic, slightly oxidizing, meteoric water. Good drainage during seasonally low water tables promoted the downward movement of dissolved constituents, mostly silica, alumina, and base cations from the dissolution of feldspars, chlorite, and detrital dolomite. A soil B horizon, enriched in kaolinite and iron, developed within the zone of ground-water fluctuation. The absence of coal at the top of the crevasse-splay underclay (Fig. 9) demonstrates that peat was not necessary for pedogenesis. However, the preservation of flora in growth position at the top of the underclay and

rootings within the paleosol does suggest the importance of organic activity.

The average low stand of the water table occurred at the zone of sphaerosiderite nodules near the base of the crevasse-splay paleosol. Retallack (1976, 1981) used siderite to indicate similar water-table conditions. In the Harold sandstone, the average low water-table position is inferred to be about 5 m below the top of the underclay and is represented by the intersection of the kaolinite-ferroan dolomite point count plots (Fig. 12d).

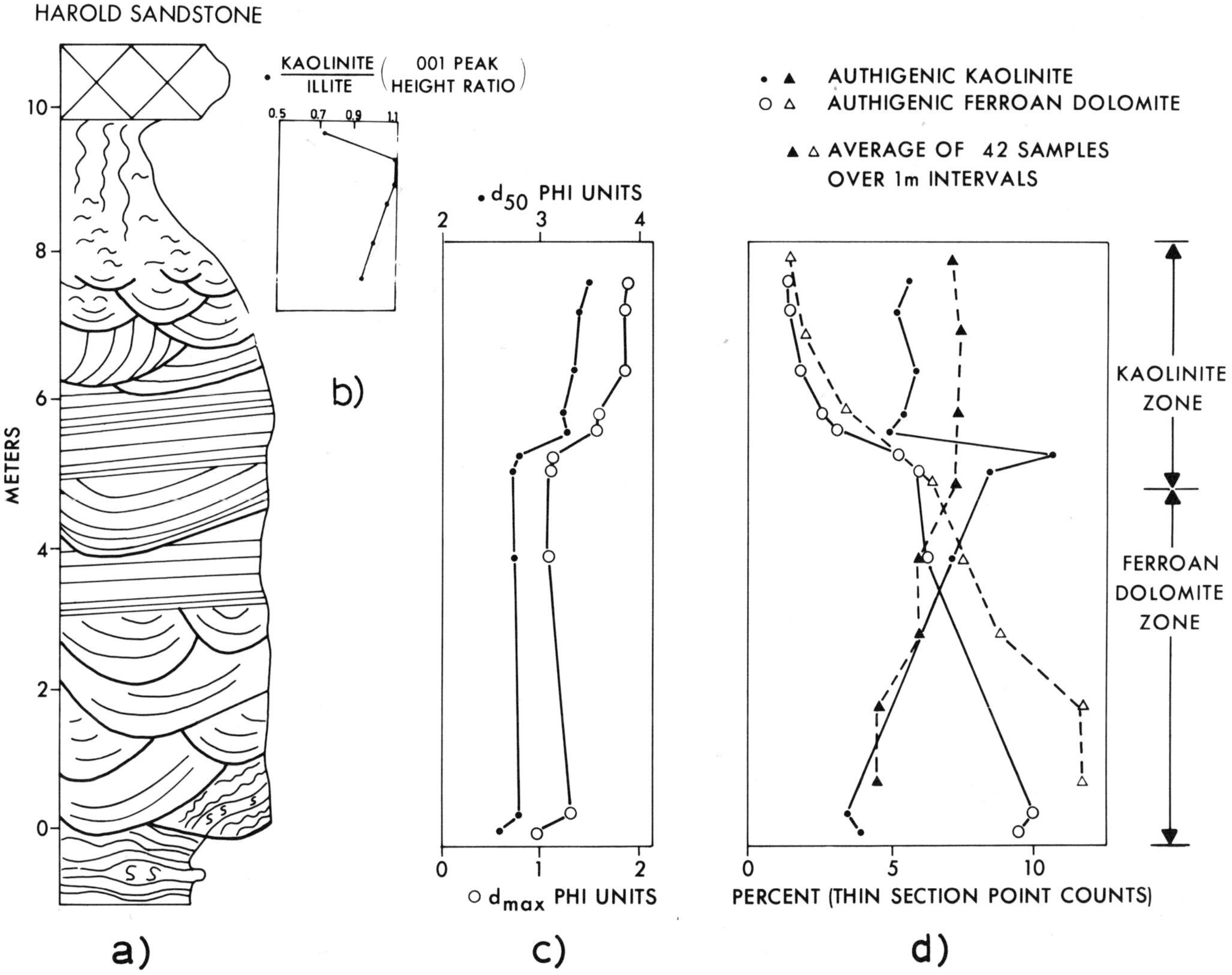

HAROLD SANDSTONE

Figure 12. a, Stratigraphic column for Harold sandstone measured at Harold, Kentucky. b, Vertical clay mineral profile in underclay. c, Grain-size distribution through a vertical section of the sandstone. d, Plot showing vertical variation in percentage of alteration minerals in the sandstone. Solid and open circles in figure part d represent authigenic kaolinite and ferroan dolomite, respectively, for stratigraphic column measured at Harold, Kentucky. Open and closed triangles represent average authigenic kaolinite and ferroan dolomite, respectively, for 42 thin sections from samples collected at equally spaced vertical intervals along 5-km outcrop length of Harold sandstone.

Importantly, kaolinization of feldspars in the Harold sandstone demonstrates that underclay pedogenesis produced kaolinite in situ. Kaolinization to depths well below the rooted zone (Fig. 12d) further demonstrates the downward migration of acidic surface water. Ferroan dolomitization of both feldspar and detrital dolomite with minor authigenesis of chlorite and siderite occurred below the general level of the ground-water table in the Harold sandstone. Stability fields for siderite (Berner, 1964; Garrels and Christ, 1965; Curtis and Spears, 1968; Maynard, 1983)

suggest low sulfur activities, high partial pressure of carbon dioxide, negative Eh, and slightly alkaline conditions for the ground water. The close association of authigenic chlorite, ferroan dolomite, and siderite, the preservation of detrital dolomite, and the absence of pyrite are consistent with those physicochemical constraints on a fresh ground-water system. Furthermore, the presence of detrital siderite and dolomite and the constant position of the ferroan dolomite zone within the Harold Sandstone, together with its conformity to paleotopography, are factors consistent

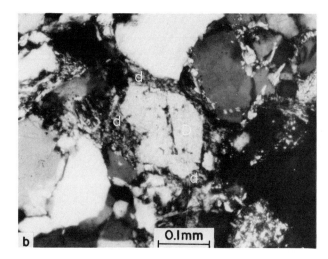

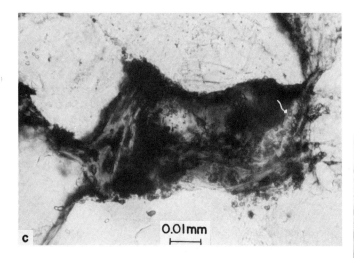

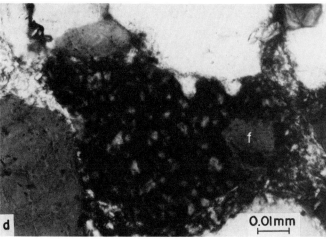

Figure 13. a, Microphotograph showing ferroan dolomite (d) replacement of feldspar (f). Diagnostic
d-spacings for carbonates are from Lippmann (1973). An X-ray diffraction peak occurring at 2.89 Å
indicates presence of dolomite in this sample. Alizarin red S and potassium ferricyanide stains impart a
blue color to the replacement cement, suggesting that it is ferroan dolomite. Note dog-tooth crystals
(arrows) along left and top edge of ferroan dolomite cement (crossed-nicols). b, Detrital dolomite grain
(center of photograph), which remains unstained is surrounded and partially replaced by ferroan
dolomite cement (d). c, Green chlorite fills pore between quartz grains. Dark centers are organic
material. Small rhombedral crystals are siderite (arrow). Siderite rhombs are slightly red in color and
where abundant give x-ray diffraction peaks at 2.80 Å. (Plane, transmitted light.) d, Nearly complete
kaolinization of a yellow stained feldspar (f). X-ray diffraction peak for typical kaolinite books is 7.15 Å.
Thin sections were stained for feldspars, calcite, dolomite, ferroan dolomite, and ankerite following
methods described by Carver (1971, p. 515–523).

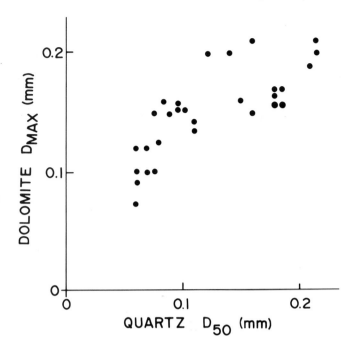

Figure 14. Plot of dolomite (d_{max}) versus quartz (d_{50}) for individual thin sections; d_{max} represents longest measurable axis of each dolomite grain and is used because partial replacement of all dolomite grains gives only minimum lengths.

with an early pedogenic origin. However, later diagenetic carbonates have been reported from Pennsylvania cyclothems in Kansas (McKibben and Walton, 1985).

In the second stage of the pedogenic model (Fig. 15b), compaction, subsidence, and/or marine transgression caused groundwater table levels to rise, eventually reaching the land surface. Pedogenesis with downward movement of soil water ceased. Peat accumulation or renewed sedimentation began on the old soil surface.

Despite the evidence for strong weathering in many sections, the underclays do not exhibit the marked horizon zonation of modern well-drained soils, which led McMillan (1956) to interpret them as analogues of modern gleys, which are gray, poorly drained soils. Because the gleying process involves mainly the removal of iron under reducing conditions, it seems unlikely that gleying can account for the vertical variation in clay minerals observed in some of the underclays. Accordingly, a two-stage process of underclay formation similar to that initially proposed by Williams and others (1965) is more appropriate: namely, a well-drained phase of podzolization followed by the poorly drained gleying process, which would remove the iron oxide zonation produced during the initial phase of podzolization.

Tectonic Control of Lateral Variation in Underclay Mineralogy

The foregoing analysis of vertical variation in underclay mineralogy has provided evidence for in situ weathering. Two new parameters—weathering ratio and mica loss ratio for the Lower Kittanning underclay—are used to document vertical, as well as areal, variability. Both parameters show similar geographical distributions that can be related to paleotopography. Williams and Bragonier (1974) outlined four orders of paleotopographic control over sedimentation in western Pennsylvania: (1) the shape of the basin, (2) major folds, (3) minor folds and faults, and (4) local paleotopography resulting from erosion and sedimentation. First- and second-order paleotopographic controls are shown in Figure 16.

Williams and Bragonier (1974) have shown that the northern Appalachian Basin had much the same shape in Pennsylvanian time as it has today. Thus, the present structural low also defines the basin axis during Pennsylvanian time. Gwinn (1964) outlined the major folds in the basin that correspond to second-order paleotopographic controls. Isopach data show that these folds were active growth features during Pennsylvanian time. Using faunal data, Williams (1960) concluded that the lower Kittanning basin axis follows an east-northeast trend about 45 km south of the northern outcrop limit.

The average kaolinite/mica ratio for the Lower Kittanning underclay is contoured in Figure 17. Kaolinite/mica ratios are high along the northern basin margin and in the folded Allegheny Mountain region to the southeast. Underclays that occur near the basin axis have the lowest ratio. Sections containing chlorite occur primarily in topographic and structural lows where the kaolinite/mica ratio is less than 1. Thus, there is a general correspondence between paleotopographic control (Williams and Bragonier, 1974) and average underclay mineralogy. The greater abundance of kaolinite and the loss of chlorite on paleotopographic highs suggest that these sites had better soil drainage and were exposed for longer times.

Parham (1963) and Schultz (1958) observed similar regional variations in the areal distribution of underclays, suggesting that these patterns resulted from differential sedimentation and/or marine authigenesis of illite. Marine authigenesis is not a viable explanation for the variability observed in western Pennsylvania. Authigenic micas form as the 1Md polymorph (Velde and Hower, 1963). However, more than 90 percent of the 10 Å mineral in the lower Kittanning underclay is a $2M_1$ mica (Holbrook, 1973). Velde and Hower (1963) concluded that $2M_1$ micas formed at a metamorphic temperature range of 200 to 350°C. The minute quantities of 1Md mica present are insufficient to explain the higher mica contents in the Lower Kittanning interval along the basin axis.

If differential weathering is a major cause of the areal variability of the kaolinite/illite ratio (Fig. 17), then supporting evidence should be found in the areal variability of the weathering ratio and the mica loss ratio. Figure 18 is a map of the weathering

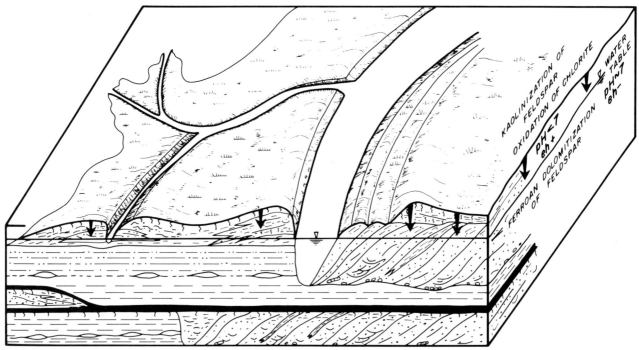

DELTA PROGRADATION, MARINE REGRESSION

(A)

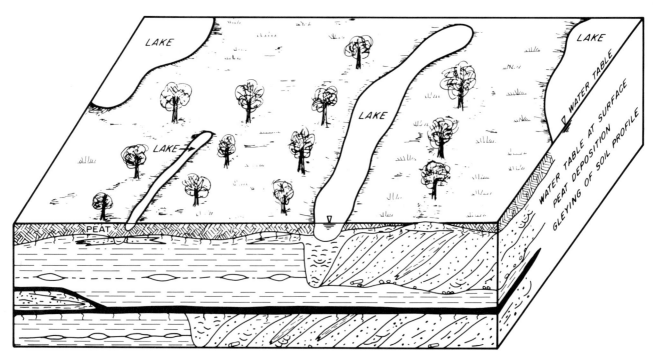

DELTA COMPACTION AND SUBSIDENCE, MARINE TRANSGRESSION

(B)

Figure 15. Two-stage model for pedogenic alteration of underclay and subjacent sandstones.

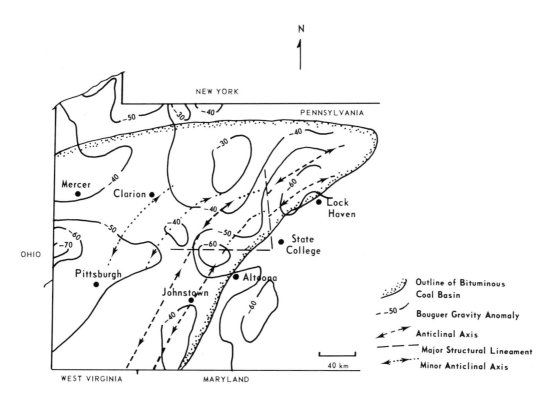

Figure 16. Map of western Pennsylvania showing the major tectonic features that controlled Pennsylvanian sedimentation (after Williams and Bragonier, 1974).

ratio of the Lower Kittanning underclay. There is a great deal of similarity between this map and the average K/M map (Fig. 17). Weathering ratios are highest (>3.0) along the stable northern basin margin, and lowest in the basin axis, where a value of 1.0 indicates that significant weathering has not occurred.

There is a striking contrast between the tectonically passive northern basin margin and the more deformed eastern basin margin. Average weathering ratios are much lower and more variable along the eastern margin, although most of the values are above 1.0, indicating that some weathering has occurred. Third-order paleotopograhy, as well as depositional relief, probably controlled much of this local variability. Sample spacing is sufficient to demonstrate regional first- and second-order paleotopographic controls on weathering, but not to demonstrate the effect of local paleotopography.

The mica loss ratio (Fig. 19) is similar in many respects to the weathering ratio map (Fig. 18) and the average kaolinite/mica ratio map (Fig. 17). Regional variation in the mica loss ratio is also related to paleotopography. Samples from the northern basin margin generally have high mica loss ratios (above 5.0), whereas the lowest ratios are in the basin axis. Values near 1.0 indicate negligible mica loss.

Determination of the exact amount of weathering at a given location depends on estimation of the regional variability of un-

weathered parent material of the underclay. Williams and others (1974) have studied such variations in the shales and siltstones above the Lower Kittanning Coal. These rocks vary from marine to fresh water, from basin axis to margins, respectively, and approximate the composition of parent material for any of the lower Pennsylvanian underclays. The kaolinite/illite ratios for the shale vary from 0.20 in the basin center to 0.50 along the northern and eastern margins. Williams and others (1974) believed such variation was probably produced by selective size sorting or differential flocculation. Corresponding values for the Lower Kittanning underclay are 0.43 along the basin axis and 1.50 along the basin margin. Thus, only approximately 30 percent of the regional variation in underclay mineralogy could be inherited from the parent materials. Furthermore, compared to the shale, the kaolinite/illite ratio has been increased in the underclay by a factor of 2 in the basin center and by 3 at the margins, a condition that supports the hypothesis of differential weathering inferred from the weathering and micas loss maps. Figure 20 illustrates the relations in graphic form between underclays and shales from which they were derived. The form of the underclay curve resembles that of the shale. The variation in the clay mineralogy of the shale is caused by differential settling or differential flocculation of kaolinite in the near-shore environment, thus accounting for the lower mica/kaolinite ratio at the margin of the bituminous

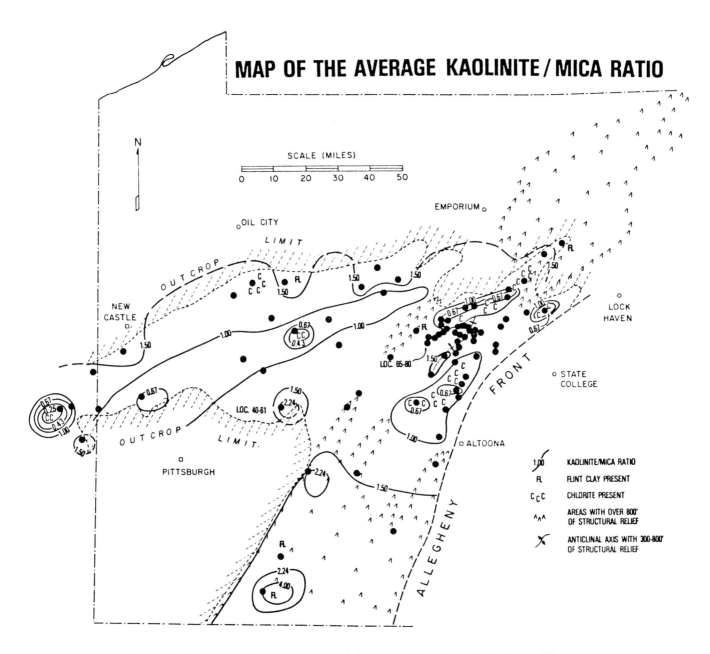

Figure 17. Contour map showing regional variation in kaolinite/mica ratio for Lower Kittanning underclay.

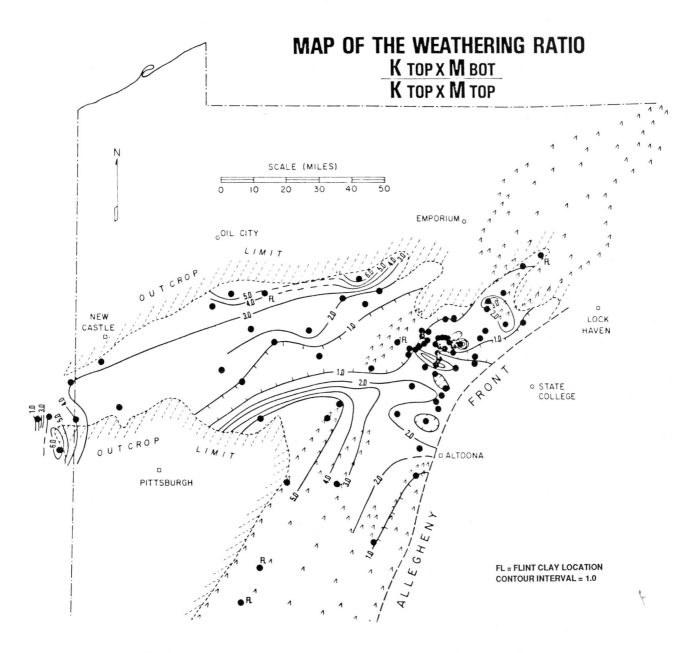

Figure 18. Contour map showing regional variation in weathering ratio for Lower Kittanning underclay.

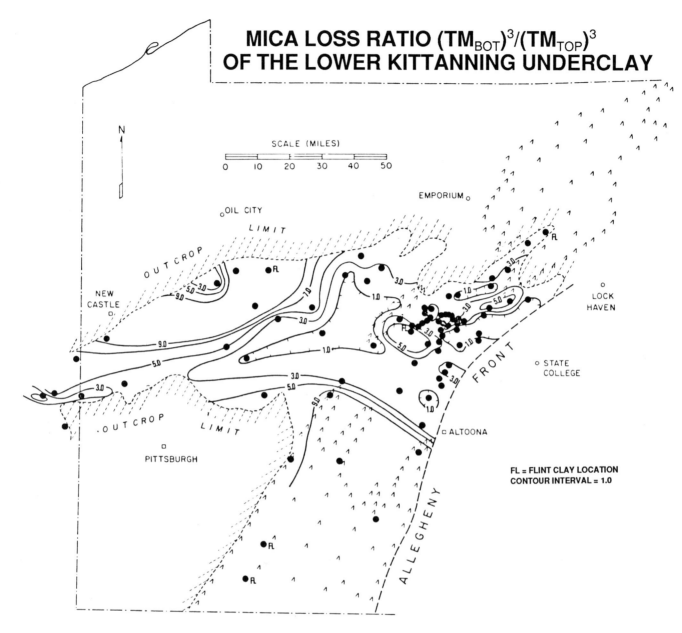

Figure 19. Contour map showing regional variation in mica loss ratio for Lower Kittanning underclay.

coal basin (Williams and others, 1968). The difference between the shale and the underclay, greatest at the elevated basin margin, resulted from in situ weathering.

SUMMARY

Given subtle topographic and ground-water level variations, soil catena sequences could be expected to develop on Pennsylvanian deltaic surfaces. Catena sequences could develop both locally on depositional topographic features or more regionally across zones of syntectonic movement (Fig. 21). Certainly, pedogenesis in continuously wet swamps or marshes would differ from that on topographically higher levees or constructional channel deposits. Complex paleosols associated with other alluvial and deltaic sediments (Bown and Kraus, 1981; Retallack, 1983) have been attributed to paleotopography, depositional setting, and/or climatic change. The vertical variation in underclay mineralogy described in this chapter originated on a portion of the land surface where the ground-water table was below the land surface during a significant portion of the pedogenic interval.

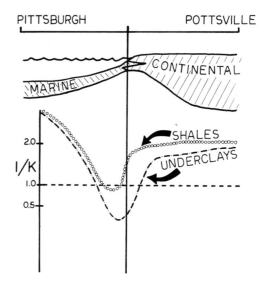

Figure 20. Generalized cross section of western and central Pennsylvania showing inferred facies changes and illite/kaolinite ratio variations for rocks of lower Allegheny Group (modified from Oldham, 1979). Cross section is approximately 300 km.

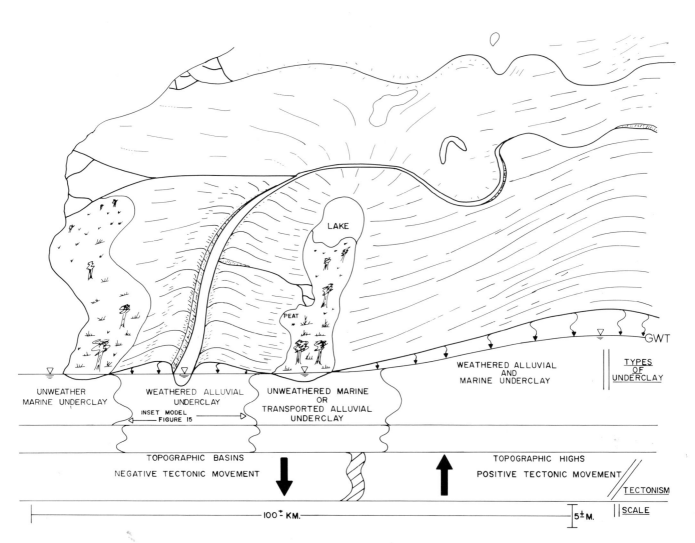

Figure 21. Regional model for underclay pedogenesis at time of most intense pedogenesis during maximum marine regression.

In conclusion, we believe that the underclays from the Lower Kittanning and Upper Elkhorn formed by pedogenic processes that occurred both prior to and during peat formation, but that the dominant vertical and lateral underclay mineralogy was established antecedent to peat formation. The degree of pedogenesis for any one underclay was controlled predominantly by the relative position of the ground-water table, which in turn was controlled by topography, climate, and syntectonism within the coal-forming basins. The pedogenic process involved extensive leaching in areas of relatively higher relief along positive tectonic areas or constructional highs and during seasonal wet-dry climates, lesser amounts toward the center of the basin, on constructional lows and during ever-wet climates.

Marine transgression, negative tectonic movement, and sur-face erosion caused a relative rise in the ground-water table, inhibiting drainage. Peat formation began, and underclays became gleyed. Iron was removed or formed siderite in amounts related to the slope and drainage, so that the clay frequently appears mottled, a characteristic feature of these soil types.

ACKNOWLEDGMENTS

We gratefully acknowledge critical comments of this manuscript by C. Blaine Cecil, Bill Casey, Al Guber, and John W. Hosterman. Partial support for this project was provided by the Fisk Laboratory of Sedimentology, University of Cincinnati, and the Mineral Conservation Section, The Pennsylvania State University.

REFERENCES CITED

Amsbury, D. L., 1962, Detrital dolomite in central Texas: Journal of Sedimentary Petrology, v. 32, p. 5–14.

Arndorfer, D., 1973, Discharge patterns in two crevasses of the Mississippi River delta: Marine Geology, v. 15, p. 269–287.

Baganz, B. P., Horn, J. C., and Ferm, J. C., 1975, Carboniferous and recent Mississippi lower delta plains; A comparison: Gulf Coast Association of Geologists Society Transactions, v. 25, p. 183–191.

Berner, R. A., 1964, Stability fields of iron minerals in anaerobic marine sediments: Journal Geology, v. 72, p. 826–834.

Bown, T. M., and Kraus, M. J., 1981, Lower Eocene alluvial paleosols (Willwood Formation, northwest Wyoming, U.S.A.) and their significance for paleoecology, paleoclimatology, and basin analysis: Palaeogeography, Palaeoecology, Palaeoclimatology, v. 34, p. 1–30.

Brownwell, W. E., 1978, Encyclopedia of sedimentology: Stroudsburg, Pennsylvania, Dowden, Hutchinson and Ross, 901 p.

Carver, R. E., 1971, Procedures in sedimentary petrology: New York, John Wiley & Sons, 653 p.

Cecil, C. B., Stanton, R. W., Neuzil, S. G., Dulong, F. T., Ruppert, L. F., and Pierce, B. S., 1985, Paleoclimate controls on late Paleozoic sedimentation and peat formation in the central Appalachian Basin (U.S.A.): International Journal of Coal Geology, v. 5, p. 195–230.

Challinor, J., 1978, Dictionary of geology: New York, Oxford University Press, 5th ed., 365 p.

Coleman, J. M., 1976, Deltas; Processes of deposition and models for exploration: Champaign, Illinois, Continuing Education Publishing Co., 102 p.

Curtis, C. D., and Spears, D. A., 1968, The formation of sedimentary iron minerals: Economic Geology, v. 63, p. 257–270.

Curtis, C. D., Pearson, M. J., and Somogyi, V. A., 1975, Mineralogy, chemistry, and origin of a concretionary siderite sheet (clay-ironstone band) in the Westphalian of Yorkshire: Mineralogical Magazine, v. 40, p. 385–393.

Deans, T., 1934, The spherulitic ironstones of west Yorkshire: Geological Magazine, v. 71, p. 49–65.

Donaldson, A. C., Renton, J. J., and Presley, M. W., 1985, Pennsylvanian deposystems and paleoclimates of the Appalachians: International Journal of Coal Geology, v. 5, p. 167–193.

Freeman, T., Rothbard, D., and Obrador, A., 1983, Terrigenous dolomite in the Miocene of Menorca (Spain); Provenance and diagenesis: Journal of Sedimentology Petrology, v. 53, p. 543–548.

Gardner, T. W., 1977, Paleohydrology, paleomorphology, and depositional environments of some fluvial sandstones of Pennsylvanian age in eastern Kentucky [Ph.D. thesis]: Cincinnati, Ohio, University of Cincinnati, 216 p.

—— , 1983, Paleohydrology and paleomorphology of a Carboniferous, meandering, fluvial sandstone: Journal of Sedimentary Petrology, v. 53, p. 991–1005.

Garrels, R., and Christ, C., 1965, Solutions, minerals, and equilibria: New York, Freeman, Cooper and Co., 450 p.

Grim, R. E., and Allen, V. T., 1938, Petrology of the Pennsylvanian underclays of Illinois: Geological Society of America Bulletin, v. 49, p. 1485–1514.

Gwinn, V. E., 1964, Thin skinned tectonics in the Plateau and northwest Valley and Ridge provinces of the central Appalachians: Geological Society of America Bulletin, v. 75, p. 863–900.

Ho, C., and Coleman, J. M., 1969, Consolidation and cementation of recent sediments in the Atchafalaya Basin: Geological Society of America Bulletin, v. 80, p. 183–192.

Holbrook, P. W., 1973, Geologic and mineralogic factors controlling the properties and occurrence of ladle brick clays [Ph.D. thesis]: University Park, The Pennsylvania State University, 318 p.

Horne, J. C., and Ferm, J. C., 1976, Carboniferous depositional environments in the Pocahontas Basin, eastern Kentucky and southern West Virginia; A field guide: Columbia, University of South Carolina, 129 p.

Huddle, J. W., and Patterson, S. H., 1961, Origin of Pennsylvanian underclay and related seat rock: Geological Society of America Bulletin, v. 72, p. 1643–1660.

Keller, W. D., 1956, Clay minerals as influenced by environments of their formation: American Association of Petroleum Geologists Bulletin, v. 40, p. 2689–2710.

—— , 1958, Flint clay and flint-clay facies: Clays and Clay Minerals, v. 16, p. 113–128.

Lindholm, R. C., 1969, Detrital dolomite in Onondaga Limestone (Middle Devonian) of New York; Its implication to the dolomite question: American Association of Petroleum Geologists Bulletin, v. 52, p. 1035–1042.

Lippmann, F., 1973, Sedimentary carbonate minerals: New York, Springer-Verlag, 228 p.

Logan, W. E., 1842, On the character of the beds of clay lying immediately below the coal seams of south Wales: Geological Society of London Proceedings, v. 3, p. 275–277.

Maynard, J. B., 1983, Geochemistry of sedimentary ore deposits: New York, Springer-Verlag, 305 p.

McKibben, M. E., and Walton, A. W., 1985, Carbonate cements in Desmoinian and Missourian limestones and sandstones of southeastern Kansas: Geological Society of America Abstracts with Program, v. 17, p. 659.

McMillan, N. J., 1956, Petrology of the Nodaway underclay (Pennsylvanian), Kansas: Kansas Geological Survey Bulletin 119, p. 187–249.

Moore, L. R., 1968, Some sediments closely associated with coal seams, *in* Murchison, D., and Westoll, T. S., eds., Coal and coal-bearing strata: New York, Elsevier, p. 105–123.

O'Brien, N. R., 1964, Origin of Pennsylvanian underclays in the Illinois Basin:

Geological Society of America Bulletin, v. 75, p. 823–832.

Oldham, D. W., 1979, Analysis of the relationships between composition and the occurrence of bloating shales and clays in the Pennsylvanian system of western Pennsylvania [M.S. thesis]: University Park, The Pennsylvania State University, 167 p.

Parham, W. E., 1964, Lateral clay mineral variations in certain Pennsylvanian underclays: Clays and Clay Minerals, Proceedings of the 12th Conference, p. 581–602.

Patterson, S. H., and Hosterman, J. W., 1960, Geology of the clay deposits in the Olive Hill district, Kentucky, *in* Swineford, A., ed., 7th National Conference on Clays and Clay Minerals Proceedings, Washington, D.C., October 1958, p. 178–194: Issued as International Earth Science Series Monograph 5, New York, Pergamon Press.

Percival, C. J., 1986, Paleosols containing an albic horizon; Examples from the upper Carboniferous of northern England, *in* Wright, V. P., ed., Paleosols; Their recognition and interpretation: Princeton, New Jersey, Princeton University Press, p. 315.

Phillips, T. L., and Peppers, R. A., 1984, Charging patterns of Pennsylvania coal swamps and implications of climate control on coal occurrence: International Journal of Coal Geology, v. 3, p. 205–255.

Retallack, G., 1976, Triassic paleosols in the Upper Narrobean Group of New South Wales; Pt. I, Features of the paleosols: Journal Geological Society of Australia, v. 23, p. 383–399.

—— , 1981, Fossil soils; Indicators of ancient terrestrial environments, *in* Niklas, K. J., ed., Paleobotany, paleoecology, and evolution, v. 1: New York, Praeger, p. 55–102.

—— , 1983, Late Eocene and Oligocene paleosols from Badlands National Park, South Dakota: Geological Society of America Special Paper 193, 82 p.

Rimmer, S. M., and Eberl, D. D., 1982, Origin of an underclay as revealed by vertical variations in mineralogy and chemistry: Clays and Clay Minerals, v. 30, p. 422–431.

Sabins, F. F., 1962, Grains of detrital secondary and primary dolomite from Cretaceous strata of the Western Interior: Geological Society of America Bulletin, v. 73, p. 1183–1196.

Schultz, L. G., 1958, Petrology of underclays: Geological Society of America Bulletin, v. 69, p. 363–402.

Smith, W. H., and O'Brien, N. R., 1965, Middle and Late Pennsylvanian flint clays: Journal of Sedimentary Petrology, v. 35, p. 610–618.

Smyth, A. L., 1984, Pedogenesis and diagenesis of the Olive Hill Clay Bed, Breathill Formation (Carboniferous) Northeastern Kentucky [M.S. thesis]: Cincinnati, Ohio, University of Cincinnati, 201 p.

Soil Survey Staff, 1975, Soil taxonomy: U.S. Department Agriculture Handbook 436, 754 p.

Staub, J. R., and Cohen, A. D., 1978, Kaolinite enrichment beneath coals; A modern analog, Snuggly Swamp, South Carolina: Journal of Sedimentary Petrology, v. 48, p. 203–210.

Stout, W. C., 1923, Coal formation clays of Ohio: Ohio Geological Survey, 4th Series, Bulletin 26, p. 533–568.

Velde, B., and Hower, J., 1963, Petrologic significance of illite polymorphism in Paleozoic sedimentary rocks: American Mineralogists, v. 48, p. 1239–1254.

Weller, J. M., 1930, Cyclic sedimentation of the Pennsylvanian period and its significance: Journal of Geology, v. 38, p. 97–135.

—— , 1931, The concept of cyclical sedimentation during the Pennsylvanian period: Illinois State Geological Survey Bulletin 60, p. 163–177.

Williams, E. G., 1960, Marine and fresh water fossiliferous beds in the Pottsville and Allegheny Groups of western Pennsylvania: Journal of Paleontology, v. 34, p. 908–923.

Williams, E. G., and Bragonier, W. A., 1974, Controls of Early Pennsylvanian sedimentation in western Pennsylvania: Geological Society of America Special Paper 148, p. 135–152.

Williams, E. G., and Ferm, J. C., 1964, Sedimentary facies in the Lower Allegheny rocks of western Pennsylvania: Journal of Sedimentary Petrology, v. 34, p. 610–614.

Williams, E. G., and Holbrook, R. P., 1985, Origin of plastic underclays: 50th Annual Conference of Pennsylvania Geologists, Bureau of Topographic and Geologic Survey, Harrisburg, Pennsylvania, p. 212–225.

Williams, E. G., Guber, A. L., and Johnson, A. M., 1965, Rotational slumping and the recognition of disconformities: Journal of Geology, v. 73, p. 534–547.

Williams, E. G., Bergenback, R. E., Falla, W. S., and Udagana, S., 1968, Origin of some Pennsylvanian underclays in western Pennsylvania: Journal of Sedimentary Petrology, v. 38, p. 1179–1193.

Williams, E. G., Holbrook, R. P., Lithgow, F. W., and Wilson, B. R., 1974, Properties and occurrences of bloating shales and clays in the Pennsylvanian of western Pennsylvanian: American Institute Mining Engineers Transactions, v. 256, p. 237–240.

MANUSCRIPT ACCEPTED BY THE SOCIETY JULY 1, 1987

Geological Society of America
Special Paper 216
1988

Calcareous paleosols in the Triassic Dolores Formation, southwestern Colorado

Robert H. Blodgett
Department of Geological Sciences
University of Texas
Austin, Texas 78713-7909

ABSTRACT

Nodular calcareous paleosols are common in the upper member of the Upper Triassic Dolores Formation in the San Juan Mountains of southwestern Colorado. These soils are developed in reddish brown, very fine-grained sandstone and siltstone of a sand-sheet facies that was deposited by eolian and aqueous processes on the margins of a large Triassic erg. Characteristics of these paleosols include nearly complete destruction of physical sedimentary structures, extensive mottling associated with burrows and root trace fossils, poorly sorted textures, and abundant carbonate nodules.

Vegetative stabilization of the sand sheet is recorded by trace fossils of long, monopodial root systems, and fine networks of rootlets. Distinctive purple pigmentation of the large root mottles appears to have been produced by more coarsely crystalline hematite, which precipitated in the presence of root-derived organic compounds.

Faunal bioturbation in these soils takes the form of meniscate and structureless burrows of the *Scoyenia* ichnofacies. The meniscate burrows are common in recent soils and pre-Holocene paleosols, and probably represent sediment reworking by arthropods.

Carbonate nodules in these soils are composed of micrite and microspar, and they contain sparry calcite crystallaria and septaria. These glaebules occur as individual "floating" entities and as stacked columns. Burrows cross-cut some nodules, indicating that at least some of the pedogenic carbonate accumulations were relatively unlithified at the time of deposition.

INTRODUCTION

Calcareous paleosols are common components of continental facies in Phanerozoic red beds (Turner, 1980). The calcic horizon of these paleosols is commonly referred to as "calcrete" or "caliche" by geologists. While a great deal of emphasis has been given to massive, laminar, and pisolitic pedogenic calcrete (James, 1972; Reeves, 1976; Esteban and Klappa, 1983; Goudie, 1983), little detailed description has been published of nodular forms. Recognition and interpretation of nodular calcareous paleosols is particularly important for two reasons. First, they record the initial stages of pedogenic carbonate accumulation (Stages I and II of Gile and others, 1966). They are thus common in depositional sequences where breaks in sedimentation were of short duration, and there was insufficient time for plugged or laminar horizons to form. Second, they are a common form of pedogenic carbonate in the transition zone between semiarid and humid climates, and in seasonal wet-dry climates. This must be considered when "calcretes" or "caliches" are used for paleoclimatic interpretations.

Carbonate nodules are important indicators of paleosol development in Upper Triassic red beds of the Dolores Formation in southwestern Colorado (Blodgett, 1980, 1982). Other evidence for pedogenesis includes root and burrow bioturbation, color mottling, destruction of primary sedimentary structures, and poorly sorted textures. Paleosol profiles also commonly exhibit gradational lower boundaries into unmodified parent material.

This chapter summarizes the criteria used to identify calcareous paleosols in one facies of the Dolores Formation, the sand-sheet facies. In a discussion of these paleosols, special emphasis is placed on the localization of carbonate nodules along Triassic roots (rhizocretions) and on the constraints in using nodular calcareous paleosols for interpreting paleoclimate.

Stacked carbonate nodules are abundant in these paleosols, and in fine-grained paleocalcic horizons of other red beds that range from Mississippian to Tertiary in age. The stacked carbonate nodules, some of which show inverse grading, are rhizocretions that formed around living roots.

The nodular calcareous paleosols of the Dolores sand-sheet facies appear to have formed in a tropical seasonal wet-dry climate similar to the Sahel or the Sudan of North Africa. These paleosols are most likely Inceptisols or Aridisols.

DEPOSITIONAL SETTING

The Dolores Formation consists of as much as 260 m of interbedded mudstone, very fine-grained sandstone to siltstone, fine- to medium-grained sandstone, and limestone pebble conglomerate. Locally it contains a basal conglomerate with abundant quartz and less common lithic pebbles. This predominantly reddish brown sequence of fluvial, eolian, and lacustrine deposits is well-exposed on the southern and western margins of the San Juan Mountains near Durango, Colorado (Fig. 1).

Lithofacies in the Dolores Formation can be correlated with portions of the Chinle and Wingate Formations in New Mexico, Arizona, and Utah (Stewart and others, 1972; Blodgett, 1984). Five genetic lithofacies are recognized in the Dolores Formation on the basis of grain size and sorting, bedding, sedimentary structures, and mineralogy. These include coarse-grained fluvial channel, fine-grained meanderbelt point-bar, fluvial flood plain, sand sheet, and continental sabkha facies.

Coarse fluvial channel facies

The coarse-grained fluvial channel facies occurs at the base of the Dolores Formation and is composed predominantly of fine- to medium-grained sandstone and quartz- and lithic-pebble conglomerate. This facies is as much as 22 m thick, and in most areas forms a tabular body overlying the basal Dolores unconformity. Internally, it contains horizontal laminations with parting lineation and small- to medium-scale trough cross-stratification. The facies geometry and sedimentary structures suggest a braided or low-sinuosity fluvial system.

Point-bar facies

Fluvial facies above the basal sandstone and conglomerate in the Dolores Formation contain cross-bedding indicative of higher-sinuosity rivers. These deposits are dominated by a fine-grained meanderbelt point-bar facies. Point-bar deposits are recognized by sets of large-scale (4 m or greater in thickness) sigmoidal cross-beds of sandstone and mudstone (Blodgett, 1984). These heterolithic cross-beds fine upward from basal limestone-pebble lags into unstratified reddish brown mudstone

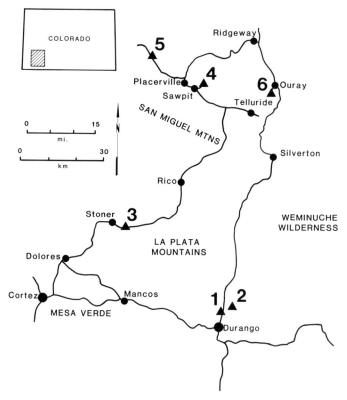

Figure 1. Map showing location of major exposures of paleosols in sand-sheet facies of Upper Triassic Dolores Formation. Appendix 1 contains detailed location of each numbered exposure.

and represent lateral accretion deposits of a migrating point bar. Internally, the sandstone in the large cross-beds contains small-scale trough cross-laminations or is parallel laminated. In many sets, the mudstone-defined lateral-accretion surfaces extend nearly to the basal scour. This suggests that flow in some of the meandering streams was ephemeral or at least highly variable (Puigdefabregas and van Vliet, 1978; Stewart, 1981).

Fluvial floodplain facies

Interstratified, very fine- to fine-grained sandstone and reddish brown mudstone of the fluvial floodplain facies are associated with the fine-grained meanderbelt point-bar facies. The tabular sandstone beds of this facies contain small-scale trough cross-stratification or horizontal laminations, and represent crevasse-splay deposition on a seasonally well-drained flood plain (Blodgett, 1984). Mudstone in this facies varies from laminated siltstone to unlaminated silty claystone.

Seasonal desiccation of the flood plain is indicated by the occurrence of sandstone casts of lungfish aestivation burrows (Blodgett, 1983; Dubiel and others, 1987) and large mud cracks. These tubular burrows are 2 to 9 cm in diameter, and occur in mudstone below crevasse-splay sandstone, on point-bar lateral accretion sets, in abandoned-channel mudstone, and at one locality, in the sand-sheet facies.

Sandstone and mudstone of the fluvial flood-plain facies locally show evidence of soil development. Evidence for these paleosols includes root mottles, slickensides, carbonate nodules, meniscate burrows (*Scoyenia* ichnofacies), and very poorly sorted (plasmic) textures. Thin beds of root-mottled, brecciated, and laminar micritic limestone occur locally in this facies. These limestones and some of the associated mudstone may represent deposition in shallow flood-plain lakes.

Sand-sheet facies

Also interbedded with the reddish brown mudstone in the upper Dolores Formation are beds of tabular, moderately well-sorted, very fine-grained sandstone to siltstone (Fig. 2). These beds range from 1 to 10 m in thickness and can be traced along depositional strike for distances of more than 3 km with little change in thickness. Both the upper and lower contacts of these reddish brown sandstone to siltstone beds are generally planar with rare evidence of scour. Commonly, the upper contact of these beds grades into dark reddish brown mudstone over a distance of a few centimeters, whereas the lower contact is marked by sand-filled desiccation cracks in the underlying mudstone.

At most localities, the very fine-grained sandstone to siltstone beds contain horizontal to wavy bedding with dark reddish brown mudstone drapes at intervals of 1 to 2 cm. Many of these drapes show evidence of *Scoyenia* burrows, desiccation cracks, and wart-like (adhesion?) structures. At several localities this facies contains broad, low-angle trough and planar cross-stratification (Blodgett, 1984). Calcareous paleosols are common, especially in the upper portion of the very fine-grained sandstone to siltstone beds.

The bedding style, contact relationships, sorting, and internal sedimentary structures suggest that the very fine-grained sandstone to siltstone facies is an extradunal sand sheet of the Late Triassic Wingate erg (Blodgett, 1983, 1984; Kocurek and Nielson, 1987). An abundance of mudstone drapes within the very fine-grained sandstone to siltstone beds indicates an episodic flooding of the sand-sheet environment.

Continental sabkha facies

Near the top of the Dolores Formation, at the western edge of the outcrop belt, are beds of very fine-grained sandstone to siltstone that are less resistant to weathering than the sand-sheet facies. These beds are characterized by contorted and discontinuous mudstone drapes, and are more poorly sorted than the sand-sheet facies. Bimodal sorting is common, with the coarse mode consisting of very well-rounded, fine-to-medium sand grains (Blodgett, 1984). Also abundant are sparry calcite pseudomorphs of discoidal gypsum, 5 to 15 cm in length.

The bimodal sorting of very well-rounded sand grains is

Figure 2. Massive-weathering beds of the sand-sheet facies, composed of very fine-grained sandstone to siltstone. These beds form parent material for calcareous paleosols described herein. Geologist's arms indicate sharp basal contact of sand-sheet bed 10 m thick.

indicative of eolian transport (Folk, 1968), while clear discoidal gypsum forms in the moist unsaturated zone of sabkhas (Miller, 1975; Kinsman, 1969). These characteristics are consistent with a continental sabkha environment that formed under conditions of increasing aridity. This sabkha appears to have formed as the Wingate erg migrated into southwestern Colorado.

Summary

The Dolores Formation consists predominantly of interbedded fluvial and eolian facies deposited on the southwestern side of remnants of the Uncompahgre highlands. Except for a basal sheet sandstone deposited by a braided or low-sinuosity fluvial system, most fluvial deposits in the Dolores Formation were formed by actively meandering rivers that produced extensive point-bar deposits.

Flood-plain deposits of these meandering rivers interfinger with sand sheets that appear to be derived from the Wingate erg. The sand sheets were periodically moist environments with overbank flooding from adjacent fluvial systems. Vegetative stabilization of the sand sheets resulted in significant periods of soil development.

Near the top of the Dolores Formation, continental sabkha deposits indicate both increased aridity and a near-surface regional ground-water table. Overall, the Dolores Formation represents fine-grained fluvial, eolian, and lacustrine sedimentation in a tropical continental setting.

EVIDENCE FOR PEDOGENESIS

Introduction

Many soil-forming (pedogenic) processes represent a continuation of geologic surficial processes in a vegetated landscape. Bioturbation, desiccation, carbonate precipitation, and the vertical translocation of clay are just a few of the processes that occur in both unvegetated and vegetated sediment. Likewise, chemical weathering begins in unvegetated sediment, and continues during soil development. Dissolution and alteration of framework grains can continue in the unsaturated zone below the soil profile (Walker and others, 1978; Wood and Petraitis, 1984; James, 1985). Evidence for pedogenesis in the rock record thus requires either an understanding of the relative timing of these processes or the identification of processes diagnostic of soil formation. In nearly all instances the overprint of saturated-zone (phreatic) diagenesis must also be considered.

Two processes, floral bioturbation and the development of soil horizons, appear to be the least ambiguous indicators of pedogenesis in the rock record. Fossil roots or root trace fossils of terrestrial plants indicate a vegetated surface, and thus—in nearly all cases—a soil. These roots may occur in environments as diverse as swamps and salt marshes (Histosols or organic-rich Entisols) and vegetated eolian dunes (Entisols). The development of distinctive surface or subsurface diagnostic horizons in soils are features that may be preserved in the rock record (Bown and Kraus, 1981; Retallack, 1983). This is especially true for horizons that contain authigenic (neoformed) minerals. Care must be taken in distinguishing pedogenic horizons from depositional beds (e.g., argillic horizons from detrital clay beds), and from subsoil unsaturated and saturated zone cementation (e.g., laminar petrocalcic horizons from speleothems).

A third and underutilized indicator of pedogenesis are soil petrographic (micromorphologic) fabrics. Repeated wetting and drying, freezing and thawing, and bioturbation destroy depositional sedimentary structures and sorting to produce a very poorly sorted sediment with patches or stringers of oriented clay minerals. The resulting "sepic plasmic fabric" (Brewer, 1976) may also occur in some unweathered glacial tills and debris flows, but it appears to be most common in soils and paleosols.

The evidence for pedogenesis in the Dolores Formation is thus a combination of field and petrographic observations that indicate the existence of floral bioturbation, soil horizonation, and early diagenetic cementation. Discussion here is limited to paleosols in the Dolores sand-sheet facies because of the relative textural and mineralogical homogeneity of its beds of very fine-grained sandstone to siltstone. This reduces the significance of textural changes in parent material as a variable in the interpretation of these paleosols. The relative homogeneity in grain size and mineralogy makes it probable that beds of this facies share a similar burial diagenetic history.

Paleosol characteristics

Paleosols of the sand-sheet facies are characterized by destruction of primary sedimentary structures, bioturbation and mottling, isolated carbonate nodules, stacked carbonate nodules, poorly sorted tecture, and graduational lower contacts. Most profiles contain all of these features. Only the stacked carbonate nodules are locally absent.

Destruction of primary sedimentary structures. Where little or no evidence of paleosol development exists, beds of the sand-sheet facies show evidence of water and wind transport as well as desiccation. Many of the physical sedimentary structures are subtle because there is little contrast in mineralogy or grain size. Horizontal to low-angle laminae, spaced 1 cm or less apart, are the most common physical sedimentary structures in the sand-sheet facies. Many of these laminae are defined by mudstone drapes that are 1 to 2 mm in thickness. These drapes commonly show evidence of desiccation and burrowing. Evidence for desiccation includes orthogonal and nonorthogonal mud cracks and delicate concave-up mudstone curls.

Desiccation and burrowing destroy physical sedimentary structures in areas of the sand-sheet facies where paleosol development has not occurred. This destruction, or turbation of the deposit, is rarely as complete or as pervasive as that found in the paleosols.

In the paleosols, rooting was added to burrowing, and wetting and drying, as processes responsible for the turbation. The combined effect, pedoturbation, may have been more effective in destroying sedimentary structures because of the duration of subaereal exposure. The nearly complete destruction of the primary sedimentary structures provides important evidence that these paleosols advanced beyond immature soils, Entisols, in their development.

Bioturbation and mottling. Much of the color mottling in the calcareous paleosols is associated with floral or faunal bioturbation. Many of the root mottles are a grayish red-purple (5RP 4/2). This contrasts with the reddish brown (2.5YR 4/4) color of the host rock. Complete, or nearly complete, removal of the hematite pigment results in a greenish gray (5GY 8/1) or light blue-green (5BG 8/2) mottle. This occurs in bleached spheres, and along some burrow and root trace fossils.

Root trace fossils. Evidence for roots in the calcareous paleosols is based on the geometry of purple mottles and on the occurrence of stacked carbonate nodules. Root trace fossils provide important information on paleosol drainage, pigmentation, and carbonate accumulation.

Root mottles in the calcareous paleosols can be categorized on the basis of size and shape. Large root mottles are those that range from 3.5 to 6 cm in width, are 18 to 67 cm in traceable length, and have a grayish red-purple (5RP 4/2) pigmentation. Their orientation is near vertical or inclined at steep angles to the depositional surface. Lateral branches to root mottles occur (Fig. 3), but are less common. Most of the large root mottles are bordered by stacked carbonate nodules (rhizocretions). These large root trace fossils appear to be monopodial root systems, consisting of a central, vertical tap-root and less well-developed secondary ramifications.

Figure 3. Downward and laterally branching root trace fossil (light colored areas). Purple (5RP 4/2) mottle of root trace fossil contrasts with red (2.5YR 4/6) color of very fine sandstone to siltstone host rock. Jacob staff is numbered in centimeters; Locality 3.

Figure 4. Rootlet trace fossils (light colored areas) associated with larger, purple, root trace fossils (Fig. 3). Branching frequency and angles (Went, 1973) suggest that these are trace fossils of rootlets rather than bleached halos around fungal rhizomorphs. Coin is 24 mm in diameter; Locality 3.

The large tap-root fossils locally decrease in size downward, where they are traced into smaller root or "rootlet" trace fossils (Fig. 4). Mottles of the rootlets are 1 to 2 mm in diameter, and are commonly light pale green (5G 8/2) to grayish white (5G 9/1). The diameter of the mottles is probably larger than the original rootlets. Their green color probably reflects pigmentation by chlorite or illite after the iron oxide or oxyhydroxide pigment was removed (McBride, 1974). Many rootlet mottles cannot be traced to larger tap roots, and may be the roots of smaller plants. The branching frequency and intersection angles of these fine mottles suggest that they are indeed roots rather than fungal rhizomorphs (Went, 1973).

Cohen (1982) has proposed that root trace fossil morphology can be used to reconstruct paleoground-water conditions in arid regions. In his model, deeply penetrating vertical and diagonal roots are indicative of a thick unsaturated zone, and shallow, horizontal, and matted root systems suggest a very shallow water

table. While this model may be applicable to phreatophytes, plants that obtain their water from the capillary fringe above the water table, it has limited applicability to xerophytes, plants that obtain their water from near-surface wetting events. Xerophytes have various combinations of vertical tap roots and horizontal ramifications (Oppenheimer, 1960). Factors other than moisture (aeration, nutrients, temperature, and genetics) control their depth of rooting (Oppenheimer, 1960).

Thus, although the large Dolores root trace fossils represent well-developed monopodial root systems, the plants that produced them were not necessarily phreatophytes. Both xerophytes and phreatophytes can develop carbonate accumulations (rhizoliths) around root systems (Semeniuk and Meagher, 1981; Cohen, 1982). In coastal dune sands of Australia, capillary draw by phreatophytes produces plugged and laminar, calcic or petrocalcic horizons close to the ground-water table (Semeniuk and Meagher, 1981). Thick carbonate accumulations with laminar caps are absent in most Dolores paleosols. This is probably because of inadequate time for their development. Rapid formation of plugged and laminar petrocalcic horizons may be restricted to marine marginal settings where the supply of calcium is virtually inexhaustible. In continental areas, development of plugged and laminar horizons takes on the order of 10^5 yr (Gile and others, 1966; Machette, 1985).

The purple-pigmented root trace fossils are distinctive chemically and mineralogically from the reddish brown paleosol matrix. Wet-chemical analysis and x-ray diffractometry of several purple root trace fossils indicates that they are areas of manganese deficiency and of decalcification. The mottles have been leached in manganese (108 to 169 ppm) relative to the surrounding reddish brown paleosol matrix (379 to 445 ppm). This deficiency in manganese is common in some unsaturated-zone root systems (Mount and Cohen, 1984). The Dolores root mottles also contain less than 1 percent carbonate, in contrast to the surrounding matrix, which commonly contains abundant calcite (5 to 46 percent) and lesser amounts of dolomite (0 to 5 percent). There is little difference in the total-iron content between the purple root mottles (2.0 to 3.6 percent) and the surrounding reddish brown matrix (1.9 to 4.2 percent), and virtually no difference in the ratio of ferrous to ferric iron.

The chemical and mineralogical data on the root mottles constrains the possible explanations for their distinctive purple pigmentation. McBride (1974) summarized four hypotheses to explain the orgin of purple pigmentation in red beds: (1) changes in the percentage of hematite, (2) mixing of red and green minerals, (3) occurrence of manganese oxides, and (4) differences in the particle size of the hematite. Based on a chemical anaylsis of pigmentation in the red beds of the Difunta Group in Mexico, McBride (1974) found no evidence to support the first three hypotheses and favored the later one, hematite particle size, as the most likely explanation for the purple mottles. Durand (1975) also reached this conclusion after examining coarse and fine clay fractions of Permian and Triassic red beds of France and Germany. He attributed purple pigmentation to hematite in the coarse-size fraction (greater than 2 μm). Folk (1976) surveyed the color of Phanerozoic and Precambrian red beds, and supported McBride's contention that hematite crystal size explains differences in red-bed pigmentation.

Recent work by Morris and others (1985) on the properties of fine synthetic hematite pigments also supports the crystal-size hypothesis. Morris and others (1985) examined both crystal size and shape to explain differences in the spectral properties of hematite. They found no relation between crystal shape and the reflectivity of hematite. Instead, they found that an increase in the mean particle-diameter of hematite pigment corresponds to a shift in color from orange to deep purple. From these investigations, it appears that the hematite in the purple root-mottles of Dolores paleosols may be more coarsely crystalline than the pigment in the adjacent paleosol matrix.

The cause for this coarseness in hematite crystal size is less clear. It may result from organic exudates of the living root, or from organic decay products. Laboratory studies of synthetic hematite have shown that organic acids (Cornell and Schwertmann, 1979) and sugars (Cornell, 1985) affect the rate of crystallization and nucleation of hematite. These kinetic factors may ultimately influence the size of the hematite crystals if selected organic compounds favor slow rates of growth at fewer nucleation sites.

The timing of the purple mottling appears to be early in the diagenesis of the paleosols, but is not well constrained. Mottles associated with burrows that are similar in color to the root trace fossils are cross-cut by a second generation of gray-to-white mottles that are amoeboid in shape. Alternatively, the purple hue of some root mottles may be initiated during pedogenesis. In Holocene fine-grained sediments of the Rio Puerco River in New

Figure 5. Meniscate burrows of *Scoyenia* ichnofacies. These burrows, abundant in calcareous paleosols and in association with mud drapes of sand-sheet facies, were probably produced by nonmarine arthropods (Frey and others, 1984). Scale is numbered in centimeters; Locality 2.

Mexico, purple-hued mottles occur around modern roots (Blodgett, 1984).

Burrows. Although faunal bioturbation occurs throughout the sand-sheet facies, it is most intense in the calcareous paleosols. Two forms of faunal bioturbation occur in this facies: burrows and chamber structures. Both forms appear to be the product of sediment reworking by arthropods.

Burrows in the paleosols range from 3 to 15 mm in diameter ($\bar{x}$ = 6 mm), and can be subdivided on the basis of internal structure. The internal structure of these burrows is either meniscate or appears to be featureless. Both type of burrows are cylindrical, nonbranching, occur at angles to bedding, and locally cross preexisting burrows. A comparison of the diameters of both types of burrows in full relief suggests that they were made by the same organism, possibly for different purposes.

Delineation of meniscate burrows is commonly enhanced by the alternation of reddish brown meniscae with drab pale red (10R 6/2) or very pale green (5G 8/2) meniscae. This alternation occurs at intervals of 0.5 to 1 mm (Fig. 5). The green meniscae appear to be selectively bleached, possibly through the decay of fecal or mucus matter concentrated during burrow construction (Frey and others, 1984).

The external morphology of these burrows can be observed on mudstone drapes of the sand-sheet facies that are unaffected by pedogenesis. These drapes display burrows in apparent convex epirelief, where they show surficial ornamentation consisting of subparallel longitudinal ridges. These ridges or striae represent casts of scratch marks on the burrow walls produced by the appendages of the burrowing organism (Bromley and Asgaard, 1979).

The taxonomy and ethology of these burrows is complex. The meniscate burrows can be assigned to several trace fossil genera (*Ancorichnus, Muensteria,* or *Scoyenia*), depending on the presence or absence of a burrow lining, and on the occurrence of external burrow markings (Frey and others, 1984). Structureless burrows are assigned to the ichnogenus *Planolites* based on their size, absence of a well-defined lining, orientation, curvature, and filling that commonly differs from the surrounding matrix (Pemberton and Frey, 1982).

The meniscate burrows are the product of active deposit-feeding (Stanley and Fagerstrom, 1974; Frey and others, 1984), while the apparently structureless burrows may be passively filled. Some of the apparently structureless burrows may actually be backfilled, but the organism produced little or no fecal/mucus material to subsequently bleach the meniscae.

The facies association of the Dolores meniscate burrows supports the suggestion that the casting medium for these burrows was moist (Stanley and Faberstrom, 1974) rather than subaqueous (Bromley and Asgaard, 1979). Morphologically similar meniscate burrows occur both in soils (Stace and others, 1968; Brewer, 1976) and in paleosols (McBride and others, 1975; Buurman, 1980; Bown and Kraus, 1981; Freytet and Plaziat, 1982). Meniscate burrows in soils are sometimes referred to as "striotubules" (Brewer and Sleeman, 1963).

The organism responsible for the construction of these meniscate burrows remains enigmatic although the likely candidates are limited. "*Scoyenia*-like" meniscate burrows have been attributed to crayfish (Olsen, 1977; Hubert and others, 1978), annelids (Häntzschel, 1975; McGowen and others, 1979; Freytet and Plaziat, 1982), and insects (Stanley and Fagerstrom, 1974; Bromley and Asgaard, 1979). However, Wells (1977) and Frey and others (1984) provided convincing arguments to exclude adult crayfish, annelids, and many insects from consideration. Frey and others (1984) concluded that an arthropod, other than an insect or a decapod, is most likely responsible for *Scoyenia* and *Ancorichnus*.

Chamber structures. In intimate association with the small invertebrate burrows are irregularly shaped areas of reddish brown siltstone and very fine-grained sandstone with pronounced bleached halos (Fig. 6). These structures are referred to as "chambers" because of their irregular shape and burrow-like extensions (Blodgett, 1984). The grain size and sorting of the chamber filling commonly appears to differ little from the very poorly sorted sandstone or siltstone of the surrounding paleosol. The bleached halos are light greenish gray (5GY 8/1) to bluish white (5B 9/1), and are most pronounced for a distance of 1 to 3 mm away from the chamber wall. Pigmentation of the halo grades into the reddish brown color of the host rock at a distance of 10 to 30 mm from the chamber wall. Most chambers have one or more branches that are cylindrical with smooth, concave terminations. These branches have cross-sectional diameters identical to surrounding meniscate and structureless burrows.

Some of these "chambers" may be the product of intersecting burrows, whereas others may actually be filled "cells" (Ratcliffe and Fagerstrom, 1980) or "nests" and "galleries" (Bown, 1982) constructed by insects or other small arthropods. The pronounced outward bleaching of the chamber walls with no inward

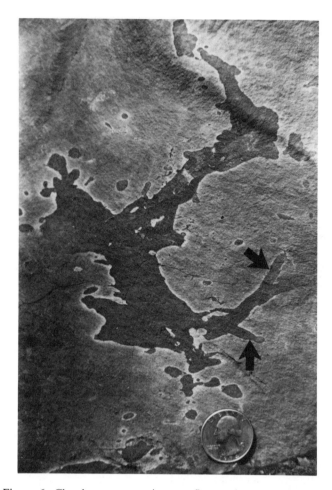

Figure 6. Chamber structure, in very fine sandstone, outlined by bleached rim; has filling similar in grain size and sorting to surrounding paleosol matrix. Some lateral extensions of chambers (arrows) have shape and diameter of adjacent burrows. Coin is 24 mm in diameter; Locality 1.

bleaching of the chamber filling suggests either syndepositional loss of pigment in the chamber wall or a deficiency of organic matter in the chamber infilling.

Carbonate nodules. Carbonate nodules composed of low-Mg calcite are the primary form of pedogenic carbonate in Dolores paleosols. These nodules are irregular in shape and commonly range from 1 to 30 mm in diameter. The nodules are generally concentrated to form paleocalcic horizons that contain up to 53 weight percent carbonate.

The term nodule is used here in both a geologic and pedogenic sense. Pettijohn (1949) differentiated nodules from concretions in sedimentary rocks on the basis of their irregular shape and lack of concentric internal structure. This distinction is also made in soils for accretionary structures called glaebules (Brewer, 1976). Pedogenic nodules are glaebules that have an undifferentiated internal fabric (Brewer, 1976).

Figure 7. Highest density of carbonate nodules observed in Dolores calcareous paleosol; this concentration would represent intermediate Stage III carbonate morphology in classification proposed by Gile and others (1966) for Quaternary soils. Jacob staff is numbered in centimeters; Locality 6.

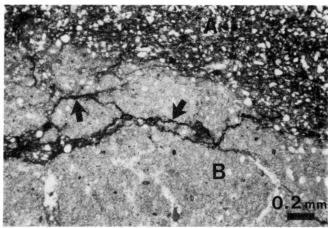

Figure 8. Contrast between grain-rich matrix of paleosol (A) and crystic plasmic fabric (B) of calcareous nodules. Concentration of hematite pigment occurs between nodules (arrows); Locality 1.

Nodules in Dolores paleosols vary in both their internal and external arrangement. Internally, they consist of micrite or microspar with varying proportions of detrital grains. The nodules may also include veins of sparry calcite referred to as crystallaria and wedge-shaped crack patterns termed septaria. Externally, they occur as individual bodies that appear to "float" in the paleosol matrix, as vertical "stacked" columns, or as dense concentrations (Fig. 7).

Micromorphology. Thin sections show that the carbonate nodules contain varying proportions of detrital quartz and feldspar. These detrital grains appear to float in the micrite or microspar cement. This texture in Holocene soils is described as a crystic plasmic or calciasepic plasmic fabric, with the floating detrital grains referred to as skeletal grains (Bal, 1975a; Brewer, 1976). Most Dolores nodules have a sharp boundary with the surrounding paleosol, although some have outer edges which appear diffuse (Fig. 8). In many stacks of nodules, stringers of clay-size hematite and clay minerals occur between individual nodules (Fig. 8).

The relationship between carbonate nodules and the surrounding soil is emphasized by Wieder and Yaalon (1974) as an indicator of the degree of nodule transport. In their model, "orthic" nodules have diffuse boundaries and formed in situ, "disorthic" nodules have sharp boundaries and moved in the soil profile by pedoturbation, and "allothic" nodules—which are dissimilar in composition to the surrounding soil—have been transported into the soil. Using these criteria, nearly all of the Dolores nodules would be classified as "disorthic," even those that formed in situ in stacks adjacent to root trace fossils.

Two problems arise in the application of the Wieder and Yaalon (1974) model. The first is that carbonate nodules appear to undergo multiple stages of in situ growth and recrystallization within a soil (Rabenhorst and others, 1984). This may transform a diffuse carbonate accumulation into a nodule with a sharply defined boundary without significant pedoturbation. Second, differential compaction of the paleosol matrix around a lithified or partially lithified nodule may produce a sharp boundary to an initially diffuse nodule.

Compaction and pressure solution may also, in part, explain the concentration of hematite-pigmented clay between individual nodules in the vertical stacks (Fig. 8). A second, as yet untested, hypothesis for this plasma concentration involves the growth rate of the nodules. Slow growth of the nodule may allow rearrangement of the crystic plasma between precipitation events. Preferential nucleation of the microspar or micrite in pores adjacent to earlier carbonate crystals would eventually exclude skeletal grains. Surface tension of the pellicular water on the crystals might exclude clay-size particles from the growing nodule.

Crystallaria and septaria. In addition to micrite and microspar, areas of sparry calcite are common in the carbonate nodules and in separate veins in the paleosol (Fig. 9). This sparry calcite fills desiccation cracks and voids that appear to be the product of decayed rootlets. Many of these voids were less than 1 mm across and now contain single crystals of spar that extend from one wall of the void to the other. In larger voids, the crystal size of the spar increases inward from the side of the void to its center. The areas of sparry calcite are analogous in size and shape to crystallaria in soils (Bal, 1975b; Brewer, 1976). Unlike the crystic plasmic fabric of the carbonate nodules, the sparry calcite in the crystallaria does not envelope detrital grains.

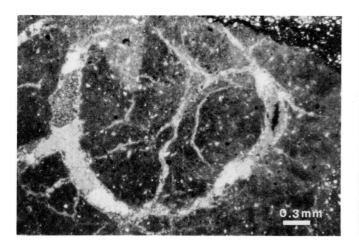

Figure 9. Crystallaria of sparry calcite filling curvilinear circumgranular cracks. Circumgranular crystallaria form within crystic plasmic fabric. Photograph taken in partially cross-polarized light; Locality 1.

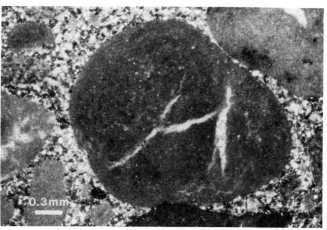

Figure 10. Internal structure of pedogenic septaria, with sparry calcite filling tapering septarian fractures within these nodules. This nodule lithified in the Triassic calcic horizon and was eroded and redeposited in fluvial channel lag. Photograph taken in partially cross-polarized light; Locality 4.

Two morphologies of the crystallaria in the Dolores nodules are also common in Holocene soils. These are curvilinear circumgranular crystallaria (Fig. 9) and wedge-shaped septaria (Fig. 10). Both apparently result from differential drying and cementation between the interior and the exterior of the nodules, and between the nodules and the surrounding soil matrix. Esteban and Klappa (1983) cited circumgranular cracks as being "indicative of caliche facies."

Septarian crystallaria narrow from the center of the nodule outward (Fig. 10). Glaebules containing these features are termed septaria, rather than nodules (Brewer, 1976). In the Dolores Formation, septaria occur in situ in calcareous paleosols of the sand-sheet facies and as clasts in intraformational, fluvial limestone conglomerates. The genesis of septaria in calcareous soils is not precisely known. However, it seems unlikely that they formed by the "syn-compactional" growth/de-watering origin proposed for septarian concretions in shale (Raiswell, 1971).

Timing of growth. Several lines of evidence indicate that the calcareous nodules in the Dolores sand-sheet facies formed near the depositional surface. In a paleosol north of Durango, Colorado, meniscate burrows can be observed to cross-cut carbonate nodules (Fig. 11). This implies that at least some of the nodules were relatively unlithified at the time of soil development, and that the nodules formed at depths shallow enough to be reached by burrowing organisms.

The second line of evidence is the overwhelming abundance of carbonate nodules in fluvial conglomerates of the Dolores Formation. These "limestone conglomerates" were derived from Dolores flood-plain and sand-sheet paleosols, and from less common Dolores lacustrine carbonates. Granules and pebbles

Figure 11. Some burrows (B) crosscutting carbonate nodules (C). This relationship indicates that some nodules were only weakly lithified at time of bioturbation, and suggests that carbonate accumulated in near-surface environment, within zone of bioturbation. Scale is numbered in centimeters; Locality 1.

that compose these carbonate conglomerates are generally unfossiliferous, are composed of micrite and microspar, and contain crystallaria and septaria. These conglomerates are moderately well sorted, suggesting that the nodules in them were lithified and able to survive at least short distances of transport. A third line of evidence is the direct association of the stacked carbonate nodules with the purple root mottles. Evidence presented below suggests that the roots were alive at the time these nodules formed.

Figure 12. Stacked carbonate nodules (rhizocretions) that coalesce vertically to form irregular tubule around grayish red-purple root trace fossil. This tubule weathers out in relief in clay-rich bed of sand-sheet facies. Scale is 15 cm long; Locality 3.

Figure 13. Vertical stacking of carbonate nodules in paleocalcic horizon of calcareous paleosol illustrated in Figure 15. Many of the stacks taper downward and are associated with burrow mottling. Proximity of stacked calcareous nodules to root trace fossils at other localities (Figs. 12, 14) suggests that these nodules are also rhizocretions. Coin is 24 mm in diameter; Locality 1.

While the timing of nodule formation is closely constrained, the formation of the sparry calcite that fills the crystallaria and the septaria is not. In soils, sparry calcite may precipitate early where local conditions channel and restrict soil drainage (Mount and Cohen, 1984). Some of the sparry calcite may have also precipitated with burial in the meteoric phreatic zone.

Rhizocretions. A distinctive feature of paleosols in the Dolores sand-sheet deposits is an abundance of calcareous nodules in vertical stacks (Fig. 12). Individual nodules in these stacks are generally 10 to 30 mm in diameter. Some stacks show an inverse grading in the size of the nodules (Fig. 13). Outcrop weathering locally results in the partial or total dissolution of these nodules, producing vertical stacks of cavities in the very fine-grained sandstone or siltstone.

The origin of the stacked configuration for these nodules is apparent at Locality 3. At this exposure, stacked nodules coalesce vertically to form irregular tubules around the purple root trace

fossils (Fig. 12). In longitudinal section these tubules have a sharp inner boundary proximal to the root trace fossil and a more diffuse outer margin (Fig. 14).

The close association of stacked carbonate nodules with root trace fossils indicates that these nodules are a type of rhizolith, a "rhizocretion," which is a root-related accumulation of mineral matter (Klappa, 1980; Blodgett, 1982). While descriptions of carbonate root sheaths or tubules extend as far back as Darwin (1860), little has been published on the genesis of nodular rhizoliths. In addition to the Dolores Formation, nodular rhizoliths occur in the Mississippian Mauch Chunk and Pennington Formations (author's observations), the Pennsylvanian Monongahela Formation (author's observations), the Permian Halgaito Formation (author's observations), the Triassic New Haven Arkose (Hubert, 1978) and Keuper Formations (Spy-Anderson, 1980/1981), and the Tertiary of Aquitaine, France (Crouzel and Meyer, 1978). Although called rhizoconcretions by some workers, these glaebules are not generally concretions in that they commonly lack a concentric internal structure.

General observations and speculation on the genesis of rhizoliths have been summarized by Johnson (1967), Amiel (1975), and Klappa (1980). Three specific questions can be asked regarding the origin of the Dolores rhizocretions: (1) Did they form when the root was dead or alive? (2) What was the source of calcium carbonate? and (3) What conditions favored their formation?

Field evidence indicating that rhizocretions form around dead roots or along voids formed after root decay is lacking. The pCO$_2$ gradient around a dead, decaying root should not differ

Figure 14. Cross section of nodular carbonate tubule (c) surrounding grayish red-purple root trace fossil (r). This carbonate rhizolith has sharp inner boundary closest to root and diffuse outer margin. Scale is 15 cm in length; Locality 3.

The actual precipitation of carbonate rhizoliths appears to be mainly the result of mass flow rather than diffusion of dissolved calcium and bicarbonate toward the root (Miller and Wilding, 1972; Barber, 1974; Amiel, 1975). Calcium builds up in the soil solution near a root because supply often exceeds the rate of absorption by the root (Barber, 1974). Precipitation next to the root may be by supersaturation caused by transpiration or by changes in pH induced by root exudates. Plants vary in their water absorption (Kramer, 1983). This may explain, in part, variations in rhizocretion development in a given paleosol.

Iron or manganese oxide pigment is generaly absent in the outer rims of the rhizocretions in the sand-sheet facies. Where present, iron or manganese oxide pigmentation of the outer rim of a carbonate nodule is referred to as a neoferran, neoferrimangan, or neomangan (Brewer, 1976). These features appaer to be most common in calcic horizons that are frequently saturated or are close to the water table (Sehgal and Stoops, 1972; Sobecki and Wilding, 1983).

Paleosol horizonation

As with Holocene soils, the genesis of paleosols can be reconstructed through the identification of diagnostic pedogenic horizons. Complete burial and preservation of a soil should include a diagnostic surface horizon, an epipedon, in addition to one or more diagnostic subsurface horizons. Once identified, these paleosol horizons must be correlated to define the vertical extent of an individual soil. This is difficult when epipedons are missing or when multiple soils are superimposed (Ruellan, 1971). Dolores calcareous paleosols lack an identifiable epipedon and are recognized by a diagnostic subsurface calcic horizon. The characteristics of the paleocalcic horizon and absence of other diagnostic horizons must be considered in interpreting the genesis of Dolores calcareous paleosols.

Absence of an epipedon. Epipedons in soils developed on unconsolidated material are generally identified by surface darkening from organic matter or by evidence of eluviation (Soil Survey Staff, 1975). Neither feature is observed in the Dolores Formation.

There are at least four possible explanations for the absence of an identifiable epipedon in the Dolores calcareous paleosols. The first explanation is that organic matter did not accumulate in the A horizon in either the quantity or the type to produce darkening (melanization) of an epipedon. In general, low surface accumulations of organic matter might be expected if Dolores paleosols formed under arid or semiarid climatic conditions. An exception to this generalization is found in grassland soils (Mollisols and some Vertisols), which have dark (mollic) epipedons even though they do not contain a high percentage of organic matter (Soil Survey Staff, 1975; Ahmad, 1983; Fenton, 1983). In these soils, the dark pigmentation comes from clay-organic complexes that form in a calcium-rich environment (Dixon, 1982). The close association of mollic epipedons with grassland vegeta-

greatly from other large fragments of decaying plant material in a soil. Horizontal lines of carbonate nodules have not been found around logs in Dolores paleosols. The void created by root decay should form a pathway for potential carbonate-precipitating solutions that differs litle from desiccation cracks, burrows, or other linear or tubular voids in the soil. Carbonate nodules are not found in stacks adjacent to large desiccation cracks or passively filled burrows in the Dolores Formation.

In contrast, rhizoliths (also known as neocalcans) are known to form around the roots of a variety of living shrubs and trees (Kindle, 1925; Johnson, 1967; Miller and Wilding, 1972; Amiel, 1975; Klappa, 1980; Howell and Hochberg, 1981; Semeniuk and Meagher, 1981). These rhizoliths may attain a considerable thickness without killing the root. Rhizoliths commonly develop along the entire length of the root, not just next to the tips of young roots. This is expected since large volumes of water are absorbed along the entire length of roots (Kramer, 1983). The inverse grading of some stacks of nodules in Dolores paleosols (Fig. 13) suggests that nodule growth was greater in the upper portions of roots. This could be because of their greater age or because they were closer to the source of the water.

Multiple sources for the calcium carbonate that forms the nodules in the Dolores paleosols are probable. Both wind and water could have provided considerable silt and sand-size calcium carbonate to the sand-sheet facies. This detrital carbonate could have been dissolved by soil waters containing a high concentration of dissolved carbon dioxide from the bacterial decay of organic matter. Some investigators have also suggested that exudates from roots, including organic acids and hydrogen, contribute to the dissolution of the detrital carbonate (Johnson, 1967; Barber, 1974).

tion suggests that they may not have formed prior to the middle Cenozoic evolution of grasses, and thus should not be expected in Triassic paleosols.

A second explanation is that any surface organic-matter accumulation was lost during burial of the paleosol under oxidizing conditions. Loss of organic matter by bacterial diagenesis is common in buried Quaternary paleosols (Stevenson, 1969; Yaalon, 1971; Hall, 1983). A third possibility is that eluvial horizons are present, but have not been recognized. Identification of eluviation is a common problem in Holocene soils with sandy epipedons (Soil Survey Staff, 1975).

Finally, epipedons are vulnerable to deflation or to removal by sheet erosion. Removal of an epipedon by wind or water in the Triassic would result in the subsequent burial of a truncated soil profile. The truncated paleosol profile would consist of one or more diagnostic subsurface horizons.

Subsurface diagnostic horizons. Identification of subsurface diagnostic horizons in paleosols is more promising (Birkeland, 1984). This is especially true if mineral accumulation has occurred. Significant clay-mineral accumulation takes the form of an argillic horizon, while carbonate mineral accumulation can form a calcic horizon.

Absence of an argillic horizon. Argillic horizons are pedogenic concentrations of silicate clay in excess of the assumed parent material and/or the overlying soil horizons (Birkeland, 1984). They are characterized by concentrations of fine clay, iluvial clay coatings (argillans), and in some soils, a reddish hue.

In homogeneous parent material, an argillic horizon is commonly identified by vertical changes in the ratio of fine to total clay. Burial diagenesis of the Dolores red beds makes reconstruction of the Triassic fine/total clay ratios impractical, if not impossible. Burial diagenetic hematite also overprints the initial color and distribution of pedogenic iron oxides or oxyhydroxides. This makes it impossible to isolate a layer with the red hue that is commonly associated with argillic horizons in warm climates.

In heterogeneous parent material, where depositional beds of clay could be mistaken for illuvial accumulations of clay, techniques other than particle-size analysis must be used to identify an argillic horizon (Soil Survey Staff, 1975). This is the case in many Dolores calcareous paleosols that occur at the top of sand-sheet beds and are overlain by thick mudstone units (Fig. 15). Such a depositional lithologic break within the paleosol profile complicates identification of an argillic horizon.

One method of dealing with parent-material inhomogeneity is to establish clay illuviation by field or petrographic recognition of oriented clay skins (argillans) on ped or grain surfaces. In the Dolores sand-sheet paleosols, only thin clay skins (simple free-grain argillans) are observed bordering some sand grains. Unlike thick, continuous argillans that form by illuviation, these thin clay cutans appear to be the product of in situ stress caused by wetting and drying (Brewer, 1976). If an argillic horizon developed in the silty mudstone (unit 3, Fig. 15) directly above the sand-sheet sandstone/siltstone facies, it could be difficult to identify in thin section. This is because argillans are disrupted by alternating

wet/dry cycles in fine-textured soils formed in desert and Mediterranean climates (Nettleton and others, 1969).

In summary, no evidence for a mollic epipedon or an argillic horizon was found in the calcareous paleosols of the sand-sheet facies. Absence of an argillic horizon is significant because it precludes assignment of these paleosols to the Alfisol order or to the Argid suborder of the Aridisols. The absence of a mollic epipedon precludes classification as a Mollisol. Thin-section observations indicate that paleosols developed in the sand-sheet facies have less than 30 percent clay and thus cannot be classified as Vertisols. Inceptisols and Aridisols are the only two remaining soil orders that contain calcic horizons.

Calcic horizons. Calcic horizons can be identified in Dolores paleosols by both the quantity and the morphology of the carbonate accumulation. In Holocene soils consisting of silt and fine sand, calcic horizons must have at least 5 percent more authigenic carbonate than the next underlying layer, and must be at least 15 cm thick. Dolores paleocalcic horizons can have in excess of 30 percent more carbonate than the underlying parent material (Fig. 15), and range from 0.5 to 1 m in thickness.

The macroscopic and microscopic morphology of carbonate accumulation in Dolores paleosols described above is similar to that in Holocene nongravelly soils (Bal, 1975a,b; Gile and others, 1981). The only feature without a close modern analog is the vertical stacking of carbonate nodules. To my knowledge, this feature has not been described in Holocene soils. This may be because detailed investigation of rhizoliths has been in sediments and sedimentary rocks (e.g., Amiel, 1975; Klappa, 1980; Bown, 1982; Loope, 1985) rather than in Holocene soils. It may also be that some rhizoliths can only be recognized as stacks of coalesced nodules when they have been lithified and subsequently weathered.

The lateral continuity of the Dolores paleocalcic horizons ranges from less than 100 m (Locality 3) to approximately 2.3 km (between Localities 1 and 2). At Locality 3, the paleocalcic horizon appears to terminate abruptly toward the western end of the outcrop. This termination is marked by the disappearance of rhizoliths and by a large, curving light green mottle. The mottle appears to partially circumscribe the portion of the outcrop containing the rhizoliths. This relationship suggests that calcic horizon development was closely related to the distribution on the Triassic vegetation.

Definition of the vertical extent of the paleocalcic horizons may provide information that is useful for interpreting the genesis of these paleosols. Relatively abrupt lower boundaries of horizons of rhizocretions may define the vertical extent of large roots (Fig. 16). The upper boundary of many of the paleocalcic horizons that contain rhizoliths is commonly within a few decimeters of the top of a sand-sheet sandstone or siltstone. This suggests that vegetative stabilization of the sand-sheets was a major factor in terminating their aggradation.

Two significantly different origins have been proposed for calcic horizons in Quaternary soils. Goudie (1973, 1983) summarized these as the *per descensum* and *per ascensum* models. In the *per descensum* model, the carbonate is essentially illuvial in

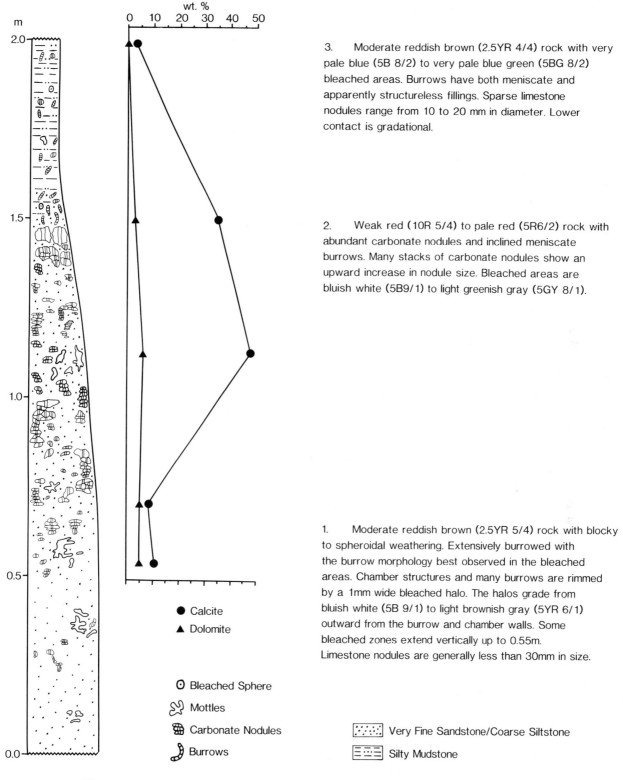

3.   Moderate reddish brown (2.5YR 4/4) rock with very pale blue (5B 8/2) to very pale blue green (5BG 8/2) bleached areas. Burrows have both meniscate and apparently structureless fillings. Sparse limestone nodules range from 10 to 20 mm in diameter. Lower contact is gradational.

2.   Weak red (10R 5/4) to pale red (5R6/2) rock with abundant carbonate nodules and inclined meniscate burrows. Many stacks of carbonate nodules show an upward increase in nodule size. Bleached areas are bluish white (5B9/1) to light greenish gray (5GY 8/1).

1.   Moderate reddish brown (2.5YR 5/4) rock with blocky to spheroidal weathering. Extensively burrowed with the burrow morphology best observed in the bleached areas. Chamber structures and many burrows are rimmed by a 1mm wide bleached halo. The halos grade from bluish white (5B 9/1) to light brownish gray (5YR 6/1) outward from the burrow and chamber walls. Some bleached zones extend vertically up to 0.55m. Limestone nodules are generally less than 30mm in size.

● Calcite

▲ Dolomite

◉ Bleached Sphere

Mottles

Carbonate Nodules

Burrows

Very Fine Sandstone/Coarse Siltstone

Silty Mudstone

Figure 15. Calcareous paleosol profile 41 m above base of exposed section at Locality 1. This columnar section shows topographic expression of lithologic units. Total carbonate content was first determined by bulk sample dissolution in 8 percent acetic acid. Relative percentages of calcite and dolomite were then determined by intensity of their respective (104) x-ray diffraction peaks compared to calibration curve of standard mixtures.

Figure 16. Lower boundary of paleocalcic horizon with underlying burrowed very fine sandstone in paleosol illustrated in Figure 15. Base of paleocalcic horizon, between 60 and 70 cm on the Jacob staff, is a relatively abrupt one and may reflect maximum rooting depth in profile; Locality 1.

origin. It precipitates, predominantly by evaporation, at the average depth of rainfall penetration. In calcic horizons formed by this mechanism, there should be a close correlation between effective precipitation and depth to the calcic horizon (Jenny and Leonard, 1934; Jenny, 1941; Arkley, 1963).

In the *per ascensum* model, the carbonate is derived by capillary draw or plant transpiration from a shallow ground-water table. The upward capillary draw of water in fine-textured soils is rarely significant at water-table depths of more than 2 m (Goudie, 1973). Alternatively, phreatophytes can draw water from as deep as 50 m (Goudie, 1973).

Shallow or perched water tables can be identified in soils by several features. Manganese and iron oxides occur in glaebules and in mottles along voids in many soils associated with shallow water tables (Sehgal and Stoops, 1972; Sobecki and Wilding, 1983; Mount and Cohen, 1984). Pumping of water by phreato-

phytes can result in the formation of a continuous sheet of massive and laminar calcrete in the zone of capillary rise directly above the water table (Semeniuk and Meagher, 1981).

None of the above features associated with a shallow water table were found in the Dolores sand-sheet paleosols. Instead, the upward coarsening of many rhizocretions and their preferential occurrence near the top of root trace fossils suggest an illuvial rather than ground-water source for the carbonate.

In summary, calcic horizons in the Dolores sand-sheet paleosols range from Stage I to intermediate Stage III morphology as described by Gile and others (1966, 1981) for Holocene soils. Root transpiration of vadose water is the major process by which carbonate accumulated in these calcic horizons.

PALEOCLIMATE

Published generalizations on the paleoclimatic significance of calcrete or caliche generally do not convey the complex relationship that exists between climate and carbonate accumulation in soils. Calcrete (caliche) is commonly interpreted to have formed in semiarid to arid (Reeves, 1976; Braithwaite, 1983) or warm, seasonally dry (Van Houten, 1982) climates. These generalizations do not fully consider variations in calcium supply (Machette, 1985), soil texture (Gile and others, 1966), seasonality of rainfall (McFadden and Tinsley, 1985), or the influence of plants on carbonate accumulation (Semeniuk and Searle, 1985; Semeniuk, 1986).

An inadequate calcium supply can limit or preclude pedogenic carbonate accumulation in any climatic regime. The effects of a low-calcium flux appear to be more pronounced with increasing precipitation (Machette, 1985). Calcium supply for Dolores paleosols came from multiple sources. The dissolved and suspended loads of Dolores rivers were derived in part from calcareous red beds of the underlying Cutler Formation and from Pennsylvanian carbonates. Wind-circulation patterns during Dolores deposition can be reconstructed from eolian stratification in the Wingate Sandstone (Poole, 1964). This reconstruction places salt-anticline outcrops of Pennsylvanian carbonate and gypsum directly upwind of the Dolores sand sheets.

The grain size of parent material is another important variable in assessing the climatic conditions under which Dolores calcareous paleosols formed. Dolores paleosols are closely comparable in particle size and initial carbonate content to the loess soils of the central United States. An east-west transect of these soils by Jenny and Leonard (1934) related annual rainfall to the shallowest depth of carbonate accumulation. The apparent shallow depth to the top of the calcic horizon in Dolores paleosols would place them close to the 400-mm value for annual rainfall on the High Plains of the United States (Jenny and Leonard, 1934).

This direct relationship between annual rainfall and depth to the top of the calcic horizon may not be applicable to climates with strongly seasonal rainfall (Arkley, 1963). In these climates, effective precipitation and the water-holding capacity of the soil appear to be better determinants for the depth of carbonate accumulation (Arkley, 1963). A strong dry season for the Triassic in southwestern Colorado is indicated by large desiccation cracks (Blodgett, 1984) and lungfish aestivation burrows (Dubiel and others, 1987) in Dolores flood-plain facies.

A seasonal moisture regime is also indicated in paleolatitudinal reconstructions for Late Triassic time. Paleomagnetic measurements from Upper Triassic and Early Jurassic red beds of the Colorado Plateau (Steiner, 1983) indicate that Dolores sandsheet paleosols formed at approximately 11°N paleolatitude. Today, this latitude in Africa is characterized by tropical desert, steppe, and savanna climates (Trewartha, 1978). Rainfall in these environments is highly seasonal, with a single three-month wet season (Lockwood, 1974). Paleoclimatic modeling supports a zonal rainfall pattern for Triassic Pangea that is analogous to tropical Africa (Robinson, 1973; Parrish and others, 1987).

Climatic controls on rhizolith formation by plants that utilize vadose water are poorly known. The only detailed investigation of the climatic distribution of rhizoliths has been by Semeniuk and co-workers in Holocene coastal dune sands of the Perth Basin, southwestern Australia (Semeniuk and Meagher, 1981; Semeniuk and Searle, 1985; Semeniuk, 1986). These rhizoliths are forming today in the unsaturated zone of mixed carbonate-siliciclastic sand, and are best developed around roots of heath and scrub vegetation. In this Mediterranean climate, the rhizoliths appear to be more abundant in humid (890 mm of rainfall and 1,200 mm of evaporation) rather than semiarid (630 mm of rainfall and 2,000 mm of evaporation) conditions (Semeniuk and Searle, 1985). This study of Australian calcrete in a seasonal, subtropical climate suggests that the overall relationship between unsaturated-zone rhizoliths and climate is not a simple one. Future investigation of Holocene rhizoliths may find that plant type, and grain size and carbonate content of parent material, also affect their climatic distribution.

In summary, the climatic limits for nodular and rhizolith carbonate accumulation in soils is poorly known. Most summaries of calcrete and caliche distributions either exclude nodular pedogenic carbonate from consideration or do not consider the effects of Quaternary climatic change on pedogenesis. Generalizations made on the basis of annual rainfall (such as arid, humid) are probably not accurate for tropical seasonal climates. The paleoclimate for Dolores calcareous paleosols appears to fit Van Houten's (1982) generalization of a warm, seasonally dry climate. Annual rainfall may have been greater than the 400-mm figure predicted by Jenny and Leonard (1934) for temperate North America, but it was probably less than the 890 mm of the southern Perth Basin in Australia because of a reduced calcium supply.

CONCLUSIONS

1. Calcareous paleosols are well developed in the sand-sheet facies of the Upper Triassic Dolores Formation in southwestern Colorado. These buried and lithified paleosols are recognized by the nearly complete destruction of physical sedimentary structures, extensive mottling associated with burrow and root trace fossils, poorly sorted and "floating" textures, and abundant carbonate nodules.

2. Triassic vegetation on these soils produced long, monopodial root systems and fine networks of rootlets. These root systems are defined by their distinctive color mottles and by their branching morphology. In the absence of evidence for a permanent, shallow water table in these soils, these plants are interpreted to have been xerophytes rather than phreatophytes. Purple pigmentation of the large root mottles appear to have produced by the coarse crystal size of the hematite rather than variations in manganese or ferrous/ferric iron content. Recrystallization of the hematite may have occurred in the presence of organic compounds derived from the root.

3. Faunal bioturbation is also pervasive in these paleosols in the form of invertebrate burrows and chamber structures. Both meniscate and structureless burrows are common. The meniscate burrows belong to the ichnogenera *Scoyenia, Anchorichnus,* and *Muensteria,* while the structureless burrows are *Planolites.* Morphologically similar meniscate burrows or "striotubules" are found in Holocene soils and in other paleosols. An arthropod, other than an insect or a decapod, is most likely responsible for these burrows of the *Scoyenia* ichnofacies (Frey and others, 1984).

4. Carbonate nodules, composed of low-Mg calcite, form paleocalcic horizons in the Dolores paleosols. These nodules occur as individual entities in the paleosol profile and as stacked columns. Internally, a number of these nodules contain veins of sparry calcite and wedge-shaped crack patterns analogous to crystallaria and septaria in Holocene soils. Evidence that these nodules formed in unconsolidated sediment near the Triassic depositional surface includes the following observations: (a) that meniscate burrows cross-cut portions of the nodules, indicating they were relatively unlithified at the time of bioturbation; (b) that large numbers of these nodules are found in fluvial "limestone conglomerates" of the Dolores Formation; and (c) that stacks of nodules are found lining the large root mottles.

5. Stacked carbonate nodules, some of which show inverse grading, are actually rhizocretions, root-related accumulations of mineral matter. Stacked rhizocretions are a macromorphologic feature that appears to be diagnostic of calcareous paleosols in red beds from Mississippian through Tertiary time. These rhizoliths probably developed around the live roots of a variety of plants. They formed by the mass flow of calcium to the semipermeable membrane of the root surface. Calcium supply commonly exceeds absorption by the root, and low-Mg calcite precipitates. This precipitation occurs by water loss in transpiration and/or by pH changes induced by root exudates.

6. Nodular pedogenic carbonate is most common in calcic horizons of finely textured soils in semiarid and seasonal wet-dry climates. It also occurs in clay-rich soils of subhumid climates, and in calcic horizons derived from shallow ground-water tables. The nodular calcareous paleosols of the Dolores sand-sheet facies appear to have formed in a tropical seasonal wet-dry climate

similar to the Sahel or the Sudan of North Africa. These paleosols were most likely Inceptisols or Aridisols.

ACKNOWLEDGMENTS

Financial support for this investigation was provided by the Owen-Coates Fund and other funds of the University of Texas Geology Foundation, the Geological Society of America, the Dana Foundation, the Society of Sigma Xi, the Atlantic Richfield Company, and the Marathon Oil Company, and is gratefully acknowledged. Support of manuscript preparation by the Ohio State University and by Dickinson College is also appreciated, especially the expert typing by Helen Hayes and Patricia Braught and the drafting by Karen Tyler, Philip Stuecheli, and Dana intern Randy Racis. Thanks to Earle F. McBride, Robert L. Folk, Larry Wilding, Gary Kocurek, Stephen P. Cumella, Brian R. Bracken, Mark W. ver Hoeve, J. B. Hayes, and Jeffrey A. May for their valued counsel and support. Manuscript reviews by Peter W. Birkeland, James W. Collinson, John L. Isbell, and Joseph P. Smoot were most helpful. Finally, completion of this project would have been very difficult, if not impossible, without the field assistance of Kevin Zonana and Brian Renaghan.

APPENDIX 1. PALEOSOL LOCALITIES IN THE SAND-SHEET FACIES OF THE DOLORES FORMATION

Locality No.	Location	Description
1	Roadcut on the west side of U.S. 550, 1.3 road mi north of the Durango city limits and across the highway from private campground; E1/2N1/2Sec.9,T.35N.,R.9W., La Plata County, Colorado; Durango East 7.5-minute Quadrangle.	Most of the sand-sheet beds in the 55 m of the upper Dolores Formation exposed here contain calcareous paleosols. The best-developed stacked nodules (Figs. 13, 16) occur in a paleosol 41 m above the base of the section. These nodules are best examined by climbing up the face of the cut and not at road level. (Stop 1, Blodgett, 1984)
2	East side of the Animas River valley in a tributary canyon to Reid Ditch. S1/2NE1/4Sec.3,T.35N.,R.9W., La Plata County, Colorado; Durango East 7.5-minute Quadrangle.	Includes all of the section exposed at Locality 1, as well as underlying fluvial and lacustrine deposits. Many of the paleosols found at Locality 1 can be found here, a distance of 2.3 km to the northeast.
3	Roadcut at Mile 28.5 on the north side of Colorado 145 west of Taylor Creek and 2.8 road mi southeast of Stoner, Montezuma County, Colorado. Unsurveyed SW1/4NW1/4Sec.10, T.38N.,R.13W., Stoner 7.5-minute Quadrangle.	Lower 8 m of the roadcut contains purple root trace fossils surrounded by tubules of stacked carbonate nodules (Figs. 3, 12, 14). Both sandy and silty parent materials are present; rootlet trace fossils are also common (Fig. 4). (Stop 5, Blodgett, 1984)
4	West side of unimproved county road 0.7 road mi east of intersection with Colorado 145 in Sawpit. Unsurveyed SW1/4SE1/4Sec.8,T.43N.,R.10W., San Miguel County, Colorado; Gray Head 7.5-minute Quadrangle.	Pervasive vertical and irregularly shaped white and purple mottles below scattered carbonate nodules. Lungfish burrows occur in the mottled zone. Conglomerate at road level contains abundant transported carbonate nodules.
5	Roadcut on east side of Colorado 145 approximately 2.9 road mi southeast of Goodenough Gulch and 0.3 road mi northeast of a high-voltage power transmission line in San Miguel Canyon. Unsurveyed SW1/4NW1/4Sec.14,T.44N., R.12W., San Miguel County, Colorado; Gurley Canyon 7.5-minute Quadrangle.	Septaria occur in situ, along with small, short stacks of carbonate nodules.
6	Roadcut on west side of Colorado 361 southwest of Weehawkeen Creek, Canyon Creek Valley, southwest of Ouray. Unsurveyed NW1/4NW1/4Sec.13 and E1/2NE1/4Sec.14, T.43N.,R.8W., Ouray County, Colorado; Ironton 7.5-minute Quadrangle.	Multiple paleosols in sand-sheet beds containing abundant stacked nodules. Bed with coalesced carbonate nodules (Fig. 7) represents intermediate Stage III morphology of Gile and others (1966).

REFERENCES CITED

Ahmad, N., 1983, Vertisols, *in* Wilding, L. P., Smeck, N. E., and Hall, G. F., eds., Pedogenesis and soil taxonomy; II, The soil orders: New York, Elsevier, p. 91–123.

Amiel, A. J., 1975, Progressive pedogenesis of eolianite sandstone: Journal of Sedimentary Petrology, v. 45, p. 513–519.

Arkley, R. J., 1963, Calculation of carbonate and water movement in soil from climatic data: Soil Science, v. 96, p. 239–248.

Bal, L., 1975a, Carbonate in soil; A theoretical consideration on, and proposal for its fabric analysis; 1, Crystic, calcic and fibrous plasmic fabric: Netherlands Journal of Agricultural Science, v. 23, p. 18–35.

——, 1975b, Carbonate in soil; A theoretical consideration on, and proposal for its fabric analysis; 2, Crystal tubes, intercalary crystals, K fabric: Netherlands Journal of Agricultural Science, v. 23, p. 163–176.

Barber, S. A., 1974, Influence of the plant root on ion movement in soil, *in* Carson, E. W., ed., The plant root and its environment: Charlottesville, University Press of Virginia, p. 525–564.

Birkeland, P. W., 1984, Soils and geomorphology: New York, Oxford University Press, 372 p.

Blodgett, R. H., 1980, Triassic paleocaliche in red beds of the Dolores Formation, southwestern Colorado [abs.]: American Association of Petroleum Geologists Bulletin, v. 64, p. 678.

——, 1983, Depositional environments of the Upper Triassic Dolores Formation, southwestern Colorado: Geological Society of America Abstracts with Programs, v. 15, p. 285.

——, 1984, Nonmarine depositional environments and paleosol development in the Upper Triassic Dolores Formation, southwestern Colorado, *in* Brew, D. C., ed., Field trip guidebook; Geological Society of America Rocky Mountain Section 37th Annual Meeting: Durango, Colorado, Fort Lewis College, p. 46–92.

Bown, T. M., 1982, Ichnofossils and rhizoliths of the nearshore fluvial Jebel Qatrani Formation (Oligocene), Fayum Province, Egypt: Palaeogeography, Palaeoclimatology, and Palaeoecology, v. 40, p. 255–309.

Bown, T. M., and Kraus, M. J., 1981, Lower Eocene alluvial paleosols (Willwood Formation, northeast Wyoming) and their significance for paleoecology, paleoclimatology, and basin analysis: Palaeogeography, Palaeoclimatology, Palaeoecology, v. 34, p. 1–30.

Braithwaite, C.J.R., 1983, Calcrete and other soils in Quaternary limestones; Structures, processes, and applications: Journal of the Geological Society of London, v. 140, p. 351–363.

Brewer, R., 1976, Fabric and mineral analysis of soils: Huntington, New York, Robert E. Krieger Publishing Co., 482 p.

Brewer, R., and Sleeman, J. R., 1963, Pedotubules; Their definition, interpretation, and classification: Journal of Soil Science, v. 14, p. 156–166.

Bromley, R., and Asgaard, U., 1979, Triassic freshwater ichnocoenoses from Carlsberg Fjord, East Greenland: Palaeogeography, Palaeoclimatology, Palaeoecology, v. 28, p. 39–80.

Buurman, P., 1980, Paleosols in the Reading Beds (Paleocene) of Alum Bay, Isle of Wright, U.K.: Sedimentology, v. 27, p. 593–606.

Cohen, A. S., 1982, Paleoenvironments of root casts from Koobi Fora Formation, Kenya: Journal of Sedimentary Petrology, v. 52, p. 401–414.

Cornell, R. M., 1985, Effect of simple sugars on the alkaline transformation of ferrihydrite into goethite and hematite: Clays and Clay Minerals, v. 33, p. 219–227.

Cornell, R. M., and Schwertmann, U., 1979, Influence of organic anions on the crystallization of ferrihydrite: Clays and Clay Minerals, v. 27, p. 402–410.

Crouzel, F., and Meyer, R., 1978, Varying patterns of calcretes in the Oligo-Miocene continental sediments from Aquitaine (southern France), *in* Friedman, G. M., ed., Abstract, International Congress on Sedimentology, 10th, p. 140–141.

Darwin, C. D., 1860, The voyage of the Beagle; Engel, L., ed.: New York, Natural History Library Edition, Doubleday and Co., 503 p.

Dixon, J. B., 1982, Mineralogy of Vertisols, *in* Vertisols and rice soils of the tropics: Symposium II, International Congress of Soil Science, 12th, New Delhi, India, p. 48–60.

Dubiel, R. F., Blodgett, R. H., and Bown, T. M., 1987, Lungfish burrows in the Upper Triassic Chinle and Dolores Formations, Colorado Plateau: Journal of Sedimentary Petrology, v. 57, p. 512–521.

Durand, M. M., 1975, Nature des colorations violettes et vertes de certains grès Triassiques: Comptes Rendus, v. 280, p. 2737–2740.

Esteban, M., and Klappa, C. F., 1983, Subaerial exposure environment, *in* Scholle, P. A., Bebout, D. G., and Moore, C. H., eds., Carbonate depositional environments: American Association of Petroleum Geologists Memoir 33, p. 1–54.

Fenton, T. E., 1983, Mollisols, *in* Wilding, L. P., Smeck, N. E., and Hall, G. F., eds., Pedogenesis and soil taxonomy; II, The soil orders: New York, Elsevier, p. 125–163.

Folk, R. L., 1968, Bimodal supermature sandstones; Product of the desert floor, *in* Proceedings, 23rd International Geological Congress, Prague, Czechoslovakia, Volume 8: Prague, Czechoslovakia, p. 9–32.

——, 1976, Reddening of desert sands; Simpson Desert, N. T., Australia: Journal of Sedimentary Petrology, v. 46, p. 604–615.

Frey, R. W., Pemberton, S. G., and Fagerstrom, J. A., 1984, Morphological, ethological, and environmental significance of the ichnogenera *Scoyenia* and *Anchorichnus*: Journal of Paleontology, v. 58, p. 511–528.

Freytet, P., and Plaziat, J.-C., 1982, Continental carbonate sedimentation and pedogenesis; Late Cretaceous and Early Tertiary of southern France: Stuttgart, Germany, E. Schweizerbart'sche Verlagsbuchhandlung, Contributions to Sedimentology No. 12, 214 p.

Gile, L. H., Peterson, F. F., and Grossman, R. B., 1966, Morphological and genetic sequences of carbonate accumulation in desert soils: Soil Science, v. 101, p. 347–360.

Gile, L. H., Hawley, J. W., and Grossman, R. B., 1981, Soils and geomorphology in the Basin and Range area of southern New Mexico; Guidebook to the Desert Project: New Mexico Bureau of Mines and Mineral Resources Memoir 39, 222 p.

Goudie, A. S., 1973, Duricrusts in tropical and subtropical landscapes: Oxford, Clarendon Press, 174 p.

——, 1983, Calcrete, *in* Goudie, A. S., and Pye, K., eds., Chemical sediments and geomorphology: New York, Academic Press, p. 93–131.

Hall, G. F., 1983, Pedology and geomorphology, *in* Wilding, L. P., Smeck, N. E., and Hall, G. F., eds., Pedogenesis and soil taxonomy; I, Concepts and interactions: New York, Elsevier, p. 117–140.

Häntzschel, W., 1975, Trace fossils and problematica, *in* Teichert, C., ed., Treatise on invertebrate paleontology, Part W, Miscellanea, Suppl. 1: Boulder, Colorado, Geological Society of America (and the University of Kansas), 269 p.

Howell, D. G., and Hochberg, M. C., 1981, Sedimentology photo: Journal of Sedimentary Petrology, v. 51, p. 1204.

Hubert, J. F., 1978, Paleosol caliche in the New Haven Arkose, Newark Group, Connecticut: Palaeogeography, Palaeoclimatology, Palaeoecology, v. 24, p. 151–168.

Hubert, J. F., Reed, A. A., Dowdall, W. L., and Gilchrist, J. M., 1978, Guide to the Mesozoic redbeds of central Connecticut: State Geological and Natural History Survey of Connecticut Guidebook No. 4, 129 p.

James, N. P., 1972, Holocene and Pleistocene calcareous crust (caliche) profiles: Criteria for subaerial exposure: Journal of Sedimentary Petrology, v. 42, p. 817–836.

James, W. C., 1985, Early diagenesis, Atherton Formation (Quaternary); A guide for understanding early cement distribution and grain modifications in nonmarine deposits: Journal of Sedimentary Petrology, v. 55, p. 135–146.

Jenny, H., 1941, Calcium in the soil; III, Pedologic relations: Soil Society of America Proceedings, v. 6, p. 27–35.

Jenny, H., and Leonard, C. D., 1934, Functional relationships between soil properties and rainfall: Soil Science, v. 38, p. 363–381.

Johnson, D. L., 1967, Caliche on the Channel Islands: California Division of

Mines and Geology Mineral Information Service, v. 20, p. 151–158.

Kindle, E. M., 1925, A note on rhizoconcretions: Journal of Geology, v. 33, p. 744–746.

Kinsman, D.J.J., 1969, Modes of formation, sedimentary associations, and diagnostic features of shallow-water and supratidal evaporites: American Association of Petroleum Geologists Bulletin, v. 53, p. 830–840.

Klappa, C. F., 1980, Rhizoliths in terrestrial carbonates; Classification, recognition, genesis, and significance: Sedimentology, v. 27, p. 613–619.

Kocurek, G., and Nielson, J., 1987, Conditions favourable for the formation of warm-climate aeolian sand sheets: Sedimentology, v. 33, p. 795–816.

Kramer, P. J., 1983, Water relations of plants: New York, Academic Press, 489 p.

Lockwood, J. G., 1974, World climatology; An environmental approach: New York, St. Martin's Press, 330 p.

Loope, D. B., 1985, Recognition and significance of rhizoliths in eolian sandstones: Society of Economic Paleontologists and Mineralogists Annual Midyear Meeting Abstracts, v. 2, p. 56.

Machette, M. N., 1985, Calcic soils of the southwestern United States, *in* Weide, D. L., ed., Soils and Quaternary geology of the southwestern United States: Geological Society of America Special Paper 203, p. 1–21.

McBride, E. F., 1974, Significance of color in red, green, purple, olive, brown, and gray beds of Difunta Group, northeastern Mexico: Journal of Sedimentary Petrology, v. 44, p. 760–773.

McBride, E. F., Weidie, A. E., and Wolleben, J. A., 1975, Deltaic and associated deposits of Difunta Group (Late Cretaceous to Paleocene), Parras and La Popa basins, northeastern Mexico, *in* Broussard, M. L., ed., Deltas, models for exploration: Houston Geological Society, p. 485–522.

McFadden, L. D., and Tinsley, J. C., 1985, Rate and depth of pedogenic-carbonate accumulation in soils; Formulation and testing of a compartment model, *in* Weide, D. L., ed., Soils and Quaternary geology of the southwestern United States: Geological Society of America Special Paper 203, p. 23–41.

McGowen, J. H., Granata, G. E., and Seni, S. J., 1979, Depositional framework of the lower Dockum Group (Triassic) Texas Panhandle: University of Texas Bureau of Economic Geology Report of Investigations No. 97, 60 p.

Miller, J. A., 1975, Facies characteristics of Laguna Madre wind-tidal flats, *in* Ginsburg, R. N., ed., Tidal deposits; A casebook of recent examples and fossil counterparts: New York, Springer-Verlag, p. 67–73.

Miller, M. H., and Wilding, L. P., 1972, Micromorphological features of soils in relation to plant growth, *in* Protz, R., ed., Microfabric of soil and sedimentary deposits: Guelph, Ontario, Department of Land Resource Science, University of Guelph, p. 75–110.

Morris, R. V., Lauer, H. V., Jr., Lawson, C. A., Gibson, E. K., Jr., Nace, G. A., and Stewart, C., 1985, Spectral and other physiochemical properties of submicron powders of hematite ($\propto$—Fe_2O_3), maghemite (γ—Fe_2O_3), magnetite (Fe_3O_4), goethite ($\propto$—FeOOH), and lepidocrocite (γ—FeOOH): Journal of Geophysical Research, v. 90, p. 3126–3144.

Mount, J. F., and Cohen, A. S., 1984, Petrology and geochemistry of rhizoliths from Plio-Pleistocene fluvial and marginal lacustrine deposits, east Lake Turkana, Kenya: Journal of Sedimentary Petrology, v. 54, p. 263–275.

Nettleton, W. D., Flach, K. W., and Brasher, B. R., 1969, Argillic horizons without clay skins: Soil Science Society of America Proceedings, v. 33, p. 121–125.

Olsen, P. E., 1977, Fossils from the Triangle Brick Company quarry, Genlee, North Carolina, *in* Bain, G., and Harvey, G., eds., Field guide to the geology of the Durham Triassic basin: Carolina Geological Society 40th Annual Meeting, October 7–9, Figure 18 (insert).

Oppenheimer, H. R., 1960, Adaption to drought; Xerophytism, *in* UNESCO, Plant-water relationships in arid and semi-arid conditions; Reviews of research: New York, United Nations, p. 105–138.

Parrish, J. M., Parrish, J. T., and Ziegler, A. M., 1987, Permo-Triassic paleogeography and paleoclimatology and implications for therapsid distributions, *in* Hotton, N., III, MacLean, P. D., Roth, J. J., and Roth, E. C., eds., The ecology and biology of mammal-like reptiles: Baltimore, Maryland, Smithsonian Institution Press, p. 109–132.

Pemberton, S. G., and Frey, R. W., 1982, Trace fossil nomenclature and the *Planolites-Palaeophycus* dilemma: Journal of Paleontology, v. 56, p. 843–881.

Pettijohn, F. J., 1949, Sedimentary rocks: New York, Harper and Brothers, 526 p.

Poole, F. G., 1964, Paleowinds in the western United States, *in* Nairn, A.E.M., ed., Problems in paleoclimatology: New York, Interscience Publishers, p. 394–405.

Puigdefabregas, C., and van Vliet, A., 1978, Meandering stream deposits from the Tertiary of the southern Pyrenees, *in* Miall, A. D., ed., Fluvial sedimentology: Canadian Society of Petroleum Geologists Memoir 5, p. 469–485.

Rabenhorst, M. C., Wilding, L. P., and West, L. T., 1984, Identification of pedogenic carbonates using stable carbon isotope and microfabric analysis: Soil Science Society of America Journal, v. 48, p. 125–132.

Raiswell, R., 1971, The growth of Cambrian and Liassic concretions: Sedimentology, v. 17, p. 147–171.

Ratcliffe, B. C., and Fagerstrom, J. A., 1980, Invertebrate lebensspuren of Holocene floodplains; Their morphology, origin, and paleoecological significance: Journal of Paleontology, v. 54, p. 614–630.

Reeves, C. C., Jr., 1976, Caliche: Lubbock, Texas, Estacado Press, 233 p.

Retallack, G. J., 1983, Late Eocene and Oligocene paleosols from Badlands National Park, South Dakota: Geological Society of America Special Paper 193, 82 p.

Robinson, P. L., 1973, Palaeoclimatology and continental drift, *in* Tarling, D. H., and Runcorn, S. K., eds., Implications of continental drift to the earth sciences: New York, Academic Press, v. 1, p. 451–476.

Ruellan, A., 1971, The history of soils; Some problems of definition and interpretation, *in* Yaalon, D. H., ed., Paleopedology; Origin, nature, and dating of paleosols: Jerusalem, Israel, International Soil Science Society and Israel Universities Press, p. 3–13.

Sehgal, J. L., and Stoops, G, 1972, Pedogenic calcite accumulation in arid and semi-arid regions of the Indo–Gangetic alluvial plain of erstwhile Punjab (India); Their morphology and origin: Geoderma, v. 8, p. 59–72.

Semeniuk, V., 1986, Holocene climate history of coastal southwestern Australia using calcrete as an indicator: Palaeogeography, Palaeoclimatology, Palaeoecology, v. 53, p. 289–308.

Semeniuk, V., and Meagher, T. D., 1981, Calcrete in Quaternary coastal dunes in southwestern Australia; A capillary-rise phenomenon associated with plants: Journal of Sedimentary Petrology, v. 51, p. 47–68.

Semeniuk, V., and Searle, D. J., 1985, Distribution of calcrete in Holocene coastal sands in relationship to climate, southwestern Australia: Journal of Sedimentary Petrology, v. 55, p. 86–95.

Sobecki, T. M., and Wilding, L. P., 1983, Formation of calcic and argillic horizons in selected soils of the Texas Coast Prairie: Soil Science Society of America Journal, v. 47, p. 707–715.

Soil Survey Staff, 1975, Soil taxonomy: Soil Conservation Service, U.S. Department of Agriculture, Agriculture Handbook No. 436, 754 p.

Spy-Anderson, F.-L., 1980/1981, Dolocrètes et nodules dolomitiques; Résultats de la dolomitisation directe, en milieu continental, de sédiments terrigènes de la "formation bariolée supérieure" (Keuper) de la région des Vans (Ardèche, sud-est de la France): Bulletin du Bureau Recherches Géologiques et Minieres, series 2, section 1, no. 3, p. 195–205.

Stace, H.C.T., Hubble, G. D., Brewer, R., Northcote, K. H., Sleeman, J. R., Mulcahy, M. J., and Hallsworth, E. G., 1968, A handbook of Australian soils: Glenside, Australia, Rellim Technical Publications, 435 p.

Stanley, K. O., and Fagerstrom, J. A., 1974, Miocene invertebrate trace fossils from a braided river environment, western Nebraska, U.S.A.: Palaeogeography, Palaeoclimatology, Palaeoecology, v. 15, p. 63–82.

Steiner, M. B., 1983, Mesozoic apparent polar wander and plate motions of North America, *in* Reynolds, M. W., and Dolly, E. D., eds., Mesozoic paleogeography of the west-central United States: Denver, Rocky Mountain Section, Society of Economic Paleontologists and Mineralogists, Rocky Mountain Paleogeography Symposium 2, p. 1–11.

Stevenson, F. J., 1969, Pedohumus; Accumulation and diagenesis during the Quaternary: Soil Science, v. 107, p. 470–479.

Stewart, D. J., 1981, A meander-belt sandstone of the Lower Cretaceous of southern England: Sedimentology, v. 28, p. 1–20.

Stewart, J. H., Poole, F. G., and Wilson, R. F., 1972, Stratigraphy and origin of the Chinle Formation and related Upper Triassic strata in the Colorado Plateau region: U.S. Geological Survey Professional Paper 690, 336 p.

Trewartha, G. T., 1978, Climatic regions, *in* Espenshade, E. B., Jr., and Morrison, J. L., eds., Goode's world atlas (15th ed.): Chicago, Rand McNally, p. 8–9.

Turner, P., 1980, Continental red beds: New York, Elsevier Scientific Publishing Company, 562 p.

Van Houten, F. B., 1982, Ancient soils and ancient climates, *in* Geophysics Study Committee, National Research Council, Climate in earth history: Washington, D.C., National Academy Press, Studies in Geophysics, p. 112–117.

Walker, T. R., Waugh, B., and Crone, A. J., 1978, Diagenesis in first-cycle desert alluvium of Cenozoic age, southwestern United States and northwestern Mexico: Geological Society of America Bulletin, v. 89, p. 19–32.

Wells, R. F., 1977, Fresh water invertebrate living traces of the Mississippi alluvial valley near Baton Rouge, Louisiana [M.S. thesis]: Baton Rouge, Louisiana State University, 254 p.

Went, F. W., 1973, Rhizomorphs in soil not connected with fungal fruiting bodies: American Journal of Botany, v. 60, p. 103–110.

Wieder, M., and Yaalon, D. H., 1974, Effect of matrix composition on carbonate nodule crystallization: Geoderma, v. 11, p. 95–121.

Wood, W., and Petraitis, M. J., 1984, Origin and distribution of carbon dioxide in the unsaturated zone of the Southern High Plains of Texas: Water Resources Research, v. 20, p. 1193–1208.

Yaalon, D. H., 1971, Soil-forming processes in time and space, *in* Yaalon, D. H., ed., Paleopedology; Origin, nature, and dating of paleosols: Jerusalem, Israel, International Soil Science Society and Israel Universities Press, p. 29–39.

MANUSCRIPT ACCEPTED BY THE SOCIETY JULY 1, 1987

Printed in U.S.A.

Geological Society of America
Special Paper 216
1988

Paleosols from some Cretaceous environments in the southeastern United States

Wayne Sigleo*
Juergen Reinhardt
U.S. Geological Survey
926 National Center
Reston, Virginia 22092

ABSTRACT

Paleosols are well preserved beneath Upper Cretaceous continental sediments from the eastern Gulf Coastal Plain to the northern Mississippi Embayment. These buried soils are remnants of land surfaces that weathered during Cretaceous time and formed on several rock types, including Precambrian(?) metamorphic rocks and Paleozoic limestone and sandstone. Most soil profiles have distinctive morphologic features and exhibit pedogenic horizon zonation with ferruginous and clay-rich B horizons grading downward to saprolite and parent material within 7 m. Organic matter is not preserved, but pedotubules, which we interpret as fossil roots or burrows, are present in many paleosols. Illuvial and residual concentrations of Al_2O_3 and Fe_2O_3 occur in upper soil horizons where kaolinite and halloysite are the principal clay minerals. A variety of precursor minerals, including 2:1 lattice clays, muscovite, feldspar, and biotite, are present in the lower part of the soil profiles. Variations in pedogenesis were caused by differences in parent material and by local geomorphic factors such as paleoslope and drainage. The rates of paleosol development and the residence times of the various land surfaces are uncertain, but the times of burial and preservation range from Cenomanian to early Maestrichtian. Chemical and mineralogic characteristics of these paleosols are similar to those of modern soils of tropical to subtropical climates; however, the fossil soils may be polycyclic, and their pedogenic characteristics could have been modified by postburial diagenesis. Climatic reconstructions based on paleobotanical, lithostratigraphic, and paleotemperature data from Cretaceous sediments support our interpretation that these paleosols formed in a warm, humid environment on well-vegetated piedmont surfaces.

INTRODUCTION

Paleosols are preserved at many localities beneath the pre–Late Cretaceous regional unconformity in the southeastern United States. These profiles are remnants of ancient land surfaces, which indicate long-term stability prior to landscape truncation and burial by Cretaceous terrestrial sediments. These paleosols provide a means to decipher weathering and soil-forming processes that reflect paleoenvironment and climate over long periods of geologic time. The spatial and temporal relations

of the land surfaces are also important factors in understanding the paleogeographic evolution of the southern margin of the North American continent.

This chapter documents the pedostratigraphic, geochemical, and mineralogic characteristics of paleosols formed on three different pre-Cretaceous rock units exposed from the eastern Gulf Coastal Plain to the Mississippi Embayment (Fig. 1). One profile on gneiss is described from the eastern margin of the Gulf Coastal Plain (Columbus, Georgia), and two are on Paleozoic sandstone and limestone along the southeastern margin of the Mississippi Embayment (Shady Grove and Seven Pines, Alabama).

*Deceased October 17, 1986.

124 *Sigleo and Reinhardt*

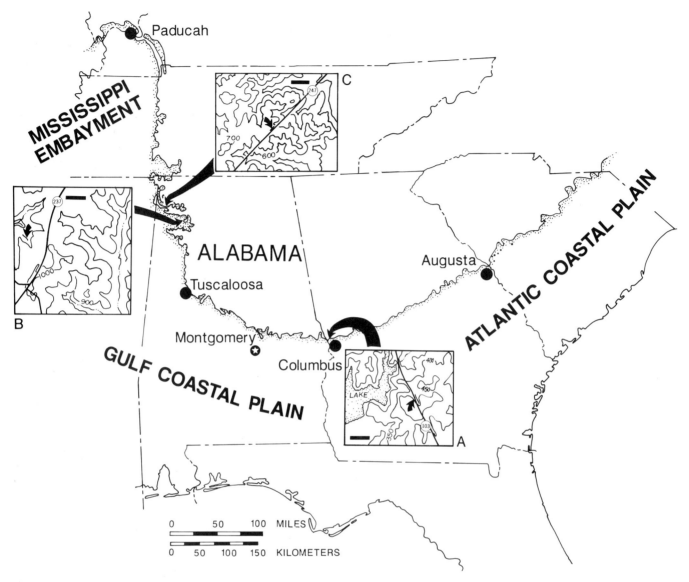

Figure 1. Map of southeastern United States showing the major physiographic provinces and the position of the Fall Line. Inset maps show the precise positions of the three paleosol profiles described in detail in the text. Inset A, Columbus profile from the Fortson, Georgia 7½-minute Quadrangle; inset B, Shady Grove profile from the Phil Campbell, Alabama 7½-minute Quadrangle; and inset C, Seven Pines profile from the Halltown, Alabama 7½-minute Quadrangle. Bar scale on insets equals 1,000 ft (300 m).

The profiles are everywhere truncated and buried by Upper Cretaceous (Cenomanian and younger) fluvial sediments that are presently mapped as the Tuscaloosa Formation or Group. These weathering profiles are the oldest associated with the Coastal Plain of the southeastern United States and are thought to be roughly comparable in age to paleosols formed at the same stratigraphic positions worldwide.

PREVIOUS RESEARCH

Paleosols, duricrusts, and residua are present over a wide range of paleolatitudes in upper Mesozoic and lower Cenozoic rock sequences (Dury, 1971). Cretaceous laterites and bauxites have been described from western and eastern Europe, the Soviet Union, and the Middle East (see Nicholas and Bildgen, 1979; Singer, 1975; Valeton, 1972). The age relations of these paleosols are not entirely certain; however, in many cases the weathered material is formed on Early Cretaceous or older rocks that are usually buried by Upper Cretaceous sediments. With few exceptions, these paleosols and weathering profiles are thought to have formed over a considerable time period—hundreds of thousands to perhaps millions of years—under relatively warm, humid conditions.

Similarly, Cretaceous paleosols have been reported from many localities in the United States, including Minnesota (Austin, 1970; Goldich, 1938) and New York (Blank, 1978). Most of these profiles are lateritic soils with morphologic and geochemical characteristics that most likely resulted from weathering under subtropical or tropical conditions. The weathering intervals range from Early to middle Cretaceous, and the paleosols are usually truncated by Upper Cretaceous sedimentary rocks.

In addition, regional studies have identified pre–Late Cretaceous paleosols and residua in the southeastern United States. For example, Russell (1889) and Sutton (1931), followed by Mellon (1937), Pryor and Ross (1962), and Pavich (1974), recognized Cretaceous profiles on Precambrian and Paleozoic rocks at several locations. Paleosols in the northern part of the Mississippi Embayment formed on Paleozoic carbonate rock units associated with an extensive paleokarst surface that extends from northwestern Alabama to western Kentucky (Miser, 1921; Stearns, 1957).

Mellon (1937) introduced the term Little Bear Residium to describe red earth, or *terra rossa*, profiles on limestone associated with the Paleozoic-Cretaceous unconformity in Alabama and Mississippi. These profiles consist mainly of kaolinite clay, quartz, and iron oxides. Transported residua derived by infilling of irregularities on the paleokarst surface also may be present. Paleosols and siliceous deposits of tripolitic earth, thought to be residua, occupy the same stratigraphic position in Tennessee and western Kentucky (McGrain, 1970). Pre–Late Cretaceous paleosols and residuum also have been described from a few locations in eastern Alabama and western Georgia (Drennen, 1950; Freeman, 1981; Sigleo and Reinhardt, 1985). These authors concluded that saprolite and soil profiles, formed through deep weathering of the crystalline rock, surface before truncation and burial by sediments of the Tuscaloosa Formation.

Most of the previous studies described Cretaceous profiles in widely scattered localities. Few attempted to provide a pedostratigraphic framework to aid in the interpretation of the paleosols. To our knowledge, this study is the first to present a regional comparison of morphological and analytical data from apparently equivalent paleosols on different parent materials and to provide a synthesis of Cretaceous paleogeography and climate.

METHODS OF STUDY

Paleosols are recognized by the same criteria used to identify modern soils—principally, evidence of physical and geochemical horizon zonation that parallels the existing landscape (Morrison, 1967). Numerous paleosols were observed in each study area, and the descriptions contained in this chapter are from the best preserved profiles. Horizons were differentiated by depth functions, including soil texture and structure, color, biogenic features, oxide distribution, clay mineralogy, and concretions. Horizon nomenclature follows that recommended by the Soil Survey Staff (1975). Soil colors are described using the Munsell color system (Munsell Soil Color Charts, 1954).

Textural data from the principal sites were determined by dispersal in water and settling times, using Stokes' Law to estimate grain-size distributions (Krumbein and Pettijohn, 1938). Splits of the whole-rock fraction from different depths within the profiles were analyzed for major and minor oxides by using atomic absorption methods developed by the U.S. Geological Survey (Table 1). Clay mineralogy was determined on an automatic x-ray diffraction unit using copper ($CuK\alpha$) radiation. Sample preparation followed the method of Hosterman and Whitlow (1983), and mineral species were identified by using standard references. Determinations are qualitative; the relative amount of each clay was estimated from both intensity and area enclosed by the strongest diffraction peaks. Transmission electron microscopy (TEM) was used to investigate the crystallinity of kaolinite and as an aid in mineral determinations in some samples. Several iron-rich glaebules (nodules and concretions) from the Columbus profile were investigated petrographically and mineralogically by means of standard microscopy and x-ray diffraction. Nomenclature to describe and classify these soil features follows that of Brewer (1964) and Fitzpatrick (1984).

PALEOSOL DESCRIPTIONS

This section is intended to provide textural, mineralogical, and chemical descriptions of specific sites where paleosols are well preserved and buried by Cretaceous sedimentary deposits in the southeastern United States, specifically along the inner margin of the Gulf Coastal Plain. The information is presented in two parts: a section on a paleosol in the eastern Gulf Coastal Plain, where the fossil soils are preserved on crystalline rocks, and a section on two paleosols along the southeastern margin of the Mississippi Embayment, where the fossil soils are on sandstone and limestone.

Eastern Gulf Coastal Plain

Paleosols are exposed beneath Upper Cretaceous sediments at several locations in the Chattahoochee River Valley near Columbus, Georgia (Sigleo and Reinhardt, 1985). These profiles formed on a variety of Piedmont metamorphic rocks and are easily recognized as a roughly 2-m-thick, red, deeply mottled zone that can be traced along the crystalline rock–Coastal Plain contact. The parent rocks here consist mainly of layered migmatitic hornblende-biotite gneiss and amphibolite of intermediate mafic composition (Schamel and others, 1980; Hanley, 1986), belonging to the Uchee belt (Precambrian?).

The weathered material is everywhere truncated and buried by alluvial sediments of the Tuscaloosa Formation (Cenomanian), a poorly sorted, arkosic sand probably equivalent to the Gordo Formation (Tuscaloosa Group) of western Alabama (Reinhardt and Gibson, 1981). In the Chattahoochee Valley, these sediments are typically organized into fining-upward sequences as much as 5 m thick and are interpreted as low-sinuosity, sandy stream deposits (Reinhardt, 1980; Smith, 1984).

TABLE 1. CHEMICAL DATA (IN PERCENT) FOR CRETACEOUS PALEOSOLS

Depth (cm)	SiO_2	Al_2O_3	Fe_2O_3	FeO	MgO	CaO	Na_2O	K_2O	H_2O^{+1}	H_2O^{-1}	TiO_2	P_2O_5	MnO	CO_2	Total
						Columbus Profile										
10	48.6	24.8	13.7	0.08	0.13	0.02	0.03	0.41	9.5	1.1	0.91	0.17	0.04	0.02	100
40	69.4	17.4	5.2	0.04	0.04	0.01	0.01	0.01	6.3	0.85	0.75	0.07	<0.01	0.01	100
90	47.0	17.5	25.0	<0.01	0.03	0.01	0.01	0.04	7.0	1.0	0.65	0.14	<0.01	0.01	99
175	76.6	15.4	1.7	0.04	0.05	0.02	0.01	0.03	5.2	0.51	0.66	0.05	<0.01	0.01	100
300	62.3	17.4	11.8	<0.01	0.05	0.01	<0.01	0.04	7.6	0.46	0.83	0.08	<0.01	<0.01	101
450	63.5	16.3	3.0	0.20	3.1	0.14	0.05	1.1	5.3	7.1	0.39	0.29	0.05	<0.01	101
Gneiss	58.8	19.1	1.0	5.3	1.7	3.1	4.0	3.1	1.8	0.78	0.90	0.51	0.25	<0.01	100
						Shady Grove Profile										
20	66.0	20.9	2.2	<0.01	0.28	0.10	0.09	1.1	6.5	1.2	0.97	0.05	0.01	0.01	99
60	68.4	14.1	9.7	<0.01	0.11	0.05	0.02	0.07	5.3	1.0	0.89	0.07	0.01	0.02	100
120	69.2	15.2	7.7	<0.01	0.08	0.09	0.02	0.06	5.1	0.88	0.82	0.10	0.02	0.02	99
180	63.4	17.9	9.8	<0.01	0.07	0.04	0.02	0.08	6.4	0.94	0.87	0.08	<0.01	0.03	100
300	67.2	17.9	5.5	<0.01	0.10	0.03	0.02	0.29	6.5	0.80	1.0	0.09	<0.01	0.01	99
						Seven Pines Profile										
10	73.8	11.2	8.0	<0.01	0.32	0.12	0.03	0.33	4.3	1.1	0.63	0.08	<0.01	0.02	100
50	70.4	12.7	8.6	<0.01	0.21	0.16	0.03	0.23	5.0	1.3	0.66	0.07	0.01	0.01	99
100	64.0	18.1	7.1	<0.01	0.25	0.27	0.02	0.08	6.8	2.3	0.76	0.09	0.01	0.01	100
200	72.6	14.5	1.1	0.04	0.92	0.39	0.06	0.60	5.1	3.5	0.47	0.04	<0.01	<0.01	99
330	72.2	13.7	1.3	0.08	1.2	0.49	0.07	0.93	4.2	4.1	0.45	0.05	0.01	0.01	99
Limestone	25.9	2.6	1.2	0.12	2.9	34.3	0.05	0.31	1.0	0.66	0.10	0.03	0.03	29.8	99

The contact at the Fall Line between the Tuscaloosa Formation and the crystalline rock surface is irregular, with probably less than 10 m of local relief (Drennen, 1950). Near Columbus, the unconformity is preserved in a zone some 3 to 4 km wide that dips to the south at 7 to 11 m/km. In many sections, the contact is masked by Quaternary weathering and consequently is difficult to define.

The best exposed paleosol crops out near the intersection of 54th Street and River Road about 3 mi (5 km) north of Columbus (A, Fig. 1). The exposure is on the north side of a low hill of gneiss some 30 m above the thalweg of the Chattahoochee River. A description of the Columbus profile (Fig. 2) follows.

Unconformity

0 to 70 cm, B horizon; silty clay, red (2.5YR 5/6); fine to medium, white (7.5YR 7/10) mottles common; very coarse, prismatic to locally blocky structure to massive; thin, discontinuous argillans; few to common rounded red glaebules as much as 15 mm in diameter, some with white halos; few, very coarse quartz grains and granules; upper 10 to 15 cm reddish yellow (7.5YR 6/8) with few downward-branching tubules as much as 1 cm in diameter filled with white clay and fine sand;

Diffuse smooth boundary

70 to 180 cm, B_t horizon (mottled zone); silty clay, white (5Y 8/1); many fine to coarse, strong brown (7.5YR 6/5) and dark red (10R 3/6) mottles and glaebules densely packed in distinct vermiform pattern; very coarse prismatic structure to massive; glaebules rounded to irregularly shaped as much as 20 mm in diameter; mottles increase in size and chroma with depth but are less densely packed than above; very coarse quartz grains and granules common;

Gradational to diffuse boundary

180 to 550+ cm, C horizon (saprolite); silty to sandy clay, white (5Y 8/1); few faint to distinct, dusky red (10R 3/4) mottles; massive; very coarse quartz grains and granules common; texture becomes coarser with depth; horizon grades downward into saprolite that contains in situ quartz veins and corestones.

Irregular boundary, partly covered

550+ cm, R horizon; gneiss, gray (10R 5/1) on fresh surfaces, weathered reddish brown (5YR 5/3); medium- to coarse-

Figure 2. Contact between the paleosol profile and the overlying Tusca-loosa Formation at Columbus, Georgia, locality. Note the changes in coloration and structure within the profile. Entrenching tool handle = 52 cm long.

Figure 3. Downward-branching, sand-filled structure, interpreted as root trace, in the upper part of the paleosol profile at Columbus, Georgia. Truncation of the structure and the profile is sharp and irregular; the contact with Tuscaloosa is immediately above the knife handle.

grained, some pale yellow (5YR 8/4) concordant layers, 1 to 2 mm wide.

The A horizon is missing and presumably was eroded. The upper part of the profile, interpreted as the B horizon, consists mainly of red to reddish yellow clay with coarse prismatic structure. Argillans or clay films are poorly developed and discontinuous. Pedotubules of various shapes, including some prominent downward-branching structures (Fig. 3), are present and are interpreted as the traces of fossil roots. Iron-rich glaebules occur throughout the profile, either singly spaced in the soil matrix, as in the B horizon, or concentrated near its base in a more or less continuous mottled zone (Fig. 4). This zone is as much as 2 m thick and can be traced continuously for several hundred meters north and east of the paleosol exposure.

Glaebules form about 10 percent of the B horizon matrix. Most are prominent, rounded, ovoid to subspherical features that are 5 to 15 mm in diameter. Their surfaces are wavy to rough, and boundaries with the enclosing matrix are generally clear to diffuse. Most are enveloped by a halo of white clay as much as 1 mm in diameter. In the upper part of the B horizon, glaebules are randomly distributed with little or no relationship to other macroscopic features; however, they increase in size and number downward in the underlying mottled zone or B_t horizon.

In comparison, glaebules in the mottled zone make up about 50 percent of the matrix, and are organized in a complex vermi-form pattern with large, irregular mottles. These glaebules are prominent, and tend to be larger and more irregular than those in the B horizon. Most are clustered within mottles that are in turn surrounded by irregular areas of white clay.

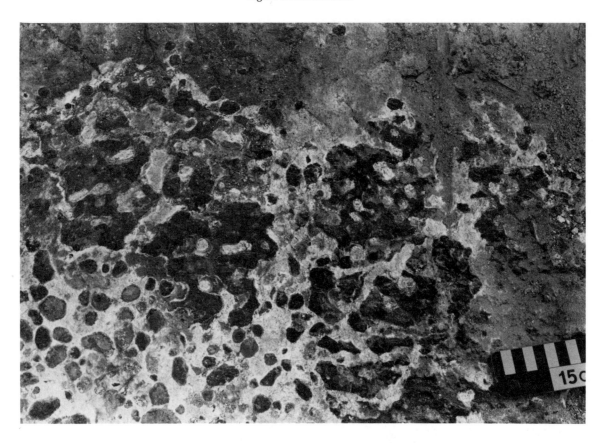

Figure 4. Pattern of pedotubules and glaebules in mottled zone of the Columbus profile. Whereas most of this zone appears to be the result of in situ weathering, the large iron-rich glaebules or concretions (left center) exhibit evidence of downward movement. Scale given in centimeters.

Petrographic examination of some glaebules in the B horizon indicates that they are opaque to translucent features characterized by an undifferentiated fabric (Fig. 5a). Most are strongly adhesive, ovoid nodules with diffuse boundaries and range from 0.5 to 1.0 mm in diameter. Several are enclosed by light-colored halos of clay with diffuse external boundaries. Nearly all contain silt-sized quartz grains around which the nodule has formed. Hematite, kaolinite, and quartz are the dominant minerals. The enclosing soil fabric consists predominantly of skeletal quartz grains in a red, iron-rich, clay matrix (skel-insepic fabric). The quartz grains are generally angular; grain surfaces are extensively pitted and contain solution embayments.

Glaebules in the mottled zone have properties similar to those of glaebules in the B horizon, but many exhibit concentric fabrics with well-developed laminae formed around quartz grains (Fig. 5b). External boundaries are generally sharp and halos are absent. Goethite, kaolinite, and quartz are the dominant minerals.

The mottled zone grades downward into a white to light gray C horizon at depths of 5 to 6 m below the top of the profile. The upper part of this horizon is nearly structureless and shows very weak schistosity as well as relict quartz veins and scattered

corestones. The composition of the gneiss (R horizon) varies considerably; petrographic analysis indicates that is consists locally of plagioclase (50%), biotite (27%), quartz (18%), garnet (4%), and opaque minerals (1%).

The contact between the paleosol and the overlying sediments of the Tuscaloosa is sharp and irregular. Well-rounded pedoliths, feldspar, and quartz are contained in the lower 30 cm of the Tuscaloosa. The composition of the sands at this location is derived from eroded paleosols, saprolite, and crystalline rock, and the grains show little evidence of the pedogenic alteration.

The textural, chemical, and mineralogical properties of the Columbus paleosol show systematic variation with depth (Fig. 6). Clay-sized material is most abundant in the B horizon and shows a typical pedogenic relationship with sand at the base of the profile. Silt occurs throughout but shows a slight increase at the top of the B horizon. The sand fraction increases with depth and is coarsest near the base of the profile, where it contains abundant granules of quartz and a few plagioclase grains little altered from the gneiss.

Silica, iron oxides, and alumina are the principal oxides, together making more than 98 percent of the B horizon. In

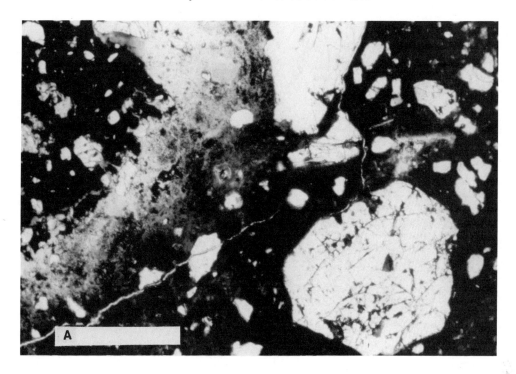

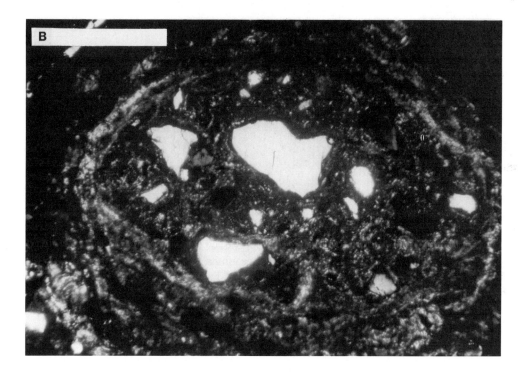

Figure 5. Photomicrographs of glaebules (nodules) from the Columbus profile. A, Hematite-cemented glaebule (upper left) with iron-depleted halo. The mottled zone consists of coarse, angular, and embayed quartz sand with locally very well-rounded quartz silt in an iron oxide and kaolinite groundmass. B, Glaebule with crude concentric laminations enclosing angular quartz, hematite-cemented microclasts, and mottled groundmass. Scale bar in both photos equals 1 mm.

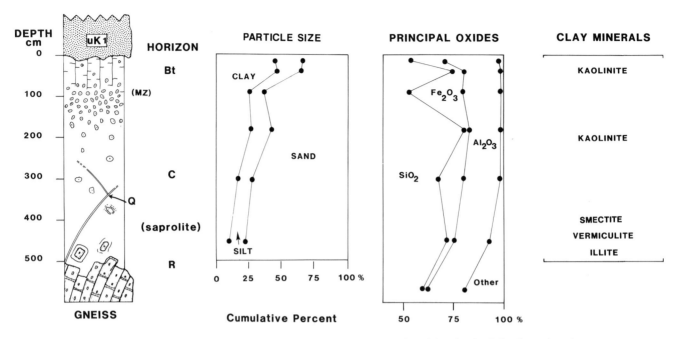

Figure 6. Generalized summary of textural, chemical, and clay-mineral data for the Columbus paleosol profile. Contact relationship between the overlying Tuscaloosa Formation (uK_1) and the underlying parent rock is schematic; a quartz vein (q) cuts the underlying gneiss and extends into the C horizon of the paleosol. Standard symbols show relative positions of inferred soil horizons; MZ shows position of the "mottled zone." In the generalized chemical data, "other" includes alkalis and alkaline earths.

contrast, alkalis and alkaline earths (Na, Ca, K) are nearly absent in the solum and are present in minor amounts only near the base of the profile. Silica contents are low in the upper part of the B horizon and show an inverse relationship with iron. Oxides of iron are most abundant in the mottled zone and at the top of the B horizon. Both iron oxide and silica decrease in abundance in the C horizon or saprolite. There is little variation in alumina abundance except near the top of the B horizon where it increases substantially relative to silica.

The distribution and relative abundance of clay minerals in the profile closely parallel those of the principal oxides. Kaolinite is the dominant clay mineral and shows little variation in the upper 300 cm of the profile. TEM analysis suggests that the kaolinite has a greater degree of crystallinity in the B horizon than in the C, and the average crystal size appears to decrease with depth in the profile. In samples below 300 cm, the 2:1 lattice clay of illite, vermiculite, and smectite are common, with smectite being most abundant near the base of the C horizon. A small amount of illite or mica is present near the top of the B horizon, principally in the zone where argillans are best developed.

Cristobalite occurs in trace amounts throughout the profile but is relatively more abundant in the C horizon where the amount of kaolinite is least. Halloysite, a hydrated aluminum kaolin, is present in very small amounts throughout the profile, as determined by TEM analysis. Its characteristic rolled and tubelike crystals contrast with the platy hexagonal

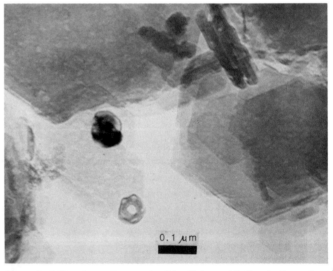

Figure 7. TEM photomicrograph of kaolinite and halloysite from the B horizon of the Columbus paleosol.

forms of kaolinite (Fig. 7); in a few places, tubes of halloysite appear to be partially unrolled. Iron oxides and hydroxides were not detected by x-ray diffraction in the C horizon except in the glaebules; most, if not all, of the iron in the lower part of the profile seems to be poorly crystallized or amorphous.

Figure 8. Limestone pinnacles buried by coarse chert gravel deposits (Cretaceous) in northern Mississippi Embayment. This locality, about 20 mi (32 km) east of Paducah, Kentucky, illustrates the local relief due to karstification of the pre-Cretaceous land surface.

Southeastern Mississippi Embayment

The paleosols described in this region are developed on a variety of upper Paleozoic sedimentary rocks, specifically on sandstone of the Pottsville Formation (Pennsylvanian) and on the Bangor Limestone (Mississippian). Detailed description of these rocks and their regional stratigraphic relations are given by Adams and others (1926) and Welch (1958, 1959). Relief on the unconformity may locally be 30 m or more. Variations in the bedrock surface are primarily due to differences in lithology; there is greater relief on limestone than on sandstone terrains. Paleokarst features, including dolines, collapse breccias, and limestone pinnacles, are present in outcrop exposures as well as in the shallow subsurface (Peace, 1963). The paleokarst topography is present farther to the north in Tennessee and western Kentucky (Fig. 8) along the margin of the Mississippi Embayment (Miser, 1921; Marcher and Stearns, 1962).

The overlying Tuscaloosa sediments vary considerably, from massive conglomerates to well-bedded sands with clay and silt lenses typically organized into fining-upward sequences. The gravel fraction consists predominantly of well-rounded chert locally containing polycrystalline quartz pebbles; the matrix is composed almost entirely of quartz silt and kaolin. It is difficult to determine the extent of erosion on the underlying bedrock during deposition of the basal Tuscaloosa, but in many localities, the Tuscaloosa sediments appear to have been deposited in and around topographic irregularities associated with the original paleokarst surface.

The Cretaceous paleosol at Shady Grove is formed on a fine-grained, quartz arenite of the Pennsylvanian Pottsville Formation. This exposure is in a shallow coal strip mine about 4 mi (6.5 km) southeast of Phil Campbell, Alabama (B, Fig. 1). The megascopic description of the paleosol (Fig. 9) consists of:

Unconformity

0 to 40 cm, E(?) horizon; silty clay, white (5YR 8/1) to light gray (5YR 6/1); few, fine and indistinct, yellowish brown (10YR 5/6) mottles; medium to coarse, subangular blocky structure, locally massive; few indistinct root traces;

Figure 9. Upper part of the paleosol profile at Shady Grove, Alabama, showing the erosional truncation of the profile by the overlying Cretaceous gravel deposit and gross horizon zonation and structure within the profile.

Gradual wavy to smooth boundary

40 to 205 cm, B_t horizon; sandy clay, dark red (2.5YR 3/6); common medium to coarse light gray (5YR 6/1) mottles distinct and common; very coarse subangular blocky structure to locally massive; few indistinct argillans near top, poorly developed and thin; few, dark reddish brown (2.5YR 3/4) glaebules as much as 10 mm in diameter in a mottled zone between 180 and 220 cm;

Diffuse, irregular boundary

205 to 400⁺ cm, C horizon; sandy clay, light yellowish brown (10YR 6/4) to reddish yellow (5YR 7/6); medium to coarse dark reddish brown mottles common; structureless; indistinct cross-bedding preserved near base;

Irregular boundary

400⁺ cm, R horizon; sandstone, light gray (10YR 7/2); fine grained, micaceous, thin to medium bedded, cross-bedded; interbedded with dark gray shale, coal, and underclay; Pennsylvanian age (Pottsville Formation).

The top of the profile is probably eroded, but the light-colored, silty material above the B horizon may be either part of the original surface horizon (A) or part of the E horizon; it is hereafter referred to as the E(?) horizon. This horizon could also have been modified by postburial diagenesis. The B horizon has a distinct reddish hue and shows blocky ped structure with few weakly developed argillans. The C horizon is structureless at the top and grades downward into cross-bedded sandstone. Weakly adhesive glaebules and mottles are mostly concentrated in a thin zone as much as 50 cm thick near the base of the B horizon (Fig. 10). A very coarse, reticulate pattern of mottling is present throughout the profile.

The contact between the basal Cretaceous conglomerate and the paleosol is sharp and irregular. Locally, the top of the paleosol has been deeply scoured, and the profile described here seems to represent the maximum preserved in the area. The overlying Tuscaloosa sediments consist of discoid, imbricated chert and quartz gravel interbedded with fine to medium sand. Thin and irregular hematite-cemented beds are contained in the conglomerate; these generally follow, but do not conform to, the erosional unconformity between the paleosol and the basal Tuscaloosa (Fig. 9).

The textural, chemical, and mineralogical properties of the Shady Grove profile show typical pedologic distribution (Fig. 11). As in the Columbus paleosol, clay-size material is concentrated in the B_t horizon. The silt content is more variable but has a distinct maximum in the E(?) horizon.

The profile shows little geochemical differentiation. There is a small increase in silica near the base of the B horizon (see Table 1). Iron oxide shows a significant increase from the E(?) horizon due to illuviation or in situ formation. Alumina has an inverse relationship with iron oxide and is at a maximum in the surface horizon of the profile. Alkalis and alkaline earths are present in very small amounts throughout and show little variation.

Kaolinite is the predominant clay in both the B and C horizons, and traces of halloysite are present throughout. The kaolinite is moderately well-crystallized throughout. Illite and traces of mixed-layer clays (smectite and illite) occur in the fine-textured surface horizon. Hematite occurs in the clay fraction of the B horizon, but it is absent from the clay fraction in both the E(?) and C horizons; iron compounds may be present in a poorly crystalline or amorphous form, particularly in the C horizon. Traces of quartz, cristobalite, and mixed-layer smectite and illite occur through the profile. Muscovite and quartz dominate the silt fraction and are especially abundant in the E(?) horizon.

The paleosol at Seven Pines (C, Fig. 1) provides a contrast-

Figure 10. Reticulate pattern of pale and iron-oxide enriched zones within the mottled zone of the Shady Grove profile. Most of the glaebules (nodules) are weakly adhesive and considerably smaller than the glaebules at Columbus, Georgia.

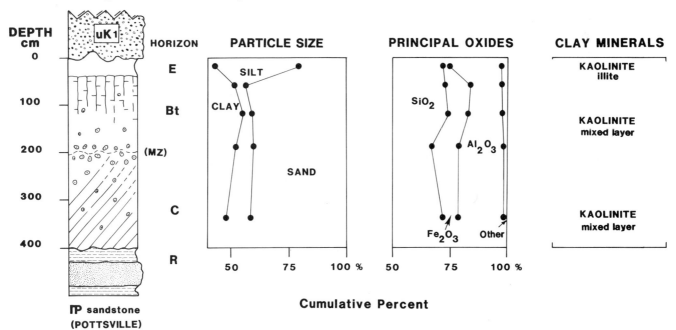

Figure 11. Generalized summary of relevant textural, chemical, and clay mineral data for the Shady Grove paleosol profile. UK_1 is the basal Cretaceous sedimentary deposit in northwestern Alabama. Data presentation comparable to Figure 6.

Figure 12. Seven Pines, Alabama, paleosol profile showing strong color change from B to C horizon. The top of the profile is just above the level of the geologist's hat. Abundant chert rubble is concentrated near the transition from the B to the C horizon.

ing example to those described from Shady Grove and Columbus. This profile is exposed along a country road near Little Bear Creek approximately 6 mi (10 km) northeast of Red Bay, Alabama. The parent material is Bangor Limestone (Mississippian) and consists of bioclastic, argillaceous limestone with interbedded chert lenses. The megascopic description for the profile (Fig. 12) is as follows:

Unconformity

0 to 180 cm, B horizon; clay, moderate red (5R 3/6); common, fine, distinct pale red (5R 6/2) mottles common in upper 50 cm; coarse to very coarse primsatic structure to locally massive; continuous argillans, dark red and distinct near top; few mangans(?); few small fragments of weathered chert; below 180 cm clay becomes dark yellowish brown (10YR 6/8), with few distinct pale red mottles; structure becomes massive to locally very coarse prismatic;

Diffuse, smooth boundary

180 to 450 cm, C horizon; clay, white (10YR 9/1), faint, pale red mottles common in a zone between 180 and 220 cm; massive throughout; few fossiliferous chert lenses as much as 5 cm thick in upper part, thin (<5 cm) ironstone (siderite) lenses in lower part; few fragments of weathered limestone throughout;

Clear, smooth to locally broken boundary

450⁺ cm, R horizon; light gray (10 YR 7/2), dense to medium crystalline to locally oolitic limestone; in part argillaceous; interbedded with light gray siltstone and a few, thin chert lenses.

The Seven Pines paleosol shows moderately well-developed horizon zonation. The B horizon has moderate to strong ped structure with well-developed argillans on ped faces (Fig. 13), is

Figure 13. Upper part of the Seven Pines profile illustrating the coarse prismatic ped structure that results from the clayey nature of the paleosol. Trowel = approximately 20 cm long.

weakly mottled, and contains small chert fragments. In contrast to the other two profiles, the paleosol at Seven Pines shows only a weakly developed mottled zone near the base of the B horizon. The C horizon is light colored and structureless, and grades down into thin-bedded argillaceous limestone containing fossiliferous chert lenses.

The contact between the paleosol and the basal Cretaceous sediments is sharp and irregular, but in most exposures the surface of the unconformity is obscured by thick colluvial deposits. At this locality, the overlying Tuscaloosa sediments consist mainly of thin- to medium-bedded fine quartz sand overlying a basal chert conglomerate.

Textural, chemical, and mineralogical data from the profile support the macroscopic horizon zonation seen on the outcrop (Fig. 14). Clay-size material is abundant in all horizons above the limestone and is most abundant near the top of the B horizon. The sand distribution is inversely proportional to that of the clay; the abundance of silt-size material is relatively uniform with depth but shows a slight decrease toward the bottom of the profile. The distribution of silica parallels that of clay. Iron oxide increases in abundance at the top of the B horizon; hematite occurs in the silt fraction of the B horizon. Alumina shows little variation overall but increases slightly near the middle of the B horizon. Alkalis and alkaline earths are largely absent in the solum but increase toward the base of the profile where calcium becomes abundant.

Moderately crystalline kaolinite is the dominant clay mineral in the B horizon; halloysite is a minor component near its base and in the C horizon. Smectite, some poorly crystalline kaolinite, and halloysite constitute nearly the entire clay-mineral assemblage in the C horizon. Small amounts of quartz and cristobalite occur throughout the profile, particularly in the lower part. Chlorite and illite with traces of kaolinite are the most abundant clay minerals in the C horizon.

DISCUSSION

All three paleosols exhibit distinctive morphologic features, with well-developed horizon zonation that is readily discernible in the field. In general, the macroscopic evidence of soil develop-

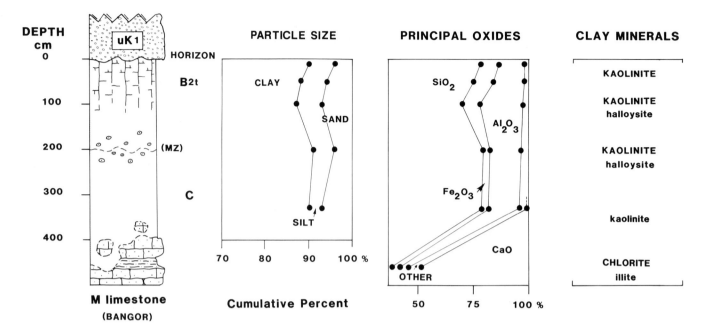

Figure 14. Generalized summary of textural, chemical, and clay mineral data from the Seven Pines paleosol profile. Erosional nature of contact between the overlying Cretaceous unit (uK_1) and the underlying Mississippian limestone is shown schematically. Data presentation is comparable to Figures 6 and 11.

ment includes ferruginous and clay-rich B horizons with structural development and argillans, the depth distribution and abundance of iron-rich nodules and mottles in the solum, and consistent color differences between soil horizons. Downward-branching structures and root mottles provide evidence of biogenic activity as a soil-forming factor in addition to physical and chemical weathering. Original profile characteristics, such as horizon thickness and lateral continuity, are difficult to reconstruct because of extensive erosion. The paleosols are truncated, and organic A horizons are not evident or preserved. In most cases, the zone of weathering ranges from 3 to 10 m in thickness from the top of the B horizon to the parent material.

The three profiles vary considerably in their morphologic and geochemical characteristics. These variations are thought to reflect differences in parent material and topography during pedogenesis, but other factors, such as duration and intensity of weathering, may be important in reconstructing the paleoenvironmental conditions responsible for paleosol formation (see Jenny, 1941).

Paleosol morphology

The clay-rich paleosol on argillaceous limestone at Seven Pines shows a higher degree of ped organization and thicker argillan development than do the other profiles, which formed on coarser and more acidic parent material. The clay coatings in the B horizon at Seven Pines are also better formed and more contin-

uous than are those on the other two profiles. These argillans provide physical evidence that clay translocation or illuviation was a factor in the soil-forming process. Their exact significance is uncertain without more detailed micromorphological study because the oriented silt or clay coatings may represent only a small part of the total clay in an argillic horizon (Fitzpatrick, 1980; Yaalon, 1971).

In contrast, the B horizon on gneiss at Columbus has mostly coarse and weakly developed peds with thin, discontinuous coatings of silt and clay. This relatively weak ped development may be a function of the crystal grain size and bedrock composition, or alternatively, of more intense bioturbation during weathering (Birkeland, 1984). In addition, the weakly developed argillans in the Columbus profile are not consistent with the amount of clay in the B horizon (see Fig. 2), and in situ clay formation may have been a significant factor in soil development (Oertel, 1968). The grain-size data support this interpretation because the upper part of the profile contains more clay than would be accounted for by the decomposition of feldspars and mafic minerals in the parent gneiss.

By comparison, the Shady Grove profile has gross morphologic features that are intermediate between those observed at Columbus and at Seven Pines. The sandstone parent material contains a considerable amount of silt- and clay-size material, which undoubtedly influenced the consistency and moderate degree of ped development in the B horizon. As at Seven Pines, the thin argillans indicate some clay illuviation during weathering;

however, the distribution of clay in the B horizon is more similar to that in the Columbus profile, and in situ clay formation also could have been an important process.

The origin of the silt-rich surface horizon at Shady Grove is not fully understood. This light-colored material may be a true eluvial horizon (E) or part of the original surface horizon (A). This latter hypothesis seems unlikely given the gradational contact between the silt unit and the underlying B horizon of the paleosol. Whatever its origin, the silt unit seems to have been weathered at the same time as the underlying sandstone.

The nature of the mottled zone in each profile indicates soil–ground water interactions during weathering. Some factors influencing the development of mottles and nodules in soils include the permeability of the soil, composition of the parent material, local topography and drainage, and climate, especially rainfall and its seasonality (Duchaufour, 1982; Hallsworth and Costin, 1953).

The Columbus paleosol has an exceptionally conspicuous mottled zone at the base of the B horizon with glaebules and mottles organized in a vermiform pattern. It can be traced continuously and appears to be more or less parallel to the overlying B horizon. The zone of closely packed glaebules at the contact between the solum and the saprolite resembles that found in certain lateritic soils in Africa (see McFarlane, 1976). These soils form in many different environments but are common in areas with marked seasonal or intermittent ground-water fluctuations. Similar paleohydrologic conditions were probably responsible for the Columbus profile. The distribution and abundance of iron in the zone implies long-term ground-water fluctuations with vertical variations of as much as 2 m. The lateral continuity of the mottled horizon suggests that it formed beneath a relatively low-relief land surface with impeded drainage. The profile is most likely polygenetic because the isolated nodules found in the B horizon indicate some sesquioxide enrichment by downward migration of soil solutions (Ollier, 1959).

A polygenetic origin for the profile is also supported in part by the micromorphological data from the glaebules. The exact origin of these features is uncertain, but limited interpretations may be made from their fabric and mineral composition. The nodules in the B horizon that show an undifferentiated fabric may represent accumulation of soluble constituents through either diffusion or recrystallization (Brewer, 1964). The iron is most likely derived from in situ decomposition of ferromagnesian minerals in the gneiss. The presence of hematite in some nodules supports this mechanism of formation. Alternatively, some glaebules in the mottled zone exhibit a concentric fabric with thin, distinct laminae. These concretionary structures suggest that each lamina was deposited during alternating wetting and drying of the soil, probably due to a fluctuating ground-water table. Iron may be transported as soluble ferrous hydroxides in wet periods and precipitate as ferric hydroxides or oxides during desiccation (Nahon and others, 1980). The occurrence of goethite in some concretions in the mottled zone supports a more hydrated origin for these features.

In contrast, mottles and glaebules are only moderately well developed in the paleosols at Shady Grove and Seven Pines. The Shady Grove profile shows a distinct zone of mottles and glaebules at the base of the B horizon. Glaebules are small and only weakly adhesive; the organization and segregation of individual mottles are not nearly as extensive as at Columbus.

The thin mottled zone at Shady Grove suggests freely drained conditions, probably due to the permeable nature of the parent material. Vertical ground-water fluctuations were probably minimal and of shorter duration than at Columbus. The very coarse reticulate pattern of mottling that pervades the entire profile probably represents lateral ground-water movement under some hydrologic gradient, either during or following soil profile development. The original geomorphic surface is difficult to reconstruct, but it appears to have been undulating and freely drained, perhaps similar to the low-relief topography found in the area today.

The paleosol at Seven Pines shows only weak development of a mottled zone. This profile may have formed in a poorly drained setting with impeded ground-water flow. The clear, smooth boundary between the B and C horizons supports this interpretation and suggests that ground-water fluctuations were negligible, probably the least of all three paleosols. The distribution and amount of iron in the B horizon indicates that surface oxidation was an important process; but the light-colored, gleyed C horizon more reasonably evolved under reducing conditions resulting from permanent ground-water saturation. The depletion of iron in this horizon relative to the solum is consistent with an interpretation of impeded drainage in the subsurface, as is the abundance of smectite.

The weathering profiles and residuum on limestone are associated with a complex paleokarst land surface. Reconstruction of the original geomorphic surface is constrained by subsequent erosion and poor exposure of the profiles. The paleokarst surface seems to have varied considerably, from areas of rocky pinnacles with little or no residuum to relatively flat land surfaces with moderately thick soil profiles, possibly similar to areas of low-lying cockpit karst (Tricart and Cailleux, 1972).

Profile chemistry and mineralogy

The geochemical and mineralogic properties of these three paleosols are thought to result primarily from pedogenic alteration of the exposed bedrock surfaces. Primary minerals in the parent material have been altered to secondary clay minerals in the solum, especially the 1:1 lattice varieties. Except for concentrations of iron compounds, most soluble constituents have been leached from the upper part of the profiles. In contrast, the C horizons contain various 2:1 lattice minerals, as well as relative concentrations of alkalis and alkaline earths. These depth-function relationships indicate that two principal geochemical processes—kaolinization of the parent material and oxidation-reduction reactions involving iron compounds—were responsible for profile differentiation.

Kaolinization in soils involves complex mineral-water interactions that are well documented (Dixon, 1977; Millot, 1970). In general, the process occurs readily in oxidizing environments where precipitation exceeds evaporation, and soluble bases, such as alkali and alkaline earths, have been removed in solution (Grim, 1951, 1968; Keller, 1970). Kaolinite formation is enhanced by the presence of organic acids and weathering of permeable rocks rich in aluminum silicates. Temperature and duration of weathering are also important factors because the rate of base release increases with temperature but decreases with time (McClelland, 1950). Halloysite is often associated with kaolinite in modern soils (Loughnan, 1969). This hydrated 1:1 lattice mineral has a crystal structure similar to that of kaolinite and may form over long periods in poorly drained soils or in humid environments (Bates, 1952). Mohr and Van Baren (1954) reported that halloysite is a characteristic clay mineral in red soils formed on limestones in tropical regions, but it also forms in other soils and climates. Profile desiccation causes halloysite to dehydrate irreversibly to metahalloysite, an intermediate species similar to disordered kaolinite. It is possible that much of the kaolinite in the paleosols, especially the Shady Grove profile, may have formed from halloysite after profile truncation or climate change.

Clay-mineral alterations from 2:1 lattice clays to halloysite or kaolinite, such as those inferred for these profiles, probably occurred by mineral transformation or neoformation (Duchaufour, 1982; Valeton, 1972). The first process involves alteration of primary silicates or clay minerals to secondary clays by the loss of silica (e.g., smectite $\rightarrow$ kaolinite). In the second process, new minerals are formed or recombined by the reaction of amorphous colloids or ions in solution (e.g., Al-hydroxide + silicic acid $\rightarrow$ kaolinite). Kaolinite and other clay minerals also may be inherited from the parent material or concentrated as weathering residua.

The 1:1 lattice clay minerals in the B horizons could have formed by either or both processes and may in part be inherited in the Shady Grove profile. Kaolinite is a relatively stable clay mineral, and its abundance in the B horizons indicates that the profiles evolved over a considerable time period, or at least over sufficient time to nullify the chemical imprint of the parent material (Chesworth, 1973).

It is difficult to determine precise pathways of clay-mineral alteration, particularly in profiles older than the Quaternary. However, some assertions are made on the basis of the clay mineral distributions. The 2:1 clay minerals in the C horizons are interpreted as kaolinite precursors (see Jackson and others, 1948) and are thought to be transition products derived by the weathering of primary minerals. Differences in mineral assemblages in the C horizons are related primarily to the composition and texture of the parent material. The smectite, vermiculite, and illite in the Columbus profile could have formed in several ways through alteration of the plagioclase, biotite, and other ferromagnesian minerals in the gneiss (Borchardt, 1977; Douglas, 1977; Ismail, 1970). Some of the kaolinite in the Shady Grove profile could be derived from weathering of mica in the silt fraction (Fanning and Keramidas, 1977) and from mixed-layer clay minerals in the clay fraction. The smectite at the base of the Shady Grove profile is most likely derived by degradation of chlorite inherited from the limestone parent material (see Barnhisel, 1977).

The distribution of iron compounds is related primarily to redox potential of the soil environment (Ollier, 1969), but chelation and relative removal of other cations may have been important. The greater concentration of iron oxides and hydroxides in the B horizons suggests more oxidizing conditions in the solum than in the subsurface. Eh-pH conditions are difficult to reconstruct, but the B horizons were probably more acidic and of a higher Eh than the C horizons (Birkeland, 1984). In the Columbus profile, iron may have been oxidized in the solum by hydrolysis during clay-mineral genesis. Some of the iron in the solum may be derived from ferrous compounds that were chelated by organic matter and transported in solution from surface horizons (Fitzpatrick, 1980). Illuviation and oxidation of iron could have been important in the formation of the B horizons at Shady Grove and Seven Pines, given the red hue and chroma of the argillans.

Most of the iron in the profiles is thought to be concentrated by pedogenic processes. Because the profiles are truncated by a regional unconformity, it is possible that some iron accumulated through ground-water flow after burial by the Tuscaloosa sediments (Pavich, 1974). However, the zones of color banding (i.e., ferruginous B horizons and mottled zones) are essentially parallel and do not cross the unconformity that truncates the paleosols. Furthermore, none of the paleosols exhibits the pervasive red coloration, iron pans, and liesegang banding that typify surface weathering of the overlying Mesozoic and Cenozoic sediments in the region.

As described earlier, the mottled zone in the Columbus profile probably developed in a fluctuating ground-water regime with alternating conditions of oxidation and reduction near the original ground surface. Iron oxidation to form glaebules and mottles would have occurred in an aerobic condition, with some iron removed as ferrous compounds during subsequent waterlogging (McFarlane, 1976). The mottled zone may be a horizon of absolute iron accumulation formed by both lateral ground-water movement and capillary rise (Sirarjasingham and others, 1962). Reduction and removal of iron are thought to be dominant processes in the formation of the C horizon at Columbus and Shady Grove.

Weathering environment and climate

Our interpretation of the paleoweathering conditions implied by the morphological and geochemical data is based largely on analogy with modern soils and their environments of formation. The paleosols are difficult to place into modern soil classification systems for two reasons: because the profiles are incomplete, with part or all of their surface horizons missing due to erosion, and because some part of the present geochemistry and mineralogy may result from several episodes of weathering or diagenetic change.

Diagenetic effects may include physical compaction and desiccation, long-term transformation of ferric gels and geothite to limonite and hematite, silicification, and clay-mineral genesis (Keller, 1962; Retallack, 1981; Roeschmann, 1971). Disrupted peds, occasional skew planes, and slickensides occur in all paleosols examined and attest to compaction by overlying sediments. The irreversible hardening of iron glaebules in the Columbus profile to form plinthite and ironstone suggests diagenetic change due to desiccation. The small amounts of cristobalite in the clay fractions may be silica released during weathering of primary silicate minerals in excess of that necessary to form kaolinite (Oehler, 1976; Wilding and others, 1977). Other than the inferred transformation of halloysite to kaolinite during profile desiccation, there is little evidence to indicate clay mineral diagenesis.

On the basis of morphologic and geochemical characteristics of modern analogs, the profiles at Columbus and Shady Grove resemble oxisols or ultisols; the paleosol at Seven Pines on limestone may be an alfisol, possibly a type of rhodoxeralf (see Buol and others, 1973; Soil Survey Staff, 1975; Duchaufour, 1982). The soils are strongly leached with B horizons rich in sesquioxides of iron and/or aluminum and are devoid of organic matter, soluble bases, and primary silicates. Both in situ and illuvial formation of clay occur, and the B horizons usually contain quartz and 1:1 clay minerals. Such soils are found in wet equatorial to subtropical wet-dry climates under original vegetation ranging from rain forest to savanna. Similar deeply weathered soils also occur in a wide range of temperate latitudes, include the southeastern United States, where they may have developed over a long period of time (Buol and others, 1973; Loughnan, 1969; Grant, 1964). Although clay-mineral and oxide assemblages are not always definitive indicators of paleoclimate (Singer, 1980), the abundance of kaolinite in these Cretaceous paleosols strongly suggests that they formed under warm, humid conditions. This interpretation is consistent with conclusions from previously cited research on Cretaceous paleosols in the southeastern United States and elsewhere on the North American continent.

The duration of weathering is not known. Because the paleosols are truncated by Tuscaloosa sediments, they have a minimum age of late Cenomanian. Soil development and inferred ground-surface stability most likely occurred on vegetated landscapes during either a still stand or slowly rising sea level. The maximum age of the profiles may be approximated from inferred strand line positions during middle Cretaceous time. Weathering could have started after the drop in sea level at the beginning of the Cenomanian (Fig. 15). Thus, the available time for weathering could have been as much as 4 m.y., according to the eustatic sea-level curve of Ziegler (1982). This amount of time does not seem unreasonable when compared with the formation of Tertiary paleosols in Africa and Australia (Goudie, 1973; McFarlane, 1976; Stephens, 1971).

Paleogeographic and climatic reconstructions based on other data for the Cretaceous support our interpretaton that the paleosols formed in warm, humid to temperate environments.

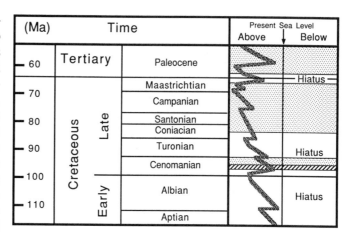

Figure 15. Coastal onlap curve for middle and Late Cretaceous time, based on Atlantic margin seismic stratigraphy by Exxon Production Research Company (after Ziegler, 1982). Hachured area is the inferred weathering period.

During the middle Cretaceous, the southeastern United States was at approximately 30°N latitude, or about the same position as today (Hospers and van Andel, 1968; Smith and Briden, 1977). The Gulf of Mexico, the western extension of the Tethys sea, was nearly open and was connected to the Western Interior seaway. This configuration and the apparent proximity of the study area to the sea would have favored a relatively equable and humid maritime climate. Models of oceanic and atmospheric circulation place the region in the subtropical anticyclonic belt between tropical easterlies and midlatitude westerlies (Lloyd, 1982). It was adjacent to the zone of intertropical convergence during summer months with an inflow of warm tropical air masses. Paleotemperature data for surface and bottom waters based on oxygen isotopes from various taxonomic groups indicate that mean annual temperatures may have been as much as 15°C higher worldwide than they are now (Savin, 1982).

Paleobotanical studies from Coastal Plain deposits located several hundred kilometers from the paleosol localities suggest a warm, humid climate during Early Cretaceous time (Smiley, 1967). The floras were predominantly tropical, characterized by assemblages of ferns, gymnosperms, and cycadophytes. Angiosperms became increasingly abundant during the Late Cretaceous and apparently represent cooler, and possibly drier, subtropical conditions (Darrah, 1960; J. Wolfe, oral communication, 1986).

Several authors have compiled terrestrial paleoclimatic indicators for the Cretaceous, including the global distributions of bauxite, coal, evaporite minerals, carbonates, and red beds (Bardossy, 1982; Frakes, 1979; Habicht, 1979). The zone of laterites and bauxites occurs mainly in paleolatitudes between about 5°S and 30°N (Fig. 16). These weathering products are interpreted to have formed in warm, humid environments and, with the exception of bauxite, are similar to the paleosols described in this study. There is no direct means to judge the synchroneity of paleosol

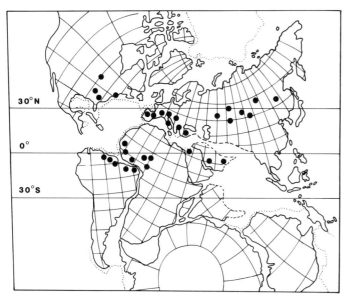

Figure 16. Paleogeographic map of the Earth during middle Cretaceous time, showing the distribution of lateritic paleosols and bauxite. Data from Bardossy (1982), Habicht (1979), and Nicholas and Bildgen (1979).

development over these widely spaced geographic regions, but we believe that intense weathering probably occurred throughout much of Cretaceous time, where land surfaces were relatively stable and well vegetated.

CONCLUSIONS

The Cretaceous paleosols from the southeastern United States are remnants of an ancient land surface that weathered prior to their truncation and burial by continental sediments of the Tuscaloosa Formation or Group. The profiles occupy the same position relative to the regional unconformity and may be facies of a widespread pedostratigraphic unit or geosol (Morrison, 1967; North American Commission on Stratigraphic Nomenclature, 1983). The paleosols have similar physical and geochemical properties despite differences in parent material. Variations in profile development seem to be related closely to paleogeomorphic setting.

The profiles are similar to intensely leached soils in modern tropical to subtropical climates, and, by analogy, probably formed under similar conditions. Diagenetic processes have superficially modified the profiles but seem to have had little overall effect on the present composition of the paleosols. The time represented by soil formation is uncertain, but weathering may have occurred over several million years. Because these paleosols represent a hiatus with no apparent stratigraphic equivalent in the region, they are the best record of the paleoenvironment and climate during a considerable time interval. As such, they are an important means of local and regional correlation.

The transition from weathering to erosion and deposition of the Tuscaloosa sediments represents a fundamental change in tectonic setting and probably resulted from a change in base level, or uplift in the southern Appalachians. Regional uplift is thought to be the principal factor influencing widespread clastic sedimentation during the late Cenomanian (Reinhardt and others, 1986). In either case, the effective change in regional base level provided sufficient gradient for the erosion of parts of the paleosols and the associated land surfaces in conjunction with the development of a major clastic wedge (Tuscaloosa Formation or Group) in the eastern and central Gulf Coastal Plain.

Further research is necessary to understand better the lateral continuity and temporal relationships of the paleosols. Similarly, more analytical data are needed to more closely define variations in the development and preservation of paleosol profiles, both locally and regionally. Because Cretaceous paleosols are present over such a broad geographic region, continued study of these profiles will enhance our knowledge of the late Mesozoic paleogeography and tectonic history of North America.

REFERENCES CITED

Adams, G. I., Butts, C., Stephenson, L. W., and Cooke, C. W., 1926, Geology of Alabama: University, Alabama, Geological Survey of Alabama, Special Report No. 14, 312 p.

Austin, G. S., 1970, Weathering of the Sioux Quartzite near New Ulm, Minnesota, as related to Cretaceous climates: Journal of Sedimentary Petrology, v. 40, p. 184–193.

Bardossy, G., 1982, Karst bauxites; Bauxite deposits on carbonate rocks: Amsterdam, Elsevier, 441 p.

Barnhisel, R. I., 1977, Chlorites and hydroxy interlayered vermiculite and smectite, *in* Dixon, J. B., and Weed, S. B., eds., Minerals in soil environments: Madison, Wisconsin, Soil Science Society of America, p. 331–356.

Bates, T. F., 1952, Interrelationships of structure and genesis in the kaolinite group; Problems of clay and laterite genesis: American Institute of Mining and Metallurgy, p. 144–153.

Birkeland, P. W., 1984, Soils and geomorphology: New York, Oxford University Press, 285 p.

Blank, H. R., 1978, Fossil laterite on bedrock in Brooklyn, New York: Geology, v. 6, p. 21–24.

Borchardt, G. A., 1977, Montmorillonite and other smectite minerals, *in* Dixon, J. B., and Weed, S. B., eds., Minerals in soil environments: Madison, Wisconsin, Soil Science Society of America, p. 293–330.

Brewer, R., 1964, Fabric and mineral analysis of soils: New York, John Wiley & Sons, 470 p.

Buol, S. W., Hole, F. D., McCracken, R. J., 1973, Soil genesis and classification: Ames, Iowa State University Press, 360 p.

Chesworth, W., 1973, The parent rock effect in the genesis of soil: Geoderma, v. 10, p. 215–225.

Darrah, W. C., 1960, Principles of paleobotany: New York, Roland Press Co., 232 p.

Dixon, J. B., 1977, Kaolinite and serpentine group minerals, *in* Dixon, J. B., and Weed, S. B., eds., Minerals in soil environments: Madison, Wisconsin, Soil Science Society of America, p. 357–403.

Douglas, L. A., 1977, Vermiculites, *in* Dixon, J. B., and Weed, S. B., eds., Minerals in soil environments: Madison, Wisconsin, Soil Science Society of America, p. 259–292.

Drennen, C. W., 1950, Geology of the Piedmont–Coastal plain contact in eastern Alabama and western Georgia [M.S. thesis]: Tuscaloosa, University of Alabama, 42 p.

Duchaufour, P., 1982, Pedology: London, George Allen and Unwin, 448 p.

Dury, G. W., 1971, Relict deep weathering and duricrusting in relation to paleoenvironments of middle latitudes: Geographical Journal, v. 137, p. 511–522.

Fanning, D. S., and Keramidas, V. Z., 1977, Micas, *in* Dixon, J. B., and Weed, S. B., eds., Minerals in soil environments: Madison, Wisconsin, Soil Science Society of America, p. 195–258.

Fitzpatrick, E. A., 1980, Soils: London, Longman, 353 p.

—— , 1984, Micromorphology of soils: New York, Chapman and Hall, 433 p.

Frakes, L. A., 1979, Climates throughout geologic time: Amsterdam, Elsevier, 310 p.

Freeman, R. F., 1981, The interpretation of the occurrence and the chemical analysis of the Columbus laterite: unpublished manuscript, Columbus, Georgia, Columbus College, 19 p.

Goldich, S. S., 1938, A study of rock weathering: Journal of Geology, v. 46, p. 17–58.

Goudie, A., 1973, Duricrusts in tropical and subtropical landscapes: Oxford, Clarendon Press, 174 p.

Grant, W. H., 1964, Chemical weathering of biotite-plagioclase gneiss: Clays and Clay Minerals, v. 12, p. 455–464.

Grim, R. E., 1951, The depositional environments of red and green shales: Journal of Sedimentary Petrology, v. 21, no. 4, p. 226–232.

—— , 1968, Clay mineralogy: New York, McGraw-Hill, 525 p.

Habicht, J.K.A., 1979, Paleoclimate, paleomagnetism, and continental drift: American Association of Petroleum Geologists Studies in Geology No. 9, 31 p.

Hallsworth, E. G., and Costin, A. B., 1953, Studies in pedogenesis in New South Wales; 4, The ironstone soils: Journal of Soil Science, v. 4, p. 24–45.

Hanley, T. B., 1986, Petrology and structural geology Uchee Belt rocks in Columbus, Georgia, and Phenix City, Alabama, *in* Neathery, T. L., ed., Southeastern Section of the Geological Society of America: Boulder, Colorado, Geological Society of America, Centennial Field Guide v. 5, p. 297–300.

Hospers, J., and van Andel, S. I., 1968, Paleomagnetic data from Europe and North Atlantic ocean: Tectonophysics, v. 6, p. 475–490.

Hosterman, J. W., and Whitlow, S. I., 1983, Clay mineralogy of Devonian shales in the Appalachian Basin: U.S. Geological Survey Professional Paper 1298, 31 p.

Ismail, F. T., 1970, Biotite weathering and clay formation in arid and humid regions, California: Soil Science, v. 109, p. 257–261.

Jackson, M. L., Tyler, S. A., Willes, A. L., Bourbeau, G. A., and Pennington, R. P., 1948, Weathering sequences of clay size minerals in soils and sediments: Journal of Physical Colloid Chemistry, v. 52, p. 1237–1260.

Jenny, H., 1941, Factors of soil formation: New York, McGraw-Hill, 281 p.

Keller, W. D., 1962, Diagenesis in clay minerals; A review; Clays and clay minerals: Proceedings of the Eleventh National Conference on Clays and Clay Minerals: Clays and Clay Minerals Monograph No. 13, Oxford, Pergamon Press, p. 136–157.

—— , 1970, Environmental aspects of clay minerals: Journal of Sedimentary Petrology, v. 40, p. 788–813.

Krumbein, W. C., and Pettijohn, F. J., 1938, Manual of sedimentary petrography: New York, Appleton-Century-Croft, 549 p.

Lloyd, C. R., 1982, The mid-Cretaceous earth; Paleogeography; Ocean circulation and temperature; Atmospheric circulation: Journal of Geology, v. 90, p. 393–413.

Loughnan, F. C., 1969, Chemical weathering of silicate minerals: New York, Elsevier, 154 p.

Marcher, M. V., and Stearns, R. G., 1962, Tuscaloosa Formation in Tennessee: Geological Society of America Bulletin, v. 73, p. 1365–1386.

McClelland, J. E., 1950, The effects of time, temperature, and particle size on the release of bases from some common soil-forming minerals of different crystal structures: Soil Science Society of America Proceedings, v. 15, p. 301–307.

McFarlane, M. J., 1976, Laterite and landscape: London, Academic Press, 151 p.

McGrain, P., 1970, Economic geology of Marshall County, Kentucky: Kentucky Geological Survey series 10, County Report 5, 33 p.

Mellon, F. F., 1937, The Little Bear residium: Mississippi State Geological Survey Bulletin, v. 34, 36 p.

Millot, G., 1970, Geology of clays: New York, Springer, 429 p.

Miser, H. D., 1921, Mineral resources of the Waynesboro Quadrangle, Tennessee: Tennessee Geological Survey Bulletin 26, 171 p.

Mohr, E.C.J., and Van Baren, F. A., 1954, Tropical soils: New York, Uitgeverij W. Van Hoeve, Interscience Publishers, 498 p.

Morrison, R. B., 1967, Principles of Quaternary soil stratigraphy, *in* Morrison, R. B., and Wright, H. E., eds., Quaternary soils: International Association of Quaternary Research (INQUA), 9th Congress, 1965, Proceedings, v. 9, p. 3–69.

Munsell Soil Color Charts, 1954: Baltimore, Maryland, Munsell Color Company, 16 p.

Nahon, D., Carozzi, A. V., and Parron, C., 1980, Lateritic weathering as a mechanism for the generation of ferruginous ooids: Journal of Sedimentary Petrology, v. 50, p. 1287–1298.

Nicholas, J., and Bildgen, P., 1979, Relations between the location of karst bauxites in the North Hemisphere, the global tectonics and the climatic variations during geological time: Palaeogeography, Palaeoclimatology, and Palaeoecology, v. 29, p. 205–239.

North American Commission on Stratigraphic Nomenclature, 1983, North American stratigraphic code: American Association of Petroleum Geologists Bulletin, v. 67, p. 841–875.

Oehler, J. H., 1976, Hydrothermal crystallization of silica gel: Geological Society of America Bulletin, v. 87, p. 1143–1152.

Oertel, A. C., 1968, Some observations incompatible with clay illuviation: Ninth International Congress on Soil Science, Transactions, v. 5, p. 481–488.

Ollier, C. D., 1959, A two-cycle theory of tropical pedology: Journal of Soil Science, v. 10, p. 137–148.

—— , 1969, Weathering: New York, Elsevier, 304 p.

Pavich, M. J., 1974, A study of saprolite buried beneath the Atlantic Coastal Plain in South Carolina [Ph.D. thesis]: Baltimore, Maryland, Johns Hopkins University, 133 p.

Peace, R. R., 1963, Geology and ground water resources of Franklin County, Alabama: University, Alabama, Geological Survey of Alabama Bulletin 72, 55 p.

Pryor, W. A., and Ross, C. A., 1962, Geology of the Illinois parts of the Cairo, Lacenter, and Thebes Quadrangles: Illinois State Geological Survey Circular 332, 39 p.

Reinhardt, J., 1980, Tuscaloosa Formation (Cenomanian) from eastern Alabama to Central Georgia; Its stratigraphic identity and sedimentology: Houston, Texas, Gulf Coast Section, Society of Economic Paleontologists and Mineralogists, Research Conference, Program and Abstracts, p. 25–26.

Reinhardt, J., and Gibson, T. G., 1981, Upper Cretaceous and Lower Tertiary geology of the Chattahoochee River Valley, western Georgia and eastern Alabama: Georgia Geological Society, 16th Annual Field Trip Guidebook, 88 p.

Reinhardt, J., Smith, L. W., and King, D. T., Jr., 1986, Sedimentary facies of the Upper Cretaceous Tuscaloosa Group in eastern Alabama, *in* Neathery, T. L., ed., Southeastern Section of the Geological Society of America: Boulder, Colorado, Geological Society of America, Centennial Field Guide v. 5, p. 363–367.

Retallack, G. J., 1981, Fossil soils; Indicators of ancient terrestrial environments, *in* Kiklas, K. J., ed., Paleobotany, paleoecology, and evolution: New York, Praeger, v. 1, p. 55–102.

Roeschmann, G., 1971, Problems concerning investigations of paleosols in older sedimentary rocks, demonstrated by the example of Wurzelboden of the Carboniferous system, *in* Yaalon, D. H., ed., Paleopedology; Origin, nature, and dating of paleosols: Jerusalem, Israel Universities Press, p. 311–320.

Russell, I. C., 1889, Subaerial decay of rocks and origin of the red color of certain formations: U.S. Geological Survey Bulletin 52, 65 p.

Savin, S. M., 1982, Stable isotopes in climatic reconstructions, *in* Climate in earth history; Studies in geophysics: Washington, D. C., National Academy Press, p. 164–171.

Schamel, S., Hanley, T. B., and Sears, J. W.., 1980, Geology of the Pine Mountain Window and adjacent terranes in the Piedmont province of Georgia and Alabama: University, Alabama, Geological Society of America, Southeastern Section Guidebook, Alabama Geological Society, 69 p.

Sigleo, W. R., and Reinhardt, J., 1985, Cretaceous paleosols from the eastern Gulf Coastal Plain: Southeastern Geology, v. 25, p. 213–223.

Singer, A., 1975, A Cretaceous laterite in the Negev Desert, southern Israel: Geological Magazine, v. 112, p. 151–162.

—— , 1980, The paleoclimatic interpretation of clay minerals in soils and weathering profiles: Earth Science Reviews, v. 15, p. 303–326.

Sirarjasingham, S., Alexander, L. T., Cady, J. G., and Cline, M. G., 1962, Laterite: Advances in Agronomy, v. 14, p. 1–60.

Smiley, C. J., 1967, Paleoclimate interpretations of some Mesozoic floral sequences: American Association of Petroleum Geologists Bulletin, v. 51, p. 849–863.

Smith, A. G., and Briden, J. C., 1977, Mesozoic and Cenozoic paleocontinental maps: Cambridge, Cambridge University Press, 63 p.

Smith, L. W., 1984, Depositional setting and stratigraphy of the Tuscaloosa Formation, central Alabama to west-central Georgia [M.S. thesis]: Auburn, Alabama, Auburn University, 125 p.

Soil Survey Staff, 1975, Soil Survey Manual: U.S. Department of Agriculture, Agricultural Handbook No. 436, 754 p.

Stearns, R. G., 1957, Cretaceous, Paleocene, and Lower Eocene geologic history of the northern Mississippi embayment: Geological Society of America Bulletin, v. 68, p. 1077–1100.

Stephens, C. G., 1971, Laterite and silcrete in Australia: Goederma, v. 5, p. 5–52.

Sutton, A. H., 1931, A pre-Cretaceous soil horizon in western Kentucky: American Journal of Science, 5th series, v. 11, p. 449–452.

Tricart, J., and Cailleux, A., 1972, Introduction to climatic geomorphology: London, Longman, 295 p.

Valeton, I., 1972, Bauxites: Amsterdam, Elsevier, 226 p.

Welch, S. W., 1958, Stratigraphy of upper Mississippian rocks above the Tuscumbia Limestone in northern Alabama and northeastern Mississippi: U.S. Geological Survey, Oil and Gas Investigations Chart OC 58.

—— , 1959, Mississippian rocks of the northern part of the Black Warrior Basin, Alabama and Mississippi: U.S. Geological Survey, Oil and Gas Investigations Chart OC-62.

Wilding, L. P., Smeck, W. E., and Dress, L. R., 1977, Silica in soils; Quartz, cristobalite, tridymite, and opal, *in* Dixon, J. B., and Weed, S. B., eds., Minerals in soil environments: Madison, Wisconsin, Soil Science Society of America, p. 471–552.

Yaalon, D. H., 1971, Soil forming processes in time and space, *in* Yaalon, D. H., ed., Paleopedology; Origin, nature, and dating of paleosols: Jerusalem, International Society of Soil Science and Israel Universities Press, p. 29–39.

Ziegler, P. A., 1982, Geological atlas of western and central Europe: New York, Elsevier, 112 p.

MANUSCRIPT APPROVED BY THE DIRECTOR ON MARCH 5, 1987 FOR PUBLICATION OUTSIDE THE U.S. GEOLOGICAL SURVEY.

MANUSCRIPT ACCEPTED BY THE SOCIETY JULY 1, 1987

Geological Society of America
Special Paper 216
1988

Pedofacies analysis; A new approach to reconstructing ancient fluvial sequences

Mary J. Kraus
Department of Geological Sciences
University of Colorado
Boulder, Colorado 80309-0250

Thomas M. Brown
U.S. Geological Survey
MS 913, Box 25046
Denver Federal Center
Denver, Colorado 80225

ABSTRACT

Paleosols formed on overbank deposits of the lower Eocene Willwood Formation in the Bighorn Basin, Wyoming, can be differentiated on the basis of pedogenic maturity. The least mature soils generally formed close to the channel margin where sediment accumulation rates were rapid, whereas the most mature soils developed on distal flood plains where accumulation rates were significantly slower. The term pedofacies is introduced to delimit laterally contiguous bodies of sedimentary rock that differ in their ancient soil attributes as a result of distance from areas of relatively rapid sedimentation.

Vertical successions of Willwood overbank deposits show three orders of pedofacies sequences. Simple sequences consist of one or more paleosols bounded below and above by crevasse-splay deposits. They were generated by slow and sporadic alluviation and soil modification that were periodically interrupted by more rapid crevasse-splay deposition. On a larger scale, compound pedofacies sequences are composed of multistory paleosols sandwiched between channel sandstones. Pedogenic maturity of the paleosols progressively increases and then decreases upward in response to episodic channel avulsion. Development of compound and simple pedofacies sequences was largely controlled by local patterns of deposition that produced vertical variability in the rate of sediment accumulation.

Superimposed on these smaller-scale cycles are pedofacies megasequences that are hundreds of meters thick. Megasequences show a distinct upward change in the overall maturity of their constituent compound sequences. They provide evidence for changes in the rate of sediment accumulation produced by allocyclic processes including varied tectonic activity. Comparison between Willwood deposits in the northern and central parts of the Bighorn Basin reveals that areally differing sediment accumulation rates, and thereby basin subsidence rates, can also be interpreted from large-scale pedofacies sequences.

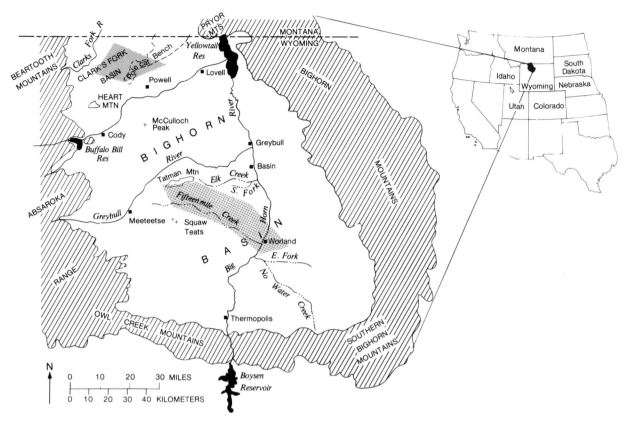

Figure 1. Map of Bighorn Basin in northwest Wyoming, showing the two principal study areas (shaded).

INTRODUCTION

During the past 20 years, facies analysis has been widely used to reconstruct ancient fluvial environments. Sedimentologists have evinced great interest in developing fluvial models (e.g., Allen, 1970; Miall, 1978; Walker and Cant, 1984) and in examining the various intra- and extrabasinal factors controlling cyclicity in vertical facies sequences (e.g., Beerbower, 1964; Miall, 1980). Despite the fact that many alluvial sequences are dominated by fine-grained overbank deposits, fluvial models and most field studies have focused on channel deposits, and, with few exceptions (e.g., Allen, 1974; Leeder, 1975; Bridge, 1984), have tended to examine overbank sediments only cursorily.

This bias is certainly understandable. Channel deposits can readily be subdivided into different facies on the basis of texture and sedimentary structures. Furthermore, the internal organization and structures of channel deposits allow paleohydraulic interpretation through analogy with empirical studies of stream processes and bedform generation. In contrast, internal stratification is not always well-developed or preserved in overbank deposits. Although levee and crevasse-splay deposits exhibit a variety of primary structures and are amenable to facies subdivision and analysis (e.g., Steel and Aashiem, 1978; Bridge, 1984), stratification in flood-plain mudrocks is commonly obliterated by bioturbation. Moreover, many modern examples of overbank sediment are obscured by vegetation so that both individual and composite depositional units are difficult to recognize in the field, to correlate laterally for any distance, and to relate to coeval channel deposits.

We demonstrate herein that the behavior of ancient stream systems and the intrabasinal and extrabasinal processes that generated individual alluvial successions can be better understood by more thorough examination and documentation of lateral and vertical variability in overbank deposits. In studying the lower Eocene Willwood Formation, we have subdivided paleosols developed on overbank sediments into five arbitrary developmental stages that vary in their geochemical and morphologic properties. This chapter describes these five paleosol stages and shows how the different maturity (time to form) of each is intrinsically related to distance from the active channel margin. Vertical sequences of overbank deposits are also subdivided by means of the developmental paleosol stages and are analyzed in conjunction with the channel deposits. Also discussed are the intrabasinal and extrabasinal factors that generated cyclic repetitions of paleosols of different maturity in the Willwood Formation.

GEOLOGIC SETTING

The Willwood Formation is a fluvial sequence that is exposed throughout the Bighorn Basin of Wyoming (Fig. 1). Be-

Figure 2. Exposures of Willwood Formation in northern study area, showing variegated mud rocks and very fine-grained sandstones of overbank origin that dominate the sequence. Sheet sandbody caps the sequence. View to east-northeast; NW¼,SE¼,Sec.20,T.56N.,R.101W., Park County, Wyoming.

cause it contains abundant fossil mammals, the Willwood is readily subdivided into biostratigraphic zones. In the northern part of the basin (Fig. 1), preserved Willwood rocks range from middle Clarkforkian (earliest Eocene) through early Wasatchian (early early Eocene) in age and have a maximum thickness of nearly 850 m (Rose, 1981). The base of the formation becomes younger to the south, and, in the central part of the basin (Fig. 1), the sequence encompasses early through late Wasatchian (early early through late early Eocene) time.

Deposition of the Willwood Formation was coeval with Laramide structural development of the Bighorn Basin, which spanned Late Cretaceous through early Eocene time (e.g., Foose and others, 1961). The basin was open to the south and west until the principal structural elevation of the Owl Creek Mountains (probably in early Eocene time) and the formation of the volcanic Absaroka Range (beginning in the middle Eocene: Bown, 1980; Wing and Bown, 1985). Floral and faunal data indicate that early Eocene climate in the Bighorn Basin was warm-temperate to subtropical with seasonal precipitation. Based on the Clarkforkian megafloras, Hickey (1980) reconstructed a mean annual temperature of 14°C; similar temperatures characterized Wasatchian time (Wing, 1981). The properties of Willwood paleosols are consistent with these climatic interpretations and also show that precipitation, although relatively abundant, was seasonally spaced (Bown and Kraus, 1981).

Willwood sediments are dominated by variegated mudrocks and very fine-grained sandstones of extra-channel origin (Fig. 2). Channel sandstones compose no more than 25 percent, and commonly as little as 10 percent, of measured stratigraphic sections, depending on their location in the basin. Most sandstones

are lithic arenites (Neasham and Vondra, 1972; Kraus, 1979) that contain a variety of crystalline and sedimentary lithic fragments eroded from surrounding mountain ranges.

Willwood channel sandstones display two basic geometries and corresponding depositional styles. Sheet sandbodies, with width-to-thickness ratios in excess of 20, are multistory in nature, with thicknesses that typically range from 8 to 20 m. In exposures perpendicular to paleoflow, Willwood sheet sandbodies exhibit well-developed lateral accretion sets as much as 5 m thick. This sedimentary feature, coupled with significant variation in paleocurrents between adjacent stories, indicates that Willwood sheets were deposited by meandering streams. In contrast, ribbon sandstones exhibit width-to-thickness ratios of less than 15, and, depending on whether they are simple or multistory, thicknesses approximately 6 to 7 m or less. Although exhumed ribbon sandbodies are sinuous as well as straight in plan view, they show little or no evidence of lateral migration and are interpreted as the deposits of laterally fixed streams. Ribbon sandstones probably represent crevasse-splay channels. Paleocurrent patterns show that major streams flowed to the north, following the Tertiary structural axis of the basin (Neasham and Vondra, 1972; Kraus, 1980), and were fed by tributaries from the west and east.

Willwood channel sandstones are enveloped by thick sequences of overbank deposits that are the focus of this study. The most coarse-grained and thickest overbank deposits accumulated adjacent to channels as levees and proximal crevasse splays. Willwood levee deposits consist of very fine-grained sandstones thinly interbedded with siltstones. Some levee deposits exhibit a depositional dip that is usually subtle but can be greater than 10° and is oriented away from the channel margin. Where internal stratification is preserved, it is typically small-scale cross-lamination. Interspersed with the levee deposits are coarser grained, proximal crevasse-splay sandstones. Proximal-splay deposits display varied internal stratification including large- and small-scale cross-bedding and horizontal stratification. Gradual accretion of Willwood levee and splay deposits produced alluvial ridges, or elevated parts of the alluvial plain occupied by channels.

Willwood overbank deposits also contain abundant siltstones and mudstones that accumulated in flood-plain areas beyond the alluvial ridge. The mudrocks are interspersed with fine- and very fine-grained sandstones and sandy siltstones that are generally interpreted as crevasse-splay deposits. Some of the thin, very fine-grained sandstone units could represent episodes of sheet flooding.

DEVELOPMENTAL SEQUENCE

With the exception of proximal crevasse-splay deposits, nearly all Willwood overbank deposits show evidence of Eocene pedogenesis. Willwood paleosols are characterized by spectacular color banding as a result of the concentration of organic carbon in A horizons and iron and manganese sesquioxides in B horizons. Other criteria for recognizing Willwood paleosol profiles were described by Bown (1979) and Bown and Kraus (1981).

Approximately 10 percent of the paleosols in the Willwood Formation are readily assigned to the spodosols (Bown and Kraus, 1981). Some of the remaining soils resemble the spodosols in one or several features, whereas others bear little similarity to them. We discovered that by first examining and becoming familiar with the Willwood spodosols and then working backward from the more similar to the more dissimilar, all of the Willwood paleosols underwent similar pedogenic processes. However, certain soils had more time to develop than other soils; that is, the Willwood soils exhibit different stages of *maturity* (Bown, 1985b). Although Willwood paleosols exhibit continuous intergradation in maturity, it has been possible to recognize landmarks in a soil maturation sequence. These are termed maturation stages 1 through 5 (Bown, 1985a,b), in which stage 1 is the least mature soil and stage 5 the most mature. Only the very mature Willwood paleosols (stages 4 and 5) can be assigned to the spodosols. Some of the less mature varieties (stages 2 and 3) appear to be alfisols; the least mature (stage 1) are entisols.

Briefly, maturation stages 1 through 5 for paleosols of the Willwood Formation are identified based on the following characteristics (see Fig. 3):

Stage 1. The least mature Willwood paleosols are entisols characterized by the absence of soil horizons. They are recognized by their yellow or orange mottling and occasional development of yellow or orange beds with or without reddish streaks and mottles. Color contacts in stage 1 paleosols are diffuse, and calcium carbonate accumulation, where present, is incipient.

Stage 2. Stage 2 paleosols differ from those of stage 1 because they show the first incipient horizonation of the soil profile. An eluvial A (Ae) horizon is present but thin, and is

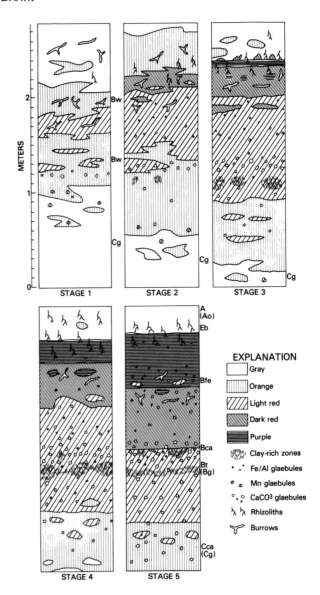

Figure 3. Developmental sequence of Willwood paleosols from incipient (stage 1) through relatively mature (stage 5) profiles. This is a composite sequence based on numerous profiles; only stage 5 represents an actual paleosol.

underlain by a red upper B horizon and orange lower B horizon. Color contacts remain diffuse. During stage 2 development, the first significant translocation of clay and soil plasma occurred, and accumulation of calcium carbonate, if present, was rapid in the lower profile. Stage 2 paleosols are assigned to the alfisols.

Stage 3. Marked profile horizonation typifies stage 3 paleosols, which are classified as alfisols or spodosols. The Ae horizon is present and relatively thick, and the B horizon is purplish at the top, dark and/or light red in the middle, and orange at the bottom. Impersistent incipient spodic horizons occur in some stage 3 soils at the top of the B horizon. Color contacts remain relatively diffuse. Major soil plasma translocation occurred during stage 3 of soil formation; much of this material has accumulated in the form of soil glaebules. By early stage 3, calcium carbonate accumulation reached its peak and began to decline, and clay translocation neared its peak by late stage 3.

Stage 4. These are spodosols that exhibit profound profile horizonation, including a thick Ae horizon and an incipient Ao (organic epipedon) horizon. Clay eluviation from the Ae horizon was complete and declining elsewhere by stage 4. The B horizon is much thicker than in stage 3, and Al and Fe sesquioxide accumulations are at their peaks. There is an overall decrease in mottling, and color contacts are more distinct. Well-defined spodic horizon(s) are present.

Stage 5. The most mature Willwood paleosols are spodosols showing profound horizonation. An epipedon (Ao horizon) is invariably present. The entire A horizon (Ae and Ao horizons) and the upper part of the B horizon are much thicker than in stage 4 paleosols. Because mottling is less important than in stage 4 paleosols, even rare, color contacts are generally very distinct. Spodic horizons are invariably present and well developed.

LATERAL PALEOSOL RELATIONS AND THE PEDOFACIES

Identification of the maturation stage of paleosols is important because it permits study of the relation of soil maturity to sediment accumulation in both the temporal and lateral dimensions. The lateral relations among Willwood paleosols of differing maturities and channel sandstones were examined in the central part of the Bighorn Basin (Fig. 1), where exposures are laterally extensive, although topographically subdued.

In the lateral dimension, field studies have shown that the least mature Willwood paleosols formed on alluvial ridge deposits closest to ancient channel margins, whereas the most mature soils developed on distal flood-plain sediments farthest from their coeval channels. Moreover, there is a gradual and continuous lateral progression from stage 1 through stage 5 soil maturities with increasing distance from the channel margin. These lateral changes are consistent in all parts of the Willwood sequence.

Because the thickness of alluvium deposited by overbank floods decreases systematically away from the channel (Alexander and Prior, 1971; Kesel and others, 1974) and because overbank areas farther from the channel may be flooded less frequently than areas close to the channel, the sediment accumulation rate diminishes with increasing distance from the channel. Consequently, the lateral changes in Willwood paleosols demonstrate that there is an inverse relationship between soil maturity and sediment accumulation rates, as was suggested by Leeder (1975) for pedogenic carbonates. We use the term pedofacies to denote these laterally adjacent packages of sedimentary rock that vary in their ancient soil properties as a function of their distance from areas of relatively high sediment accumulation. In the Willwood Formation, these areas were the channel belts. The term

facies was coined by Gressly (1838) to describe lateral change in sedimentary rock units; the facies concept as it is applied today (e.g., Walker, 1984) is well suited to denote lateral changes in unconsolidated or cemented sediment related to sedimentologically controlled pedogenic processes.

The pedofacies differs from the "soil facies" of Richmond (1962) and Morrison (1967) in that, by definition, "soil facies" refers to lateral changes in geosols, in which a geosol is "a body of rock that consists of one or more pedologic horizons developed in one or more lithostratigraphic, allostratigraphic, or lithodemic units and (is) overlain by one or more formally defined lithostratigraphic or allostratigraphic units" (North American Stratigraphic Commission, 1983). Because "soil facies" is stratigraphically confined by this definition, the concept is not applicable to alluvial units such as the Willwood Formation, which consist of numerous multistory paleosols.

Other workers have employed various terms to define lateral soil variability (e.g., the catena: Milne, 1935; the chronosequence: Vreeken, 1975; and the lithosequence: Miles and Franzmeier, 1981). Because soil catenas form on hillslopes, and soil property differences along the catena are due to topography, catenas are poor analogues of the lateral variation seen in Willwood paleosols. Moreover, inherent to the catena concept is the viewpoint that pedogenic activity accompanies a geologically lengthy period of nondeposition or net degradation. In contrast, the Willwood paleosols formed during lengthy periods of net aggradation; their variability is due not to topographic position but to areal position relative to local depositional centers. Although the chronosequence is indeed related to length of pedogenesis, this term does not conceptually embrace a lateral maturation sequence and is actually used quite differently. The lithosequence is likewise inadequate because the development of pedofacies is not solely dependent on lateral variability in parent material. Furthermore, use of the term sequence to describe lateral variability in soils or paleosols is confusing because of the vertical connotation of the word to geologists.

VERTICAL SEQUENCES OF OVERBANK DEPOSITS

The developmental paleosol sequence and the lateral pedofacies relations described above have made it possible to analyze vertical sequences of Willwood overbank deposits in more detail than any previous fluvial study. This aspect of the study was undertaken in the northern part of the Bighorn Basin (Fig. 1) where vertically continuous exposures form prominent ridges. Examination of nearly 300 m of section revealed two orders of well-developed pedofacies sequences that developed principally as a result of autocyclic fluvial controls, and a larger scale pedofacies sequence that reflects an allocyclic mechanism.

Simple Pedofacies Sequences

Simple pedofacies sequences range from 3 to 6 m in thickness, and are the smallest recognized in the Willwood For-

148   *Kraus and Brown*

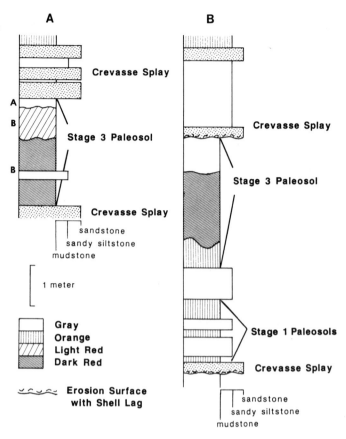

Figure 4. Stratigraphic sections of typical simple pedofacies sequences. A, Single stage 3 paleosol; letters on left side of column refer to soil horizons. B, Several stage 1 profiles overlain by stage 3 paleosol.

mation. At the base of each cycle is a very fine- or fine-grained sandstone that displays little if any pedogenic modification. In the simplest examples, the basal sandstone is overlain by a single paleosol, usually a stage 2 or 3 profile, that developed on mudrocks (Fig. 4). In other cases, the basal sandstone is immediately overlain by interstratified fine-grained sandstones and siltstones on which stage 1 paleosols formed; these in turn are overlain by a stage 2 or 3 paleosol (Fig. 5). Each cycle is capped by another pedogenically unmodified sandstone that forms the base of the superjacent simple sequence.

Because most simple pedofacies sequences contain a stage 2 or 3 paleosol, they probably developed in flood-plain areas somewhat distant from the channel margin. Initially, there was an episode of channel flooding and crevassing, which caused fine sand to be discharged onto the flood plain. Basal sandstones exhibiting few observable pedogenic features probably represent the deposits of single crevasse-splay episodes. Pedogenic modification of these sandstones was inhibited by rapid sediment accumulation and by their thickness. In examples where stage 1

paleosols developed on splay sandstones and siltstones, there were probably several episodes of splay deposition with enough time between splay events for pedogenesis to be initiated.

Following abandonment of the crevasse-splay lobe, fine-grained alluvium gradually accumulated on the flood plain as a result of periodic overbank flooding. Because new increments of parent material were very thin and introduced sporadically, moderately mature stage 2 or stage 3 soils developed. Minor crevasse-splay episodes interrupted this gradual sediment accretion, but in most cases, these silty or sandy layers were simply incorporated into the cumulative soil (e.g., the coarser layer in the red B horizon in Fig. 4). Eventually, another major crevassing event deposited the splay sandstone that caps each sequence. Because the upper sandstones are fairly thick, the underlying soil profile was usually buried deep enough to curtail further pedogenesis.

Compound Pedofacies Sequences

Willwood overbank deposits can also be subdivided into compound pedofacies sequences comprising multistory paleosols that are bounded below and above by ribbon or sheet channel sandstones. These sequences are tens of meters thick and contain several simple cycles (Fig. 6). The constituent paleosols gradually increase in pedogenic maturity upward through each pedofacies sequence and then commonly decrease in maturity in the upper part of the sequence.

Figure 6A depicts a representative compound pedofacies sequence. The basal channel sandstone is overlain by a succession of interbedded sandstones and gray siltstones several meters thick, interpreted as levee deposits on the basis of their lithology and primary dip away from the channel margin. The rocks show evidence of bioturbation and also contain numerous cylindrical orange nodules that Kraus (1985) interpreted as in-situ tree stumps replaced by calcite. There are no additional signs of pedogenic modification (such as mottling); thus the deposits are assigned a developmental stage of 0. Thinly interbedded, very fine-grained sandstones and gray siltstones that show yellowish brown mottles and root traces occur slightly higher in the sequence. These deposits are interpreted as vertically stacked stage 1 paleosols with each sand/silt couplet representing a single profile. Because individual paleosols are so thin, they are illustrated only schematically in Figure 6A.

The entisols are capped by a fine-grained sandstone that is interpreted as a crevasse channel because of its channelized shape and relatively coarse grain size. Above this sandstone there is a distinct change in paleosol maturity. The crevasse channel forms the base of a simple pedofacies sequence containing a stage 2 paleosol, and higher in the compound pedofacies sequence are simple sequences composed of well-developed stage 3 paleosols. The middle stage 3 paleosol represents the most mature paleosol (between a stage 3 and 4 profile) within the entire compound pedofacies sequence. Above this, the successive paleosols are less and less mature and overlain by levee and splay deposits exhibiting litte orr no pedogenic modification and consequently assigned

Figure 5. Simple pedofacies sequence with stage 3 paleosol (indicated by 3) underlain by stage 1 paleosols (1). Sequence capped by fine-grained sandstone of crevasse-splay origin (C). Scale indicated by person (arrow). View to northeast; NE¼,SW¼,Sec.20,T.56N.,R.101W., Park County, Wyoming.

to stage 0. The levee/splay rocks are in turn overlain and scoured by a sheet sandstone that terminates the sequence.

Compound pedofacies sequences are attributed primarily to intrabasinal controls on fluvial sedimentation and record a series of channel avulsions. The sequence illustrated in Figure 6A was initiated by deposition in a meandering stream system. Soil development was very limited in the overlying levee deposits that formed directly adjacent to the stream. Based on lateral pedofacies relations, the more mature paleosols higher in the sequence record deposition and pedogenesis in flood-plain areas that were increasingly more distant from the active channel. This suggests that the channel moved farther and farther away from its original point on the alluvial plain through a series of avulsive events. In the upper part of the sequence, there is a decrease in maturity from stage 3 to stage 0 paleosols, reflecting the return of the channel to a location near its original position. When the channel reoccupied its former position, the upper sandstone capping the sequence was deposited.

Bridge (1984) has shown that episodes of channel avulsion appear as abrupt changes in facies and in paleoflow direction within vertical sequences of overbank deposits. Some pedofacies transitions in Figure 6A reflect avulsive events. If there is a distinct difference in the pedogenic maturity of two successive simple sequences within a compound sequence, the change can probably be attributed to an avulsive episode. For example, in the Figure 6A sequence, the stage 1 paleosols at the 5 m level are truncated by a crevasse channel and are, in turn, overlain by a significantly more mature (stage 2) paleosol. Not only does this pedofacies change indicate channel avulsion, but it also demon-

strates the direction the channel moved relative to the developing soil column, in this example, away from the paleosol sequence. Other successive simple sequences show only minor differences in degree of pedogenic development; the transition between the two sequences probably results from the formation and subsequent abandonment of crevasse splays or levees with or without channel shifting.

Pedofacies megasequences

Pedofacies megasequences are hundreds of meters thick and composed of several compound sequences. Within a megasequence, there is a distinct change in the maximum or overall maturity of paleosols in the constituent compound sequences. For example, in the northern Bighorn Basin, the lower part of the Willwood Formation (Clarkforkian or earliest Eocene: Rose, 1981) is exemplified by the compound sequence in Figure 6A, in which paleosols range from stage 1 through the well-developed stage 3. In contrast, overlying Willwood rocks (early Wasatchian or early early Eocene; P. D. Gingerich, personal communication, 1984) are dominated by well-developed stage 3 paleosols, stage 4 paleosols (Fig. 6B), and even some stage 5 paleosols. Therefore, Clarkforkian and early Wasatchian Willwood rocks in the northern Bighorn Basin constitute a pedofacies megasequence in which there is a significant upward increase in the pedogenic maturity of the component compound pedofacies sequences.

Changes in short-term sediment accumulation rates, which in large part are responsible for the pedofacies transitions in compound and simple sequences, are controlled by local patterns of

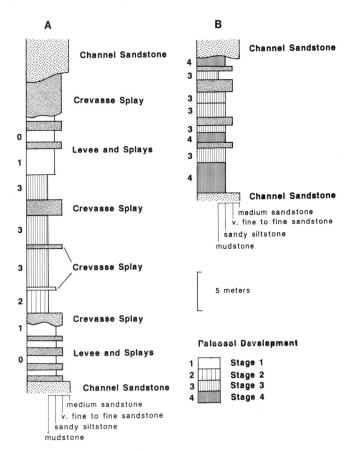

Figure 6. A, Stratigraphic section of compound pedofacies sequence. Because stage 1 paleosols at bottom and top of sequence are thin and represented by several multistory paleosols, they are illustrated schematically; see text for details. Late Clarkforkian part of Willwood Formation (NW¼,Sec.15,T.56N., R.101W., Park County, Wyoming). B, Compound pedofacies sequence from earliest Wasatchian part of Willwood Formation (Sec.10,T.55N.,R.100W., Park County, Wyoming).

satchian paleosols are significantly more mature because they develped under conditions of slowed basin subsidence and sediment acumulation.

This interpretation is strengthened by the biostratigraphic studies of Hickey (1980) and especially of Gingerich (1983), which provide independent evidence for slowed sediment accumulation rates between Clarkforkian and Wasatchian time. Furthermore, Kraus (1980) described an unusually thick (30 m) and laterally extensive (12 km perpendicular to current direction) sheet sandbody at the boundary between the Clarkforkian and Wasatchian land mammal ages. Based on computer simulation models of alluvial architecture (Allen, 1978; Bridge and Leeder, 1979) the magnitude and strongly multistory nature of this sandbody were ascribed to decreased rates of basin subsidence.

Intrabasinal variability

As has been discussed, compound pedofacies sequences reflect variability in sediment accumulation rates arising from changes in the distance between the paleosol column and the active channel caused by periodic channel avulsion. Because avulsion is a frequent process in terms of geologic time, pedofacies transitions in compound sequences record short-term changes in accumulation rate (probably on the order of 1,000 to 25,000 yr in the Willwood Formation). Because pedofacies megasequences are controlled by allocyclic processes, they represent longer term changes in sediment accumulation rate (probably on the order of 100,000 to 1,000,000 years; e.g., see Hickin, 1983).

Not only can vertical sequences of pedofacies be used to determine temporal changes in sediment accumulation, they can also be used to compare accumulation rates in different parts of a basin. For example, stage 4 or stage 5 Willwood paleosols are relatively common in the study area in the central part of the Bighorn Basin (Fig. 1), and therefore are more mature than those in the northern part of the basin, where most are no more than well-developed stage 3 paleosols. Stratigraphic thicknesses in conjunction with revised time estimates for subdivisions of the Paleogene (Berggren and others, 1985) yield sediment accumulation rates of 0.26 mm/yr for the Clarkforkian and 0.22 mm/yr for the first half of Wasatchian time in the northern Bighorn Basin. Gross sediment accumulation rates were considerably slower in the north (0.13 mm/yr during Wasatchian time). Thus the differences in paleosol maturity are construed as arising from areally differing rates of basin subsidence, which in turn could have been generated by two processes.

Because the Willwood sequence examined in the northern part of the Bighorn Basin is slightly older than Willwood rocks studied farther south (late Clarkforkian and earliest Wasatchian versus early [but not earliest] Wasatchian), subsidence may have diminished in the entire basin during early Eocene time. A second and very important factor to consider is the proximity of each study area to the Tertiary structural axis of the Bighorn Basin. Computer simulation models (Bridge and Leeder, 1979) as well as field examples (e.g., Read and Dean, 1982) of alluvial architec-

sedimentation and erosion. Over longer periods of time (on the order of 100,000 to 1,000,000 yr), allocyclic factors, such as tectonic activity or climatic conditions, can also produce variability in accumulation rates. Because pedogenic development is intimately tied to sedimentation rate, changes in pedogenic maturity should mirror the structural history of a sedimentary basin. The degree of pedogenic development should be greater during periods of slow basin subsidence and slow sediment accumulation than during periods of rapid basin subsidence and rapid sediment accumulation.

The pedofacies megasequence in the northern Bighorn Basin is attributed to changes in the rate of basin subsidence during early Eocene time. Paleosols in the older, Clarkforkian age Willwood rocks attained only moderate levels of soil maturity (stage 3) because the rate of basin subsidence, and thus the rate of sediment accumulation, were both high. Younger, earliest Wature have demonstrated that overbank deposits tend to be concentrated along basin margins where subsidence is relatively slow. In contrast, channel sandstones accumulate in areas of maximum basin subsidence, typically along the structural axis, because the major streams are localized there.

During late Paleocene and early Eocene time, the northern study area lay almost directly on the structural axis of the basin (Osterwald and Dean, 1962; Gingerich, 1983). As a result, the Willwood sequence in this area is dominated by sheet sandstones deposited by a major stream system(s), as well as by overbank deposits on which only moderately mature paleosols typically developed. During early Eocene time, the study area in the central part of the Bighorn Basin was situated at least 50 km east of the basin axis (Osterwald and Dean, 1962). As the models of Bridge and Leeder (1979) predicted, Willwood rocks in the central part of the basin consist of abundant overbank deposits that contain very mature paleosols and sandbodies, which are generally ribbons and interpreted as tributary streams. This explanation is favored because of the distinct differences in sandstone geometry between the two areas of the basin.

SUMMARY

Study of Willwood alluvial paleosols indicates that the least mature paleosols generally formed in areas of relatively rapid alluviation: on channel, levee, and crevasse-splay deposits of the proximal alluvial ridge. In contrast, mudrocks that accumulated in the distal flood plain, where net sediment accumulation rates were relatively low, contain much more mature paleosols. Paleosols of intermediate maturities are distributed in order of their stage on intervening proximal flood-plain and distal alluvial ridge sediments. These laterally adjacent packages of overbank deposits are termed pedofacies.

Determining lateral and vertical changes in pedofacies can provide valuable information on ancient stream systems. Because many ancient alluvial soil profiles are easily recognized, are exposed over broad areas, and are formed almost instantaneously in terms of geologic time (in the range of 2,000 to 30,000 years), they offer a nearly ideal method of correlating deposits (and thereby sedimentary events) from interchannel areas to the coeval alluvial ridge.

Examination of vertical sequences of Willwood rocks re-

veals three orders of pedofacies sequences. Compound and simple sequences largely reflect autocyclic fluvial controls. Small-scale or simple sequences consist of a stage 2 or stage 3 paleosol bounded above and below by crevasse-splay deposits. These sequences are generated by slow and sporadic alluviation and soil modification, which are periodically interrupted by crevasse-splay deposition. The movement of a channel away from and then back to a specific point on the alluvial plain through periodic avulsion produced compound pedofacies sequences. Each consists of a sequence of multistory paleosols that increase and then decrease in maturity or developmental stage upward through the sequence. Superimposed on these smaller scale cycles are megasequences that are hundreds of meters thick. Pedofacies megasequences are characterized by a distinct change in the overall or maximum maturity of their constituent compound sequences. Whereas compound and simple sequences record local patterns of overbank deposition, megasequences represent changes in the rate of sediment accumulation produced by allocyclic processes including varied tectonic activity.

The remarkable sequence of paleosols in the Willwood Formation clearly illustrates several important principles of soil-sediment interrelationships in aggrading alluvial systems that have broad application to other alluvial deposits. This is especially true in view of the widespread distribution of paleosols in fluvial rocks. Further study of these paleosols will contribute to increasingly more informative evaluations of the nature, tempo, and mode of alluvial deposition. Thus we believe that paleosols provide a key for integrating depositional events through time laterally across the alluvial lithotope, from the channel belt to the most distant parts of the coeval flood plain.

ACKNOWLEDGMENTS

We thank S. Y. Johnson, A. D. Miall, S. L. Wing, and J. A. Wolfe for constructive comments on the manuscript. Field assistance was ably provided by Scott Johnson, Bruce McKenna, and Virginia Yingling. Appreciation is extended to Emmett Evanoff for drafting Figures 4 and 6. This research was funded by National Science Foundation Grant EAR-8319421 to MJK and in part by a G. K. Gilbert Fellowship with the U.S. Geological Survey to TMB.

REFERENCES CITED

Alexander, C. S., and Prior, J. C., 1971, Holocene sedimentation rates in overbank deposits in the Black Bottom of the lower Ohio River, southern Illinois: American Journal of Science, v. 270, p. 361–372.

Allen, J.R.L., 1970, Studies in fluviatile sedimentation; A comparison of fining-upwards cyclothems with special reference to coarse-member composition and interpretation: Journal of Sedimentary Petrology, v. 40, p. 298–323.

——, 1974, Studies in fluviatile sedimentation; Implications of pedogenetic carbonate units, Lower Old Red Sandstone, Anglo–Welsh Outcrop: Geological Journal, v. 9, p. 181–208.

——, 1978, Studies in fluviatile sedimentation; An exploratory quantitative

model for the architecture of avulsion-controlled alluvial suites: Sedimentary Geology, v. 21, p. 129–147.

Beerbower, J. R., 1964, Cyclothems and cyclic depositional mechanisms in alluvial plain sedimentation, *in* Merriam, D. F., ed., Symposium on cyclic sedimentation: Geological Survey of Kansas Bulletin 169, p. 31–42.

Berggren, W. A., Kent, D. V., Flynn, J. J., and Van Couvering, J. A., 1985, Cenozoic geochronology: Geological Society of America Bulletin, v. 96, p. 1407–1418.

Bown, T. M., 1979, Geology and mammalian paleontology of the Sand Creek Facies, lower Willwood Formation (lower Eocene), Washakie County,

Wyoming: Geological Survey of Wyoming Memoir 2, 155 p.

——, 1980, Summary of latest Cretaceous and Cenozoic sedimentary, tectonic, and erosional events, Bighorn Basin, Wyoming: University of Michigan Papers on Paleontology, no. 24, p. 25–32.

——, 1985a, Maturation sequences in lower Eocene alluvial paleosols, Willwood Formation, Bighorn Basin, Wyoming: Abstracts, Third International Fluvial Sedimentology Conference, Ft. Collins, Colorado, p. 11.

——, 1985b, Maturation sequences in lower Eocene alluvial paleosols, Willwood Formation, *in* Flores, R. M., and Harvey, M., eds., Field guide to modern and ancient fluvial systems in the United States: Third International Fluvial Sedimentology Conference Guidebook, p. 20–26.

Bown, T. M., and Kraus, M. J., 1981, Lower Eocene alluvial paleosols (Willwood Formation, northwest Wyoming, U.S.A.) and their significance for paleoecology, paleoclimatology, and basin analysis: Palaeogeography, Palaeoclimatology, Palaeoecology, v. 34, p. 1–30.

Bridge, J. S., 1984, Large-scale facies sequences in alluvial overbank environments: Journal of Sedimentary Petrology, v. 54, p. 585–588.

Bridge, J. S., and Leeder, M. R., 1979, A simulation model of alluvial stratigraphy: Sedimentology, v. 26, p. 617–644.

Foose, R. M., Wise, D. U., and Garbarini, G. S., 1961, Structural geology of the Beartooth Mountains, Montana and Wyoming: Geological Society of America Bulletin, v. 72, p. 1143–1172.

Gingerich, P. D., 1983, Paleocene-Eocene faunal zones and preliminary analysis of Laramide structural deformation in the Clark's Fork Basin, Wyoming: Wyoming Geological Association, 34th Annual Field Conference, Guidebook, p. 185–195.

Gressly, A., 1838, Observation geologiques sur le Jura Soleurois: Neue Denkschrisgn der Allgemeinen Schweizerischen Gesellschast fur die Gesammten Naturwissen, v. 2, p. 1–112.

Hickey, L. J., 1980, Paleocene stratigraphy and flora of the Clark's Fork Basin: University of Michigan Papers on Paleontology, no. 24, p. 33–50.

Hickin, E. J., 1983, River channel changes; Retrospect and prospect, *in* Collinson, J. D., and Lewin, J., eds., Modern and ancient fluvial systems: International Association of Sedimentologists Special Publication 6, p. 61–83.

Kesel, R. H., Dunne, K. C., McDonald, R. C., Allison, K. R., and Spicer, B.E., 1974, Lateral erosion and overbank deposition on the Mississippi River in Louisiana caused by 1973 flood: Geology, v. 1, p. 461–464.

Kraus, M. J., 1979, The petrology and depositional environments of a continental sheet sandstone; The Willwood Formation, Bighorn Basin, Wyoming [M.S. thesis]: Laramie, University of Wyoming, 106 p.

——, 1980, Genesis of a fluvial sheet sandstone, Willwood Formation, northwest Wyoming: University of Michigan Papers on Paleontology, no. 24, p. 87–94.

——, 1985, Sedimentology of early Tertiary rocks, northern Bighorn Basin, *in* Flores, R. M., and Harvey, M., eds., Field guide to modern and ancient fluvial systems in the United States: Third International Fluvial Sedimentology Conference Guidebook, p. 26–33.

Leeder, M. R., 1975, Pedogenic carbonates and flood sediment accumulation rates; A quantitative model for alluvial arid-zone lithofacies: Geological Magazine, v. 112, p. 257–270.

Miall, A. D., 1978, Lithofacies types and vertical profile models in braided river deposits; A summary, *in* Miall, A. D., ed., Fluvial sedimentology: Canadian Society of Petroleum Geologists Memoir 5, p. 597–605.

——, 1980, Cyclicity and the facies model concept in fluvial deposits: Canadian Petroleum Geologists Bulletin, v. 28, p. 59–80.

Miles, R. J., and Franzmeier, D. P., 1981, A lithochronosequence of soils formed in dune sand: Soil Science Society of America Journal, v. 45, p. 362–367.

Milne, G., 1935, Some suggested units for classification and mapping, particularly for East African soils: Soil Research (Berlin), v. 4, p. 183–198.

Morrison, R. B., 1967, Principles of Quaternary soil stratigraphy, *in* Morrison, R. B., and Wright, H. E., eds., Quaternary soils: Proceedings, 7th INQUA Congress, v. 9, p. 1–69.

Neasham, J. W., and Vondra, C. F., 1972, Stratigraphy and petrology of the lower Eocene Willwood Formation, Bighorn Basin, Wyoming: Geological Society of America Bulletin, v. 83, p. 2167–2180.

North American Stratigraphic Commission, 1983, North American stratigraphic code: American Association of Petroleum Geologists Bulletin, v. 67, p. 841–875.

Osterwald, F. W., and Dean, B. G., 1961, Relation of uranium deposits to tectonic pattern of the central Cordilleran foreland: U.S. Geological Survey Bulletin 1087-I, p. 337–390.

Read, W. A., and Dean, J. M., 1982, Quantitative relationships between numbers of fluvial cycles, bulk lithological composition, and net subsidence in a Scottish Namurian basin: Sedimentology, v. 29, p. 181–200.

Richmond, G. M., 1962, Quaternary stratigraphy of the La Sal Mountains, Utah: U.S. Geological Survey Professional Paper 324, 135 p.

Rose, K. D., 1981, The Clarkforkian Land Mammal Age and mammalian faunal composition across the Paleocene-Eocene boundary: University of Michigan Papers on Paleontology, no. 26, 196 p.

Steel, R. J., and Aashiem, S. M., 1978, Alluvial sand deposition in a rapidly subsiding basin (Devonian, Norway), *in* Miall, A. D., ed., Fluvial sedimentology: Canadian Society of Petroleum Geologists Memoir 5, p. 385–412.

Vreeken, W. J., 1975, Principal kinds of chronosequences and their significance in soil history: Journal of Soil Science, v. 26, p. 378–394.

Walker, R. G., 1984, General introduction; Facies, facies sequences, and facies models, *in* Walker, R. G., ed., Facies models: Toronto, Geoscience Canada, Reprint Series 1, 2nd ed., p. 1–9.

Walker, R. G., and Cant, D. J., 1984, Sandy fluvial systems, *in* Walker, R. G., ed., Facies models: Toronto, Geoscience Canada, Reprint Series 1, 2nd ed., p. 71–89.

Wing, S. L., 1981, A study of paleoecology and paleobotany in the Willwood Formation (early Eocene, Wyoming) [Ph.D. thesis]: New Haven, Connecticut, Yale University, 391 p.

Wing, S. L., and Bown, T. M., 1985, Fine-scale reconstruction of late Paleocene–early Eocene paleogeography in the Bighorn Basin of northern Wyoming, *in* Flores, R. M., and Kaplan, S. S., eds., Cenozoic paleogeography of the west-central United States: Society of Economic Paleontologists and Mineralogists, Rocky Mountain Section, p. 93–105.

MANUSCRIPT ACCEPTED BY THE SOCIETY JULY 1, 1987

Geological Society of America
Special Paper 216
1988

Climatic influences on rates and processes
of soil development in Quaternary deposits of southern California

Leslie D. McFadden
Geology Department
University of New Mexico
Albuquerque, New Mexico 87131

ABSTRACT

Many Quaternary fan and terrace deposits of the arid and semiarid regions of the Mojave Desert and the subhumid (Mediterranean) Transverse Ranges, southern California, have similar parent material and are relatively well dated, thereby enabling evaluation of the influence of changes in climate on the rates and processes of soil development. Within soils of a given chronosequence, soil age and many morphologic, mineralogic, and chemical properties are strongly related, reflecting primarily an evolutionary, time-dependent trend of continuous soil development during Quaternary time. Comparison of soil development in Holocene deposits of similar age of arid, semiarid, and subhumid regions indicates that increases in the amount of effective soil moisture explain observed systematic differences in the rates and processes of soil development. Accordingly, major climatic changes at the end of Pleistocene time have resulted in the development of soil profiles that are, to a certain extent, polygenetic. This change in climate caused a decrease in the depth of leaching, causing accumulation of secondary carbonate and locally gypsum, materials derived from incorporation of eolian fines, in argillic B horizons of Late Pleistocene soils. Increases in dust influx and availability of calcareous dust, caused by the widespread development of playas and decreases in vegetation at the end of the Pleistocene, have probably also influenced rates of soil development.

In subhumid regions, the leaching environment favors development of noncalcic profiles during Quaternary time. This leaching environment may approximate the leaching environment experienced during late Pleistocene time by soils that are forming presently in a semiarid climate that favors accumulation of calcium carbonate. Late Pleistocene and older soils in presently semiarid regions also possess thick, clay-rich B horizons with authigenic clay and iron-oxide minerals, features that indicate soil development during past periods of increased effective moisture. The relatively rapid development of argillic horizons in latest Pleistocene soils of currently subhumid regions is attributed to attainment of a threshold of soil formation, rather than the Pleistocene-to-Holocene climatic change. The threshold is caused by the accumulation of large amounts of silt and organic matter, a process that causes decreases in permeability, increases in available water-holding capacity, and ultimately increases in the rate and magnitude of chemical weathering. Soil chronosequence studies in California demonstrate that rates and processes of soil development may be influenced by changes in climate, in a direct fashion by causing changes in leaching regime, or in an indirect fashion by causing variation in the pattern and intensity of eolian activity.

L. D. McFadden

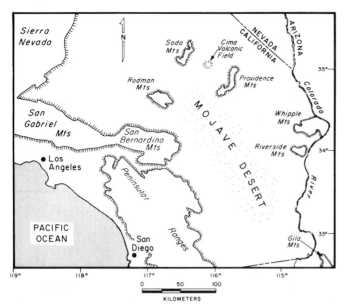

Figure 1. Index map of southern California showing important geographic features mentioned in text and locations of areas where soils were described.

INTRODUCTION

Paleosols can provide age relations in studying landscape evolution as well as paleoclimatic information used to interpret geomorphic processes. Although most studies of paleosols have focused on soil profiles formed in Quaternary deposits, paleosols in much older rocks are attracting increasingly greater interest due to the wealth of paleoenvironmental information that they contain (Retallack, 1981, 1983; other studies, this volume). Interpretation of the paleoenvironmental significance of paleosols, however, is difficult in that soils are highly complex systems influenced by many variables. The approach advanced by Jenny (1941, 1980) has provided a strategy that can be used to interpret the influence of a soil-forming factor, such as climate or parent-material composition, on the character of soil development. The relative validity of this approach has been demonstrated in many studies (Yaalon, 1975; Bockheim, 1980; Harden, 1982; Gile and others, 1981).

Soil chronosequences have been studied in arid and semiarid regions of the Mojave Desert (McFadden, 1982; McFadden and Bull, 1988; McFadden and others, 1986, 1987; Wells and others, 1987) and in the subhumid Mediterranean climate of the southern Transverse Ranges (McFadden and Tinsley, 1982; McFadden and Hendricks, 1985; McFadden and Weldon, 1987). Recent geologic studies in southern California provide age constraints for several deposits and geomorphic surfaces, ranging from middle Pleistocene to late Holocene in age (Weldon, 1985; Weldon and Sieh, 1985). Extensive paleoclimatic research conducted in the southwestern United States provides critical data

regarding the timing and magnitude of climatic change at the end of Pleistocene time (King, 1976; Smith and Street-Perrot, 1983; Spaulding and others, 1983). Such data have enabled studies of the rates and processes of soil development in these different climatic regimes, and the impacts of glacial-to-interglacial climatic changes in each region on soil development. The results of these studies indicate that soil development has occurred continuously, albeit in a complex manner, during Quaternary time, despite fluctuations in climate. This contrasts with results of studies of Quaternary soil development in regions of intermediate latitude, where extreme temperature fluctuations are inferred to have caused strongly intermittent soil development (Catt, 1986). Several lines of evidence indicate that, during long intervals of the Mesozoic Era and much of the rest of the Phanerozoic Era, global temperatures were milder than those of the Quaternary. Accordingly, if interpretation of the paleoenvironmental significance of pre-Quaternary paleosols is to rest primarily on the basis of comparison of such paleosols with Quaternary soils, it may be most appropriate to emphasize soil studies from regions that were more uniformly warm during Quaternary time, thereby more closely approximating climatic conditions that presumably influenced formation of the majority of pre-Quaternary soils.

SOIL CHRONOSEQUENCES IN THE MOJAVE DESERT

Location, parent materials, and climate

The Mojave Desert in southeastern California is a hot and arid region as a result of its location in the global subtropical arid belt and its position on the leeward side of high mountains that create a strong rain shadow (Fig. 1). Precipitation is seasonal. Mean annual precipitation is ≤12 cm, with most occurring in the winter or summer (National Oceanic and Atmospheric Administration, 1978). In the western Mojave Desert, however, little precipitation falls in the winter, as the region is too far removed from sources of moisture in the Gulf of Mexico. Maximum leaching occurs during cool, moist winters. At higher elevations, greater precipitation and cooler temperatures promote a less arid (semiarid) soil moisture regime (mean annual precipitation, 12 to 18 cm). The dry, hot climate of the Mojave Desert supports sparse vegetation. Trees are typically restricted to active channels and only small, woody shrubs and annual grasses typically grow on the piedmonts (Fig. 2).

Quaternary piedmont deposits

Piedmont deposits are typically gravelly and poorly sorted. A large proportion of mountain ranges are composed of granitic and metamorphic rocks, and consequently piedmont deposits are noncalcareous and lithic arkosic (McFadden, 1982). Locally, carbonate occurs in deposits as discontinuous abraded coatings. The source of this carbonate is older piedmont deposits or colluvial deposits in which abundant secondary carbonate is present. Once dissected, these deposits provide source materials for younger, downstream piedmont deposits.

Figure 2. Typical bar-and-swale surface form of Holocene fan deposits on the Soda Mountains piedmont, central Mojave Desert. Note increased density of vegetation on or near ephemeral drainages and moderately varnished nature of surface stones. View is to the northwest. Length of piedmont shown in photograph is approximately 1.0 km.

Bull (1974) defined eight geomorphic surfaces of Quaternary age in the lower Colorado River area of southeastern California and southwestern Arizona. The surfaces are defined on the basis of topographic position, distinctive topographic texture, and soil-weathering characteristics. Subsequent studies demonstrate that similar surfaces occur throughout the Mojave Desert and that the surfaces in most cases represent morphostratigraphic units (McFadden, 1982; Dohrenwend and others, 1984; Wells and others, 1984, 1987). The regional character of these surfaces suggests the possibility of climatic control on major periods of aggradation and degradation. For example, the most recent, major aggradational event in the region appears to have occurred between ~13 and 8 ka (latest Pleistocene to early Holocene), during which time major climatic changes occurred in the Mojave Desert (Smith and Street-Perrot, 1983; Spaulding and others, 1983). Channel aggradation at this time is attributed to increased sediment supply and water discharge from increasingly barren hillslopes (Bull and Schick, 1979; Wells and others, 1987).

Holocene geomorphic surfaces display a bar-and-swale topography inherited from the braided, distributary channel pattern of arid, ephemeral streams (Fig. 2). In contrast, geomorphic surfaces associated with older Pleistocene deposits have a flat topographic form, referred to as a desert pavement (Fig. 3). Pavement topography is the result of weathering of surface clasts, raindrop impact and sheetflooding, and eolian activity, processes that tend to eliminate topographic highs, smooth the originally bar-and-swale topography, and lift the stone pavement above a gradually developing cumulative soil (Cooke and Warren, 1973; McFadden and others, 1986; McFadden and others, 1987).

The ages of late Pleistocene units relative to the earliest Holocene to latest Pleistocene units may be inferred on the basis of climatic geomorphological evidence, but other methods that have been used to determine or estimate age relations include $^{230}Th/^{234}U$ dating of pedogenic carbonate (Ku and others, 1979); dating of varnish on stones (Dorn and Oberlander, 1981; Dorn, 1984; Wells and others, 1984); total mass of pedogenic

Figure 3. Typical pavement form of Late Pleistocene fan deposit on the Soda Mountains piedmont. Note almost complete lack of vegetation on the strongly developed, varnished pavement surface and playa of Silver Lake in middle foreground. Largest stones visible on pavement surface are ~10 cm in diameter. View is to the east.

carbonate (Machette, 1978; McFadden, 1982; Machette, 1985); and relation of piedmont deposits to dated shorelines of pluvial lakes (Wells and others, 1984) or to K/Ar-dated basalt flows (W. B. Bull, personal communication; Dohrenwend and others, 1984). Age ranges are the best constrained for piedmont deposits in arid regions of the Mojave Desert; ages of piedmont deposits in semiarid regions are estimated mostly on the basis of geomorphic criteria. Age ranges of piedmont deposits in the Mojave Desert determined on the basis of these and other data are given in Tables 1 and 2.

Soil morphology

Soils on increasingly older piedmont deposits display systematic changes in profile morphology (Tables 1, 2; Figs. 4 through 6). The first indications of soil development are the development of vesicular A (Av) horizons and horizons of secondary carbonate accumulation in late Holocene deposits. In addition, surface stones of late Holocene deposits are lightly varnished, fractured,

and pitted. The latter features are primarily indicative of physical weathering.

Vesicular pores in the A horizon have been attributed to soil gas that expands as the soil temperature increases after precipitation events during the summer (Evenari and others, 1974). Av horizons of older soils in the Mojave Desert are similar in most respects to those found on late Holocene deposits. Secondary carbonate occurs primarily as thin, discontinuous coatings on the tops and sides of most stones in late Holocene deposits (stage I of Gile and others, 1966) (Fig. 7). In currently arid climates of the Mojave Desert, secondary carbonate in late Holocene soils has accumulated in the Av horizon as well as lower soil horizons (Table 1). In currently semiarid areas, secondary carbonate accumulates below a depth of 7 cm to as deep as 62 cm (Table 2). In the arid chronosequence, increasingly older soils on Holocene and Pleistocene deposits display changes in the morphology of carbonate accumulation similar to the sequence of changes observed in increasingly older piedmont deposits of arid areas of southern New Mexico (Gile and others, 1966; Gile and others,

TABLE 1. DIAGNOSTIC CHARACTERISTICS OF SOILS FORMED ON QUATERNARY SURFICIAL DEPOSITS OF THE MOJAVE DESERT IN AN ARID, HOT CLIMATE*

Age† (yr BP)	Typical Horizon Sequence Soil Great Group	Thickness Argillic or Color B Horizon	Maximum§ Rubification	Profile** Clay (wt%-cm)	Profile** Silt (wt%-cm)	Maximum Morph. Stage, Secondary CaCO₃,††	Depth to Top of Secondary CaCO₃,††	Profile*= CaCO₃, Mass³ (g/cm²-column)	Profile§§ Index	Thickness§§ Normalized Index
Latest Holocene (100-2,000)	Av-Cu Torriorthent	0	10	0; 12.2	17.1; 71.4	0	0	0	0.30	.01
Late Holocene (2,000-4,000)	Avk-Ck1-Ck2 Calciorthid or Torriorthent	0.5	20	74.9	154.3	I	0	—	3.62	0.07
Middle Holocene (4,000-8,000)	Avk-Bwk-Bk Camborthid or Calciorthid	4; 10	90	100.0; 268.9	85.8; 137.4	I+, II	0	0.70	3.40	0.07
Early Holocene to latest Pleistocene (8,000-13,000)	Avk-Btk-Bk Camborthids or Haplargid	39	80	441.1	337.0	II	0	—	13.72	0.18
Late Pleistocene (20,000-70,000)	Avk-Btk1-Btk2-Bk Haplargids	42; 24; 44	140	312.4; 368.6; 756.0	538.3; 783.3	II+	0	3.84; 6.59	17.30 22.00	0.35; 0.39
Late Pleistocene to Late mid-Pleistocene (70,000-200,000)	Avk-Btk1, 2, 3 Bk1-Bk2 Haplargid	118	120	902.3	2076.9	III	0	29.17	55.40	0.37
Middle Pleistocene (3000,000-700,000)	Av-Btk1, 2, 3, 4 Bk1-Bk2 Haplargid or Paleargid	127	120	2907.8	1603.8	III	0	42.88	90.40	0.46

*Determined on basis of data for 16 soil profiles described on the piedmonts of the Whipple Mountains and the Soda Mountains. Profile descriptions and laboratory data for these profiles are included in McFadden (1982), McFadden and Bull (1987), and Wells and others (1987). Horizon designations and subordinate modifiers primarily after Soil Conservation Service Soil Survey Manual (1981). Modifier v signifies presence of distinct vesicular pores.

†Ages of Quaternary deposits of the Mojave Desert reported on the basis of studies of Bischoff and others (1981), Dohrenwend and others (1984), Dorn (1984); Ku and others (1977); Kukla and Opdyke (1975); McFadden and others (1986); Merriam and Bischoff (1975), Metzger and others (1973), Wells and others (1987), Olmstead and others (1973), and Ore and Warren (1971).

§Rubification after Harden (1982).

**Profile content is calculated by (a) summing the products of wt.% multiplied by horizon thickness determined for each soil horizon, and (b) subtracting the profile content calculated for the parent materials from the value obtained in step (a). For profile mass determination, soil bulk density data is used to derive mass CaCO₃, as shown by Machette (1985).

††After Gile and others (1966) and Birkeland (1984).

§§After Harden (1982).

158   *L. D. McFadden*

TABLE 2. DIAGNOSTIC CHARACTERISTICS OF SOILS FORMED ON QUATERNARY SURFICIAL DEPOSITS OF THE MOJAVE DESERT IN A SEMIARID, HOT CLIMATE*

Age (ka)	Typical Horizon Sequence; Sequence; Soil Great Group	Thickness of Argillic or Color B Horizon (cm)	Maximum† Rubification	Profile† Clay (wt%-cm)	Profile† silt (wt%-cm)	Maximum Morphologic Stage, Secondary $CaCO_3$	Depth to Top of Secondary $CaCO_3$ Accumulation	Profile§ Index	Thickness§ Normalized Index
Late Holocene (2 to 4)	Av-Coxk-Cox Torriorthent or Calciorthid	0	40	1.2	5.0	I, I	7, 35	12.25	0.13
Middle Holocene (4 to 8)	Av-ABv-Bt-Btk Ck Camborthid or Haplargid(?)	55, 55	85	28.8	107.2	I, II+	22, 39	21.16	0.21
Early Holocene to latest Pleistocene (8 to 13)	Av-Bt-Coxk1 Coxk2 Haplargid	45, 73	70	630.4	204.7	I+, II+	57, 62	23.44	0.16
Late Pleistocene to late middle Pleistocene (70 to 200)	Av-Bt1, 2, 3, 4 Coxk1 - Coxk2 Haplargid	102, 152	115	1,776.4	1,319.8	0, 1	176, >170	32.00	0.19
Middle Pleistocene (300 to 700)	Av-Bt1, 2, 3, 4, 5, 6 Coxk-Cu Paleargid	102, 168	185	1,047	723.7	I, I	86, 73	47.50	0.34

*Characteristics defined on the basis of data for 19 soil profiles described on piedmonts of the eastern San Bernardinos and the Providence Mountains. Complete soil profile descriptions and laboratory data are included in McFadden (1982), McFadden and Bull (1988), and L. D. McFadden and S. G. Wells (unpublished report).

†Data for soils of San Bernardino Mountains piedmont.

§Data for soils of Providence Mountains piedmont. Index calculations after Harden (1982).

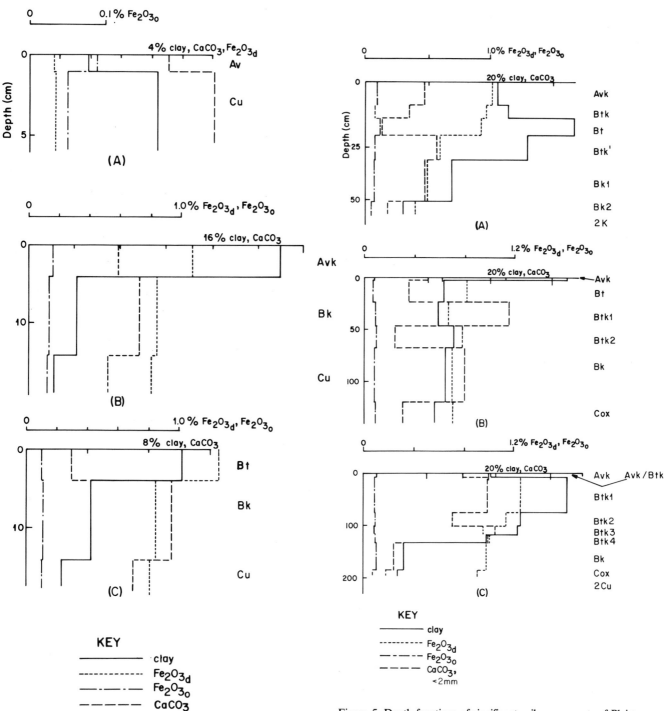

Figure 4. Depth functions of significant soil components of Holocene soils of the Whipple Mountains piedmont (arid, hot). A shows latest Holocene soil; B, middle Holocene soil formed in bar; and C, middle Holocene soil formed in swale.

Figure 5. Depth functions of significant soil components of Pleistocene soils of the Whipple Mountains piedmont (arid, hot). A shows late Pleistocene soil; B, late Pleistocene to late middle Pleistocene soil; and C, middle Mid-Pleistocene soil.

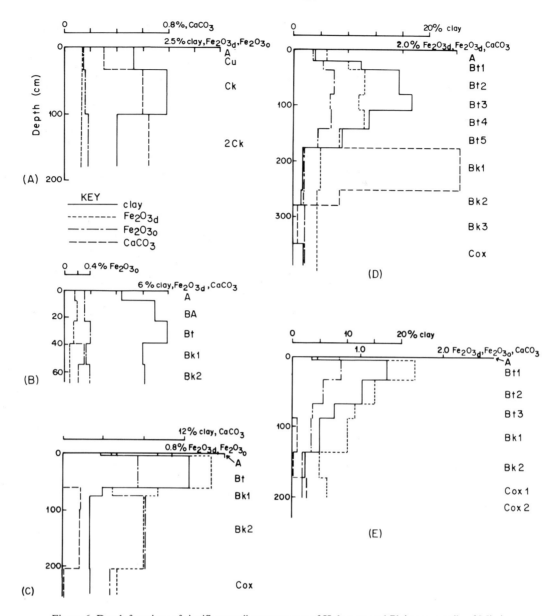

Figure 6. Depth functions of significant soil components of Holocene and Pleistocene soils of Mission Creek in the eastern San Bernardino Mountains (semiarid, hot). A shows late Pleistocene soil; B, late Pleistocene to late middle Pleistocene soil; and C, middle mid-Pleistocene.

1981). A maximum of stage III morphology is attained in the middle Pleistocene soils of the Mojave Desert (Table 1). In the currently semiarid regions of the Mojave Desert, a maximum of only stage II+ is attained in early Holocene to latest Pleistocene soils rather than the oldest soils of the chronosequence (Table 2).

In the arid chronosequence, secondary gypsum has accumulated in middle Holocene and older soils, typically at depths below 15 to 20 cm. The gypsum often occurs as euhedral needles that formed after coatings of carbonates had previously accumulated on stones. Even where gypsum is not present or has not

been detected, high values of electroconductivity (2 to 19 mmho/cm) demonstrate the presence of gypsum or other more soluble salts (McFadden, 1982).

The initial development of color B horizons is observed in middle Holocene soils. These horizons are thin and discontinuous and are located beneath boulders in the pavement. The relatively moist microenvironment beneath such stones probably favors more intense leaching, depletion of carbonates and soluble salts, and lower soil pH; it also promotes chemical alternation of ferromagnesian minerals (McFadden, 1982). Early Holocene to latthe profile index of Holocene and latest Pleistocene soils in diverse climatic settings and parent materials is nearly always less than 25.0. In the Mojave Desert chronosequences, all index values of Holocene and latest Pleistocene soils are also less than 25.0 (Tables 1 and 2). Values for older Pleistocene soils range from 17.3 to 94.0. Calculation of the thickness-normalized index, a value that does not strongly reflect differences due to varying profile thickness, yields values of 0.34 or greater for all but one of the Late Pleistocene or older soils, compared to a maximum value of 0.21 for latest Pleistocene and younger soils. This indicates that greater profile thickness of soils forming under a semiarid climate compared to an arid climate accounts for the low value of the profile index of late Pleistocene soils in the arid chronosequences.

Secondary carbonates, clay, silt, and iron oxides

In arid regions of the Mojave Desert, increasingly older soils have increasingly larger amounts of secondary carbonate (Figs. 4 and 5; Table 1). These results parallel those from a large number of studies in arid and semiarid regions that show that secondary carbonate progressively accumulates in the solum, resulting in systematic changes in soil morphology (Gile and others, 1966, 1981; Bachman and Machette, 1977; McFadden, 1981, 1982; Machette, 1985). The total mass of secondary carbonate also increases systematically in many chronosequences (Bachman and Machette, 1977; Machette, 1985; McFadden, 1982). Total mass of secondary carbonate for the soils of the Whipple Mountains piedmont also increases systematically with time (Table 1); the average rate of carbonate accumulation in this chronosequence, however, is considerably slower than the rate of carbonate accumulation determined for other areas of the southwest United States (Machette, 1985; McFadden and Bull, 1988). Thus, although total mass of secondary carbonate is a useful relative-age indicator, secondary carbonate data from one soil in a given chronosequence cannot necessarily be compared directly with secondary carbonate data for soils of other chronosequences in order to obtain age estimates (Machette, 1985; McFadden and Bull, 1988).

Comparison of data from Tables 1 and 2 also reveals distinct contrasts in the pattern of secondary carbonate accumulation. The depth to the top of the horizons of carbonate accumulation is significantly greater in soils of the semiarid chronosequence, reflecting the greater depth of soil leaching. Also, although carbonate continues to accumulate in latest Pleistocene and younger soils of the semiarid chronosequence, there is no trend of increasing carbonate accumulation in increasingly older Pleistocene soils. Clearly, carbonate morphology and content may provide useful geochronologic information when conditions are such that carbonate continuously accumulates. These conditions do not characterize the semiarid regions of the Mojave Desert, which distinguishes the chronosequence in this region from semiarid chronosequences in regions elsewhere in the southwestern United

Figure 7. Early Holocene soil exposed in trench excavated on the Soda Mountains piedmont. Note well-developed vesicular A horizon, weak argillic B horizon, and stage II carbonate morphology. Scale in tenths of meters.

est Pleistocene soils display continuous, thicker Bw or Bt horizons that have become significantly enriched in clay and silt (Figs. 4, 5, 6; Tables 1, 2). Moderately to strongly developed, reddened argillic horizons are present in late Pleistocene and older soils. Some metamorphic and plutonic stones in the argillic horizon are almost completely grussified in these soils. In the arid chronosequence, secondary carbonate has also accumulated in the argillic horizon and in some cases appears to have displaced previously accumulated clay.

Overall morphology, quantified through determination of the Harden index (Harden, 1982), systematically increases with increasing soil age (Tables 1 and 2). The index is calculated by quantifying the difference between values of several field properties and soil parent material values such as color, structure, clay films, and texture. Harden and Taylor (1983) demonstrated that

States that consistently exhibit increasing carbonate morphology and content (McFadden and Bull, 1988).

Total soil clay and silt content also increase systematically with soil age in both the arid and semiarid chronosequences (Tables 1 and 2). Much of the silt initially accumulates in the vesicular A horizon. Although physical weathering of surface clasts may have produced some fines, most of the silt is probably derived by entrapment of eolian material. Large amounts of clay also occur in the vesicular A horizons of arid chronosequence soils (Figs. 4 and 5). In increasingly older soils, the maximum clay content typically occurs in the argillic B horizon, and is interpreted to reflect primarily translocation of clay to lower horizons (Figs. 5 and 6). Much of the secondary clay in soils of the arid chronosequence consists of well-crystallized illite-mica and kaolinite, and overall clay mineralogic composition changes little with increasing soil age (Fig. 8). However, in late and middle Pleistocene soils, some palygorskite is also present.* As palygorskite is not present in the parent materials or in vesicular A horizons, it may be an authigenic mineral. Formation of palygorskite may occur by alteration of smectite in the calcareous, alkaline environment in a manner suggested by Bachman and Machette (1977). In the semiarid chronosequence, there is stronger evidence for formation of authigenic phases, as indicated by increases in the relative proportions of vermiculite compared to chlorite and illite (Fig. 9). The increasing content of kaolinite may also reflect authigenic clay-mineral formation, although the presence of kaolinite in vesicular horizons suggests that kaolinite content may increase due to incorporation of kaolinite-bearing eolian dust.

Secondary ferric-iron oxides have also accumulated in soils of arid and semiarid chronosequences (Figs. 4, 5, 6). The degree of reddening of the soils (Tables 1 and 2) also correlates strongly with increases in soil iron-oxide content (McFadden, 1982; McFadden and Bull, 1988). Childs and others (1979), Torrent and others (1980), and Schwertmann and others (1982) have demonstrated that the degree of reddening of soils is closely related to the relative amount of hematite present. The relative degree of crystallinity of iron oxides in soils can be evaluated by determination of extractable forms of iron such as oxalate-extractable iron oxides (Fe_2O_3o) and dithionite-extractable iron oxides (Fe_2O_3d) (McKeague and Day, 1966; Schwertmann and Taylor, 1977). Oxalate-extractable iron oxides consist primarily of poorly crystalline or amorphous Fe oxides, ferrihydrite (a fine-grained paracrystalline iron oxide, and organically bound iron (McKeague and Day, 1966; Schwertmann and Taylor, 1977). Dithionite-extractable iron oxides include well-crystallized iron oxides such as hematite and goethite, in addition to oxalate-extractable iron oxides (Mehra and Jackson, 1960; Schwertmann and Taylor, 1977). Analysis of the crystallinity of iron oxides of arid chronosequence soils indicates that the Fe_2O_3o content is very low relative to Fe_2O_3d content (Figs. 4, 5). This suggests

---

*Palygorskite identified on the basis of 10.2 to 10.5Å spacing; 6.44Å second-order peak; collapse of 10.2 to 10.5Å after heating to 500°C.

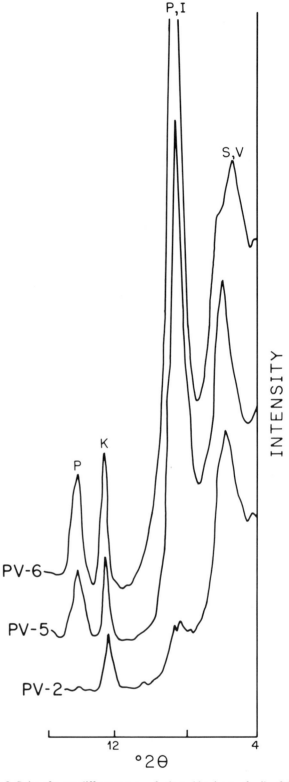

Figure 8. Suite of x-ray diffractograms of selected horizons of soils of the arid chronosequence of the Whipple Mountains. X-ray diffractograms are from Mg-saturated, gylcolated samples. PV2, middle Holocene (Bkl horizon); PV6, late Pleistocene to late middle Pleistocene (Bkl horizon); PV6, middle mid-Pleistocene (Btk3 horizon). S = smectite; V = vermiculite; I = illite/mica; K = kaolinite; P = palygorskite.

that much of the secondary iron oxide present in these soils is primarily hematite, accounting for the strong degree of reddening of these soils despite relatively small overall increases in ferric-iron oxide content (McFadden, 1982; McFadden and Bull, 1988). Because ferrihydrite forms prior to hematite, these results indicate that the transformation of ferrihydrite to hematite occurs very rapidly, or that the rate of chemical alteration is very slow, limiting ferrihydrite content, or a combination of these two processes. Soil conditions that are hot and dry, and the relative lack of organic matter favor formation of the anhydrous phase, hematite (Schwertmann and Taylor, 1977). In contrast to the arid chronosequence, analysis of the secondary iron oxides of the semiarid soils suggests (Fig. 6) that many of the secondary iron oxides typically consist of Fe_2O_3o. This indicates that the slightly moister, cooler climate of semiarid regions of the Mojave Desert is or has been in the past more conducive for ferrihydrite stability. However, in middle mid-Pleistocene soils, ferrihydrite content is very low, suggesting that much previously formed ferrihydrite has been transformed to hematite (McFadden, 1982; McFadden and Bull, 1988).

Role of eolian dust in soil development

The results of many studies indicate that much of the secondary carbonate and clay in desert soils has not accumulated due to chemical weathering, but rather is derived from external sources, principally eolian dust (Gile and others, 1966; Lattman, 1973; Bachman and Machette, 1977; Gile and Grossman, 1979; Gile and others, 1981). Yaalon and Ganor (1973) and Gile and others (1981) showed that secondary calcium carbonate occurs in Holocene soils formed in noncalcareous parent materials. More recent theoretical studies of calcic soil development support these conclusions. McFadden (1982), using a mass-balance argument, showed that the magnitude of chemical weathering of CaO-bearing aluminosilicates required to produce accumulated secondary carbonate in middle Holocene soils of the Mojave Desert should be relatively extensive and readily apparent. Yet, there is evidence for only minimal chemical alteration of the parent materials of these soils.

The observed lack of chemical alteration in an arid, hot environment is consistent with results of theoretical modeling of chemical weathering and soil development in a semiarid climate that are based on chemical mass-transfer simulations. These simulations predict very low rates of secondary clay and carbonate accumulation (Rogers, 1980). Furthermore, results of a recently developed model that integrates calcareous dust influx, soil-water balance, and carbonate solution chemistry support the hypothesis that calcareous dust influx, and to a lesser extent, dissolved Ca^{+2} in rainwater, strongly influence the pattern of calcic horizon development observed in arid and semiarid climates (McFadden and Tinsley, 1985).

The lack of significant chemical weathering indicated for soils of the Mojave Desert, as well as the presence of significant quantities of clay in vesicular A horizons, also suggest an eolian origin for much of the strongly crystalline secondary clay. This

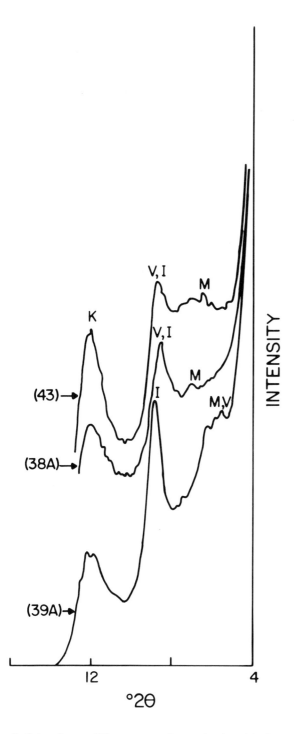

Figure 9. Suite of x-ray diffractograms of strongly altered horizons of soils of the semiarid chronosequence. All latest Pleistocene and older soils from the Mission Creek drainage, eastern San Bernardino Mountains. X-ray diffractograms are from Mg-saturated, glycolated samples. 39A, latest Pleistocene (Bt horizon); 38A, late Pleistocene to late middle Pleistocene (Bt2 horizon); 43, middle mid-Pleistocene (Btl horizon). S = smectite; V = vermiculite; I = illite/mica; K = kaolinite.

conclusion is consistent with the results of Colman (1982), who found that chemical alteration products in Pleistocene soils on gravelly tills were poorly crystalline or amorphous, suggesting that strongly crystalline clay in the B horizon of many soils in the western United States may be derived from external sources.

Much of the eolian clay and silt that is incorporated in soils of deserts initially accumulates in the vesicular A horizon (Peterson, 1980; McFadden, 1982; McFadden and others, 1986). When dry soils are subjected to rainfall, infiltration occurs rapidly through cracks in the vesicular A horizon, and dissolved solutes and suspended material may be translocated to lower horizons. Infiltration within the vesicular A peds occurs much more slowly. Reddening of the interior of vesicular A horizon peds indicates that chemical alteration of ferrous iron-bearing minerals eventually produces authigenic ferric-iron oxides (McFadden and others, 1984; McFadden and others, 1986). Oxidation of iron, iron oxide accumulation, and reddening occur below large clasts of pavements, a process that is also attributable to chemical alteration. As slow incorporation of eolian materials and vesicular A-horizon development continue, the isolated, reddened zones eventually thicken and coalesce, forming continuous gravel-poor B horizons of early Holocene to latest Pleistocene soils. Thus, according to this hypothesis, color and the formation of argillic B horizons of many desert soils are directly related to both accumulation of eolian fines and subsequent alteration of constituents present in this material (McFadden and others, 1986). The ultimate thickness attained by argillic B horizons is also strongly related to accumulation of eolian fines. Accumulation of an increasing amount of carbonate may eventually entirely engulf much of the argillic horizon, or in conjunction with gradually increasing clay content, it may cause decreases in soil permeability and increases in runoff and surface erosion (Wells and others, 1985; McFadden and others, 1986). Major advances in the study of desert soil development will certainly require much more data concerning the rates and magnitude of eolian deposition, a well as past changes in the composition of this material.

Influence of climatic change on soil development

The climate of the Mojave Desert during the last glaciation (Wisconsinan) was considerably different from the current climate. Paleoenvironmental data from plant macrofossil evidence in packrat (*Neotoma*) middens show that a juniper-pinyon-Joshua tree woodland was present throughout most of the Mojave and Sonoran deserts between 30 and 11 ka (King, 1976; Spaulding and others, 1983). These data indicate that the latest Pleistocene climate was effectively more moist than it is at present, a conclusion also reached on the basis of studies of pluvial lake chronologies throughout the southwestern United States (Smith and Street-Perrot, 1983). Disagreement exists as to the precise nature of the latest Pleistocene climate (Brakenridge, 1978); however, most recent studies indicate a cooler climate than at present, with moister winters and drier summers in desert

areas of the southwestern United States (Spaulding and others, 1983).

By calculating potential evapotranspiration for late Pleistocene climates on the basis of inferred temperatures, estimates of effective leaching during the latest Pleistocene can be derived (McFadden, 1983; McFadden and Tinsley, 1985), quantified by determination of the leaching index (Li) of Arkley (1963). These estimates indicate that the magnitude of the increase in effective leaching during latest Pleistocene climatic conditions compared to Holocene climatic conditions approximates the magnitude of the increase in effective leaching in semiarid regions compared to arid regions currently observed in the Mojave Desert (McFadden, 1982). As this change in the depth of leaching is associated with significant differences in depth of carbonate accumulation in Holocene soils of the two regions (Tables 1 and 2), it is likely that the Pleistocene-to-Holocene climatic change resulted in a significant change in depth of carbonate accumulation (McFadden, 1982; McFadden and Bull, 1988).

Machette (1985) has demonstrated that different patterns of calcic soil development in much of the western United States can be attributed to changes in the depth and magnitude of carbonate accumulation that are caused by glacial-to-interglacial changes in climate, as well as changes in the rate and spatial distribution of calcareous dust influx. As mentioned above, McFadden and Tinsley (1985) have developed a compartment model that simulates calcic soil development on the basis of soil water balance, calcite solution chemistry, and calcareous dust and dissolved Ca^{++} influx rates. Simulated development of Holocene and late Pleistocene calcic soils subjected to arid, semiarid, and xeric (subhumid) climatic regimes and to a glacial and subsequently an interglacial climatic regime is similar to development of Holocene and late Pleistocene calcic soils that occur in the Mojave Desert (McFadden and Tinsley, 1985). For example, the results of simulation of a change from a thermic, semiarid environment (latest Pleistocene) to a hyperthermic arid (Holocene) climate show that a strongly bimodal distribution of carbonate would develop as the depth of wetting and locus of carbonate accumulation decreased (Fig. 10). These results strongly support the hypothesis that bimodality of secondary carbonate distribution in late Pleistocene soils of arid regions in the Mojave Desert is at least partly the result of changes in the depth of carbonate accumulation caused by changes in climate at the end of the Pleistocene.

Schlesinger (1985) and Marion and others (1985) also concluded, on the basis of carbon and oxygen isotopic data for secondary carbonate and theoretical modeling, that changes in climate during the late Quaternary have significantly influenced the character of calcic horizon development. According to these studies, essentially all secondary carbonate present in late Quaternary soils has accumulated at a depth controlled by an effectively wetter glacial climate. However, studies of calcic soils in southern New Mexico (Gile and others, 1966; Gile and Grossman, 1979; Gile and others, 1981) and in the Mojave Desert (McFadden, 1982; Wells and others, 1984, 1987; McFadden and Bull, 1988) have demonstrated that a significant amount of sec-

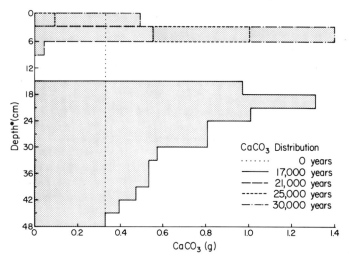

Figure 10. Predicted pattern of secondary carbonate accumulation in a late Pleistocene deposit (30,000 yr old). Dotted line shows initial carbonate distribution (0 yr). Carbonate influx is 1.0×10^{-4} g/cm^2/yr. Simulated development was determined for conditions that entailed a change from a cool, moist late Pleistocene environment to the arid, less moist environment of the Holocene. Lower gray area shows distribution of secondary carbonate after 30,000 yr of soil development. Depth* = absolute infiltration depth in the <2-mm size fraction (from McFadden and Tinsley, 1985).

ondary carbonate has accumulated in soils formed in Holocene deposits. The depth at which carbonate is accumulating in these soils is consistent with the depths predicted by the theoretical model of McFadden and Tinsley (1985) using data for the modern climate of these regions.

Machette (1985) and McFadden and Tinsley (1985) noted that the rate and pattern of calcareous dust influx also plays an important role in the rate and depth of calcic horizon development. Machette observed that calcareous dust influx is probably characterized by short-term peaks, separated by long intervening periods of relatively low calcareous dust influx. Accordingly, Late Pleistocene and Holocene soils might be expected to exhibit major differences in the apparent rates of carbonate accumulation. Unfortunately, few Late Pleistocene soils have been dated sufficiently well to permit determination of changes in the rates of carbonate accumulation. However, recent studies by Wells and others (1985) and McFadden and others (1984; 1986) of eolian deposits and soils on latest Pleistocene to Pliocene basalt flows of the Cima volcanic field, Mojave Desert, show that eolian deposition has been extremely episodic during the past ~1.0 m.y. These studies, as well as those of eolian deposits on the piedmont of the Soda Mountains (Wells and others, 1985), show that the most recent, major eolian event occurred during the latest Pleistocene to early Holocene. This eolian event is attributed to regional decline of pluvial lakes and loss of vegetation, which in turn favored deflation of exposed fine-grained, unconsolidated sedi-

ments. Subsequent to deposition of eolian materials on basalt flows of the Cima volcanic field during the latest Pleistocene to early Holocene, accumulation of large amounts of secondary carbonates and gypsum has occurred in soils formed in the eolian parent material (McFadden and others, 1986). Increasing development of saline playas during the Holocene may provide the main sources of calcareous and sulfate-rich dust that eventually are incorporated in the soils of the Cima volcanic field. It is probable, then, that soils forming on piedmont deposits of the Mojave Desert have been significantly influenced by major changes in eolian influx rates and in the composition of eolian materials, as well as changes in effective soil moisture during late Quaternary time.

SOIL CHRONOSEQUENCES IN THE TRANSVERSE RANGES, CALIFORNIA

Location, parent materials, and climate

The Transverse Ranges are a high, rugged, east-west trending belt of mountains that includes the San Gabriel and San Bernardino Mountains (Fig. 1). The rocks in these mountains are composed largely of late Mesozoic leucocratic and mesocratic plutonic rocks, Precambrian biotite-rich gneisses and schist, heterogeneous magmatitic rocks, and locally, Cenozoic marine and nonmarine sedimentary rocks. Examination of petrographic grain mounts of alluvial deposits derived from several drainage basins of the Transverse Ranges indicates a predominantly lithic arkosic composition (McFadden, 1982). The climate of the region at elevations less than 1,500 m is Mediterranean, with hot, dry summers (thermic, mean annual temperature = 15.5–16.6°C) and cool, moist winters (xeric, mean annual precipitation = 40–78 cm) (National Oceanic and Atmospheric Administration, 1978). The climate is increasingly drier toward the east along the southern front of the San Bernardino Mountains, or toward the north over the crest of the range. These trends are due to the rain-shadow effect of the high central part of the Transverse Ranges. The cool, moist winter of the Mediterranean climate supports the dense California chaparral and coastal scrub communities (Brown and others, 1980) (Fig. 11). Dominant species in these communities are chamise (*Adenostoma fascicalatum*), manzanita (*Actostaphylus glauca*), and scrub oak (*Quercus dumosa*).

Quaternary piedmont and terrace deposits

Quaternary surficial deposits of the Transverse Ranges consist mostly of valley fill terraces, erosional terraces, and extensive fan deposits (Bull and others, 1979; Ponti, 1985). Five to seven geomorphic surfaces are typically associated with these surficial deposits, recognized on the basis of geomorphic and sedimentologic data (Bull and others, 1979; McFadden and others, 1982; Weldon and Sieh, 1985). Age ranges of these surfaces (Table 3) have been determined by carbon-14 dating, paleomagnetic data,

Figure 11. Nested sequence of late Holocene (LH), early Holocene (EH), and late Pleistocene (LP) terraces of the North Fork of San Gabriel Creek drainage basin. Note the dense vegetation of the chaparral community. Small house is visible near base of cliff; exposed sediments underlying the early Holocene fill terrace are early Holocene and Late Pleistocene. Carbon-14 date on manzanita seeds collected at base of these deposits yielded an age of approximately 5.9 ka. View is to the northeast.

amount of offset by faults with known slip rates, and paleontologic evidence (Weldon, 1985).

The terrace deposits often display two distinctive sedimentologic modes: (1) very poorly sorted, water-laid deposits locally interstratified with debris-flow deposits; and (2) tightly packed, relatively well-sorted, gravelly water-laid deposits. These sedimentological differences are probably due to contrasting types of climate and climatic change–induced effects that have periodically altered the hydraulic geometries of streams during Quaternary time (Bull and others, 1979). Recently, Weldon and Sieh (1985), on the basis of several carbon-14 dates on alluvial and swamp deposits of Cajon Creek and associated tributaries, have shown that the most recent major depositional event occurred between 15,000 and 7,000 yr ago. Weldon (1985) attributed this depositional event to the Pleistocene-to-Holocene climatic change.

Ponti (1985) also attributed deposition of major alluvial units on the piedmont of the northern San Gabriel Mountains and

the southern Tehachapi Mountains to glacial-to-interglacial climatic changes during Quaternary time. Deposition of extensive Holocene and Pleistocene fan deposits of the southern piedmont of the Transverse Ranges may also reflect climatic changes during the Quaternary; however, Holocene and Pleistocene deposits are locally offset by range-front thrust faults, a process that has produced several tectonically controlled geomorphic surfaces (Bull and others, 1979; McFadden and others, 1982).

Soil morphology

Most soils in piedmont deposits of the Transverse Ranges are noncalcic, reflecting the moist, cool winters. Calcic profiles occur only on the northern and eastern piedmonts of the San Bernardino Mountains and on the northern piedmont of the San Gabriel Mountains at elevations less than 650 to 700 m, where mean annual precipitation is less than 15 cm (McFadden, 1982; Ponti, 1985). Soil chronosequence studies in the western Trans-

TABLE 3. CHARACTERISTICS OF SOILS FORMED ON QUATERNARY SURFICIAL DEPOSITS OF THE TRANSVERSE RANGES IN A SEMIARID, MEDITERRANEAN CLIMATE*

Age (ka)†	Typical Horizon Sequence; Soil Great Group	Thickness of Argillic or Color B Horizon (cm)	Maximum§ Rubification	Profiles§ Clay (wt%-cm)	Profiles§ Silt (wt%-cm)	Thickness** Epipedon (cm)	Profiles§ Index	Thickness§ Normalized Index
Latest Holocene (100-500)	A-Cox-Cu Xerorthent	0	40	6.3	283.7	21 to 50	7.08; 8.60	0.12; 0.14
Late Holocene (500-3,000)	A-AC-Cox-Cu Xerorthent or Haploxeroll	0	40	0	872.8	26 to 92	14.06	0.13
Middle Holocene (3,000-6,000)	A-AC-Cox or A-AB-Bw-Cox Haploxeroll	0 to 28	80	16.2, 0	536.1; 1,116.2	15 to 35	16.42 to 27.58	0.16; 0.22
Early Holocene (6,000-10,000)	A-Bw-Cox or A-Bt-Cox Haploxeroll	20 to 71	80	355.0; 43.3	833.8; 842.4	17 to 128	15.99; 17.29; 25.76	0.16; 0.17; 0.19
Latest Pleistocene (10,000-25,000)	A-Bt1, 2 - Cox Argixeralf or Argixeroll	37 to 67	90	246.6	1,233.3	12 to 80	22.47; 23.77	0.20; 0.22
Late Pleistocene (25,000-100,000)	A-Bt1, 2, 3 - Cox Argixeralf	130 to 223	140	1,423.4 2,182.1	3,303.8 3,200.3	1 to 20	55.74; 78.94	0.27; 0.33
Middle mid-Pleistocene (300,000-700,000)	A-Bt1, 2, 3, 4, 5 - BC-Cox Argixeralf	208 to <500	180	5,545.4 7,034.4	6,121.2 4,131.5	2 to 8	142.00; 307.74	0.36; 0.43

*Characteristics determined on basis of data for 58 soil profiles. Complete soil profile descriptions and laboratory data are included in McFadden (1982), McFadden and Hendricks (1985), and McFadden and Weldon (1987).

†Ages of Quaternary deposits reported on basis of studies of Bull and others (1978), Crook and others (1978), Weldon (1985), Weldon and Sieh (1985); and McFadden and Weldon (1987).

§Data for soils of the North Fork of San Gabriel and Cajon Creek drainages.

**Data from all soils described in the Transverse Range. Index calculations after Harden (1982).

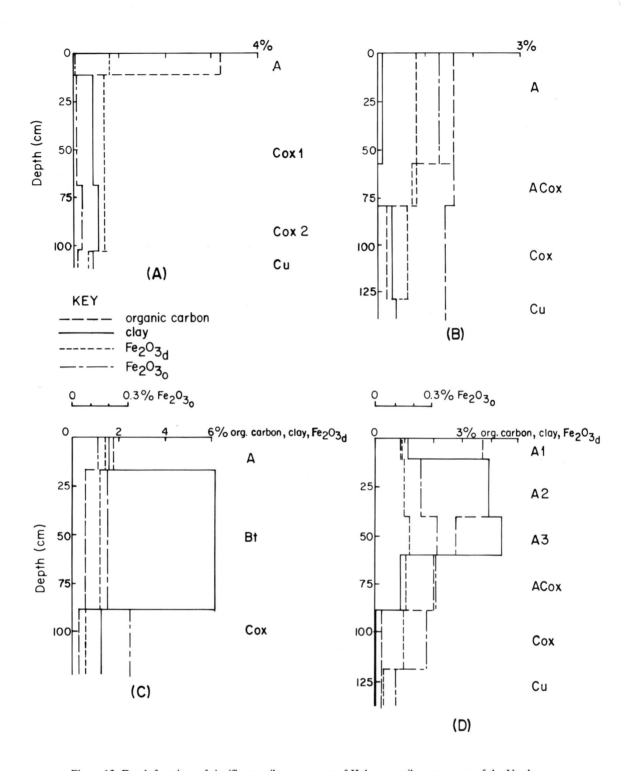

Figure 12. Depth functions of significant soil components of Holocene soils on terraces of the North Fork of San Gabriel Creek, and Day Canyon alluvial fan, San Gabriel Mountains (semiarid, Mediterranean). A shows latest Holocene soil; B, late Holocene soil; C, early Holocene soil; and D, middle(?) to early(?) Holocene soil.

verse Ranges also show that noncalcic soils have formed during the Pleistocene and Holocene (Keller and others, 1982).

A thick, darkened ochric horizon is present in late Holocene soils, and a mollic A epipedon is present in most middle Holocene soils (Figs. 12, 13; Table 3). The formation of thick horizons rich in organic matter is due to the accumulation of large quantities of organic matter in the very permeable, gravelly parent materials. A color B horizon (Bw) also is present in some middle and early Holocene soils; a weak argillic horizon is rarely present in an early Holocene soil but is typically present in latest Pleistocene soils (Fig. 13; Table 3) (McFadden, 1982; McFadden and Weldon, 1987). Coatings composed of silt and small amounts of clay and organic matter have accumulated on the tops and sides of many large clasts in Holocene soils. In addition, plutonic and schistose clasts in middle Holocene and older soils have been weathered to a grussified condition.

Increasingly older Pleistocene soils have thicker, redder argillic B horizons (Figs. 14 and 15; Table 3). In weak argillic B horizons, clay films coat the surfaces of grains and are in pores. In more strongly developed argillic horizons, films also occur in ped faces and as clay bridges. In contrast to middle and early Holocene soils, soils on latest Pleistocene and older deposits typically have increasingly thinner ochric epipedons rather than mollic epipedons (Table 3). In general, overall soil development systematically increases with soil age, as shown by consistent increases in the value of the Harden profile index and thickness-normalized index for soils of the Transverse Ranges chronosequence (Table 3).

Secondary silt, clay, and iron oxides

Large amounts of silt have accumulated in middle Holocene and younger soils (Table 3). Most of this material has accumulated in the ochric or mollic horizons. In contrast to silt, significant clay accumulation in B horizons is present only in some early Holocene soils and more typically latest Pleistocene soils. By the middle Pleistocene, the profile content of clay nearly equals or exceeds profile silt content (Table 3). Total pedogenic clay (Profile-clay) content in middle Pleistocene soils in this moisture regime greatly exceeds that in soils of approximately equivalent age that occur in arid and semiarid climates in southern California. In addition, the clay-mineral composition of soils of the Transverse Ranges changes from an initially mixed–clay mineral composition to a vermiculite +kaolinite assemblage, which ultimately changes to a dominantly kaolinite composition with subordinate vermiculute (Fig. 16a,b). The changing clay mineral composition is attributed to chemical weathering to vermiculite of ferromagnesian minerals in early Holocene to late Pleistocene soils, and to an increasing magnitude of alteration of feldspar to kaolinite in a moderately intense acidic leaching regime (McFadden, 1982; McFadden and Hendricks, 1982).

An increasingly large amount of secondary iron oxides (Fe_2O_3d) is present in progressively older soils of the Transverse Ranges chronosequence (Figs. 12, 13, and 14). As is the case with

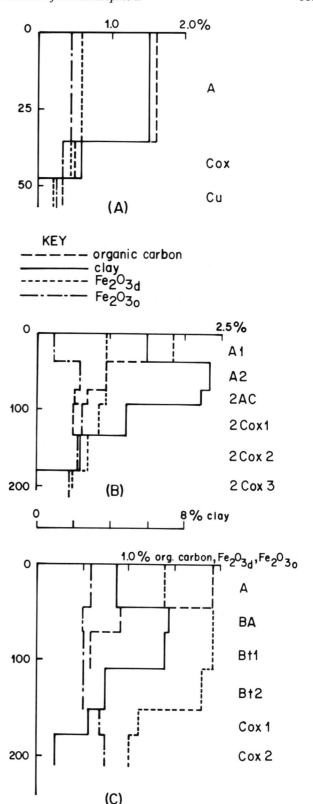

Figure 13. Depth functions of significant soil components of Holocene and latest Pleistocene soils on terraces of San Gorgonio Wash, San Bernardino Mountains (semiarid, Mediterranean). A shows latest Holocene soil; B, late Holocene soil; and C, early Holocene to latest Pleistocene soil.

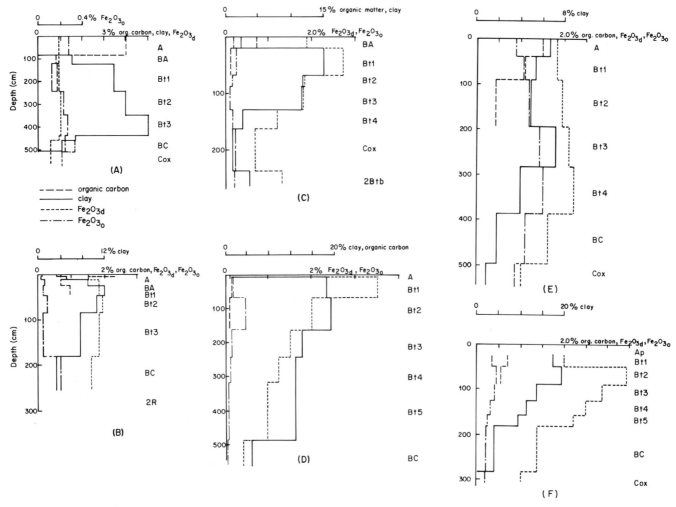

Figure 14. Depth functions of significant soil components of Pleistocene soils on terraces of the Transverse Ranges (semiarid, Mediterranean). A shows late Pleistocene soil, San Gabriel Mountains; B, late Pleistocene soil, San Gabriel Mountains; C and D, middle mid-Pleistocene soils, San Gabriel Mountains; E, Late Pleistocene soil, San Bernardino Mountains; F, middle mid-Pleistocene soil, San Bernardino Mountains.

pedogenic clay, the amount of iron oxides that have accumulated in these soils significantly exceeds the amount of accumulated iron oxides in soils of approximately equivalent age in the arid and semiarid chronosequences. The iron oxide content of a soil horizon is correlated strongly with the degree of soil reddening in early Holocene and Pleistocene soils (McFadden and Hendricks, 1985). As discussed previously, there is a strong relation between hematite content and soil reddening; thus, the increasingly redder color of older Pleistocene soils is related partly to an inferred increase in the presence of hematite, a mineral that has been detected in the reddest, most iron-oxide rich part of the argillic horizon in middle Pleistocene soil of this chronosequence (McFadden and Hendricks, 1985).

The inferred increase in hematite content is associated with a systematic change in the crystallinity of the secondary iron oxides

with time. The degree of iron oxide crystallinity, indicated by the Fe_2O_3o/Fe_2O_3d ratio, is highest in the early Holocene to late Pleistocene soils but is significantly lower in older Pleistocene soils (McFadden and Hendricks, 1985; McFadden and Weldon, 1987). Relatively high ferrihydrite content in early Holocene and Late Pleistocene soils probably owes to edaphic conditions (moderately acidic pH, high organic-matter content) that initially favor ferrihydrite rather than goethite precipitation, as discussed by Schwertmann and Taylor (1977). However, ferrihydrite is metastable, and although the presence of organic matter retards its transportation, ferrihydrite inevitably is converted to the more stable hematite. Thus, the Fe_2O_3o/Fe_2O_3d ratio ultimately attains a maximum value but thereafter decreases with a concomitant increase in the presence of crystalline hematite (McFadden and Hendricks, 1985).

Figure 15. Strongly developed soil exposed in east-facing roadcut excavated in middle Pleistocene deposits of San Gorgonio wash in the San Bernardino Mountains. Note the virtual absence of the A horizon and the near-absence of large clasts in the upper part of the argillic horizon, which extends to a depth of 210 cm. View is to the west.

Role of eolian dust in soil development

Because grussification of stones occurs in situ and little silt is produced, the large amount of silt in late and middle Holocene soils of the Transverse Ranges is attributed to incorporation of windborne dust. Seasonally strong winds blowing through passes in the Transverse Ranges carry large quantities of eolian materials derived from source areas in the Mojave Desert. Eolian dust may be transported as far west as the Channel Islands in the Pacific Ocean (Muhs, 1983). Eolian materials do not accumulate as a vesicular A horizon because, during infiltration events, entrapped silt is readily moved well below the surface. Hence, transition from the desert scrub to the chaparral community is accompanied by the change from a vesicular A horizon poor in organic matter to a thick, nonvesicular A horizon rich in organic matter.

Analysis of the iron oxide mineralogy of soils in the Transverse Ranges chronosequence indicates that much of the secondary iron oxides in middle and late Holocene soils are also derived from entrapment and incorporation of eolian material (McFad-

den and Weldon, 1987). Secondary iron oxide (Fe_2O_3d) content and silt content are very strongly correlated in soils of this age, and there is no evidence of clay accumulation that would be expected to accompany significant authigenic iron oxide accumulation, a characteristic of much older Pleistocene soils in this region. Moreover, the content of ferrous iron increases in the uppermost horizon of Holocene soils, a trend inconsistent with a significant alteration of ferrous iron to authigenic iron oxides, but more consistent with accumulation of iron oxides and ferrous iron present in incorporated dust (McFadden and Weldon, 1987). Clay, presumably present in eolian materials, is translocated through initially permeable sandy gravel below the solum by leaching that may penetrate to depths exceeding 10 m.

The accumulation of silt, as well as organic matter, during initial soil development creates a less permeable soil with commensurate increases in water-holding capacity. These changes would be expected to increasingly favor chemical weathering of soil parent materials and incorporated eolian materials. In addition, such an environment also would increasingly favor entrap-

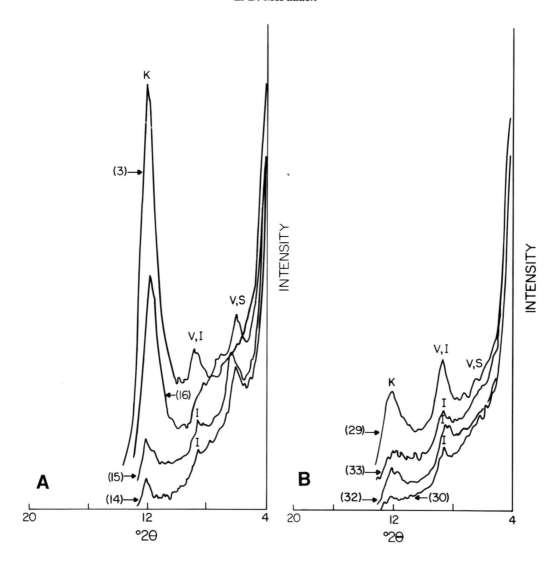

Figure 16. Suite of x-ray diffractograms of the maximal B horizon of soils from the soils of the North Fork of San Gabriel Wash and San Gorgonio drainages, San Gabriel Mountains (A), and soils of the San Gorgonio Wash drainage, San Bernardino Mountains (B). X-ray diffractograms are from Mg-saturated, glycolated samples. 14, latest Holocene (Coxl horizon); 30, late Holocene; 15, 32, early Holocene (Bt horizon); 33, latest Pleistocene (Bt4 horizon); 16, late Pleistocene (Btl horizon); 29, (Bt2 horizon), 3, (3Bt2b horizon), middle Pleistocene. V = vermiculite; I = illite/mica; K = kaolinite.

ment of clay present in incorporated eolian dust in the solum. Thus, the appearance of the argillic B horizon in early Holocene and latest Pleistocene soils reflects incorporation of clay by two different processes. McFadden and Weldon (1987) showed that this transition—from the early phase dominated by accumulation of eolian materials and organic matter to a subsequent stage that is increasingly characterized by chemical weathering and subsequent demise of the A horizon—occurs over a time span of little more than 3,000 yr. This transition constitutes a type of soil threshold that separates quite different soil environments and that may occur after differing times of soil development depending on

eolian influx rate, initial soil permeability, climate, as well as other soil variables.

Influence of the Pleistocene-to-Holocene climatic change on soil development

The latest Pleistocene full-glacial climate in the Transverse Ranges was probably effectively moister than the Holocene climate. The increase in effective soil moisture (Li) during a hypothesized full-glacial climate in the Transverse Ranges may have been about 20 percent greater than the present value (McFadden,

1982). Such an increase would have been conducive for slightly greater mean depths of leaching and associated greater B horizon thickness; however, the increase would probably not cause a significant increase in the rate of soil development. The presence of argillic horizons in latest Pleistocene soils is not attributed to a more intense Pleistocene weathering environment. These soils were subjected to little, if any, of the full-glacial, latest Pleistocene climate; therefore, the argillic horizon in latest Pleistocene soils formed during the Holocene due to the largely time-dependent threshold discussed above.

Climatic change may have indirectly influenced rates and processes of soil development by influencing variables other than soil moisture. For example, as discussed previously, Wells and others (1985) and McFadden and others (1984; 1987) proposed that significant increases in eolian activity occurred in the Mojave Desert during the latest Pleistocene and early Holocene. Increases in the rate of eolian dust supply to the gravelly piedmont and terrace deposits of the Transverse Ranges could have accelerated the rate of development of argillic horizons by causing the period of time required to attain the hypothesized soil threshold to decrease.

DISCUSSION AND CONCLUSIONS

Soil chronosequence studies in different climate regions of southern California show that soil profile development changes systematically with increasing soil age (Shlemon, 1978; McFadden, 1982; Muhs, 1982; Keller and others, 1982). Moreover, rates of change of soil properties are different in each climatic region (Fig. 17). In each chronosequence, the rate of change of several properties is initially rapid but decreases with time, although in the case of secondary iron oxide content, as well as secondary clay content, steady-state conditions do not appear to be achieved during the first 0.3 to 0.5 m.y. of soil development (Tables 1, 2, and 3; Fig. 17).

The increasing rate of secondary iron oxide accumulation in progressively less arid climates can be readily explained by an associated increase in the depth and intensity of leaching that favors chemical alteration of ferrous iron. In addition, the increasing rate of iron oxide (Fe_2O_3d) accumulation is associated with a concomitant decrease in the slope of the regression lines that characterize the relation between both profile and horizon secondary iron oxide and clay content (Fig. 18a,b). This slope decrease may be due to the decreasing role of chemical alteration (which produces significant quantities of authigenic iron oxides) relative to an increasing rate of eolian addition of clay (that is accompanied by few iron oxides) that characterizes pedogenesis in progressively drier climates.

Soils forming in the currently semiarid climatic regime of the Mojave Desert may be especially sensitive to changes in climate. During the full-glacial, late Pleistocene climate, xeric woodlands, supported by cooler and effectively moister conditions, expanded into much of the currently semiarid regions of the Mojave Desert (King, 1976; Spaulding and others, 1983). A

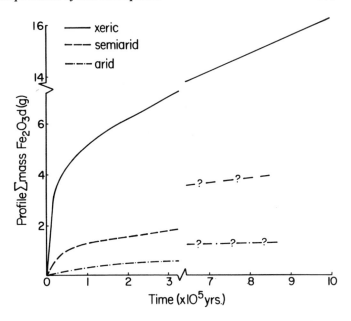

Figure 17. Change in profile content of secondary iron oxides (Σ mass Fe_2O_3d) with increasing soil age in arid, semiarid, and xeric climates of southern California.

possibly quite comparable climate presently characterizes the regions between the semiarid climate of the Mojave Desert and the subhumid, Mediterranean climate of the Transverse Ranges. As discussed previously, soils in these transitional zones that have formed on Holocene deposits are noncalcic, have thick ochric or mollic A horizons, and by the early Holocene, have color B or weak argillic B horizons with relatively large amounts of ferrihydrite. It is therefore possible that soils in the currently semiarid regions subjected to at least 10,000 yr of such a climate prior to the Holocene may have had similar profile characteristics. However, the subsequent exposure of such a soil to 8,000 to 10,000 yr of hotter, more arid Holocene conditions should have quickly converted a mollic or thick ochric A horizon to a much thinner ochric horizon. Furthermore, although rates of chemical alteration might be expected to decrease, large amounts of previously formed vermiculite and ferrihydrite might not be as quickly altered to phases more stable under semiarid conditions, because such mineral reactions proceed much more slowly than the chemical reactions by which organic matter is decomposed, and because the loss of the full-glacial plant community occurred in less than 5,000 yr. Moreover, conditions in the Holocene favoring carbonate deposition should result in accumulation of secondary carbonate in a previously noncalcareous solum (McFadden and Tinsley, 1985). Indeed, late Pleistocene soils of the semiarid Mission Creek area exhibit these characteristics (Table 2) and are therefore proposed to be polygenetic soils (McFadden and Bull, 1988).

In marked contrast to soils in currently semiarid climates, soils in currently arid regions of the Mojave Desert have probably

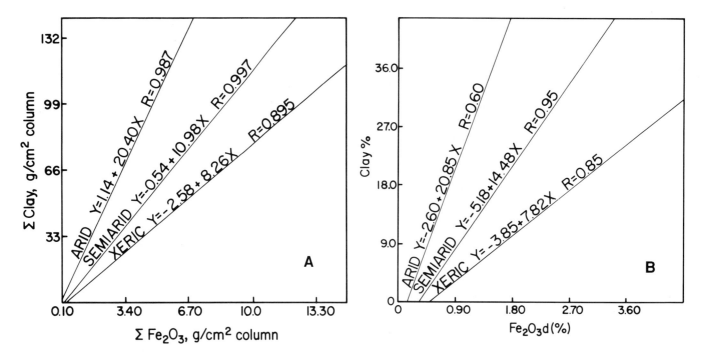

Figure 18. Relation between profile secondary clay and iron oxide content (A) and horizon-percent secondary clay and iron oxides (B) formed in arid through xeric climates in southern California.

experienced conditions throughout much of the Pleistocene that have been favorable for secondary carbonate accumulation within the solum. The small amount of secondary carbonate in late mid- and middle mid-Pleistocene soils in the semiarid chronosequence is surprising, however, because these soils were subjected to long durations of interglacial climatic regimes that presumably would have favored calcium carbonate accumulation. Furthermore, results of theoretical modeling suggest that if large amounts of secondary carbonate had accumulated during the last interglacial climate (isotope stage V), leaching during the subsequent glacial climate of the late Pleistocene would not be sufficient to remove the previously deposited calcium carbonate (McFadden, 1982). This suggests that the nature of calcic horizons in late mid- and middle mid-Pleistocene soils is probably not attributable only to the impact of changes in climate during the Pleistocene on the soil moisture regime.

As discussed previously, another variable that influences evolution of calcic soils is the influx of calcareous dust. Both variations in the amount of carbonate present in dust and variations in influx rate should strongly influence the rate and depth of carbonate accumulation (McFadden and Tinsley, 1985; Machette, 1985). In the Mojave Desert, the timing of eolian activity and the amount and composition of eolian influx could theoretically influence the evolution of calcic soils in the Mojave Desert. For example, McFadden and others (1984; 1987) and Wells and others (1985) have shown that well-developed soils have formed in loess deposits of the Cima Volcanic Field that predate 0.14 Ma,

due to very slow eolian influx rates that permitted formation of strongly developed soils during the late Pleistocene. Thus, soils forming on piedmont deposits during the last major interglacial period may also have been subjected to very slow eolian dust influx rates and associated very slow rates of secondary carbonate accumulation.

The rate of dust influx may have also been influenced by the position of a geomorphic surface relative to sources of eolian materials. For example, Lattman (1973) showed that fan surfaces located downwind of playas had more strongly developed calcic horizons than did fans farther removed from sources of calcareous dust. In the Panamint Mountains, Peterson (1980) attributed the moderately well-developed, sodic soils on distal fan surfaces to periodic deposition of carbonate and soluble-salt rich dust derived by deflation of local alkaline playa sediments.

In semiarid regions of the Mojave Desert, latest Pleistocene and Holocene deposits are inset into much older Pleistocene fan deposits. In the southwestern piedmont of the Providence Mountains, more recent fan deposits have partly overlapped and buried the proximal and medial parts of older fan deposits. The younger fans are currently prograding toward the basin and may be subject to a greater frequency and magnitude of eolian deposition than are the older Pleistocene fan deposits. Evidence supporting this is indicated by recent deposition of sand dunes on distal parts of the Holocene and youngest Pleistocene deposits of the Providence Mountains. The presence of significant amounts of secondary carbonate in Holocene and latest Pleistocene soils, relative to that in much older Pleistocene soils, may be due partly to the proximity of the younger fan surfaces to sources of calcareous dust.

In conclusion, studies of suites of increasingly older soils in three different climates of southern California reveal systematic changes in several soil properties. Because factors of soil parent materials and relief are the same for all the soils, the systematic changes must be attributed to differences in soil age and changes in climate and vegetation. Within a given suite of soils, systematic changes in some soil properties occur in Holocene soils and are thus considered to be time-dependent changes, because these soils have not been subjected to significant changes in climate or vegetation. Thus, for significant differences to occur in, for example, the degree of reddening exhibited by increasingly older Pleistocene soils does not require the existence of past climatic regimes more favorable for development of reddened soils. The process of reddening may be the inevitable result of chemical weathering over a sufficiently long period of time. Furthermore, the possibility of reaching different types of pedogenic soil thresholds indicates relatively rapid changes, in that rates of development of certain soil properties are not necessarily attributable to changes in climate.

Evaluating rates of soil development over tens of thousands of years in arid and semiarid climatic regions is very difficult because of the significant influence of glacial-to-interglacial changes on soil-water balance and the resultant effects of changes in soil-water balance on processes such as accumulation of secondary carbonates and soluble salts, processes that are highly sensitive to soil-water balance. Because climate has fluctuated during Quaternary time in such regions, increasingly older Pleistocene soils in arid and semiarid climates are increasingly more polygenetic. Climatic changes have probably also influenced the pattern of soil development in arid though subhumid climates in

southern California by dramatically changing the nature of landscapes. For example, the alternating expansion and desiccation of large pluvial lakes, changes in vegetation communities, and changes in the hillslope and stream components of the fluvial systems have probably caused variation in the magnitude and composition of dust influx on different geomorphic surfaces. This factor has strongly influenced the evolution of soil characteristics, including clay, silt, carbonate, iron oxide, and soluble salt accumulation. It is difficult to identify a soil chronofunction that is not likely to reflect the influences of at least two soil-forming factors. Moreover, because four or fewer Pleistocene surfaces are present in a given region, accurate determination of changes in rates of soil development during the Pleistocene will be exceedingly difficult. However, the factorial approach of Jenny (1941) provides an initial basis for advancing the use of pedologic data for geochronometric and paleoclimatic studies. An increased degree of interaction among researchers in the fields of pedology, geochemistry, and climatic and tectonic geomorphology will be required to further our understanding of how changing climates and landscapes have affected rates and processes of soil development during the Quaternary.

ACKNOWLEDGMENTS

Several people have considerably influenced my thinking and ideas regarding the evolution of soils as functions of soil age and climatic change, including D. Beane, P. Birkeland, W. Bull, J. Hawley, D. Hendricks, L. Lattman, J. Tinsley, S. Wells, and D. Yaalon. I have also benefitted from discussions with R. Gerson, R. Brakenridge, and J. Dohrenwend. W. Sigleo, K. Flach, and C. Olson provided useful critiques that improved this manuscript. I also thank the Geologial Survey for providing field and laboratory support.

REFERENCES CITED

Arkley, R. J., 1963, Calculations of carbonate and water movement in soil from climatic data: Soil Science, v. 96, no. 4, p. 239–248.

Bachman, G. O., and Machette, M. N., 1977, Calcic soils and calcretes in the southwestern United States: U.S. Geological Survey Open-File Report 77-794, 163 p.

Birkeland, P. W., 1984, Soils and geomorphology: New York, Oxford University Press, 372 p.

Bischoff, J. L., Shlemon, R. J., Ku, T. L., Simpson, R. D., Rosenbauer, R. J., and Budinger, F. E., 1981, Uranium-series and soil-geomorphic dating of the Calico archeological site, California: Geology, v. 9, p. 576–582.

Bockheim, J. G., 1980, Solution and use of chronofunctions in studying soil development: Geoderma, v. 24, p. 71–85.

Brakenridge, G. R., 1978, Evidence for a cold, dry full-glacial climate in the American Southwest: Quaternary Research, v. 10, p. 1–44.

Brown, D. E., Lowe, C. H., and Pase, C. P., 1980, Digitized classification for ecosystems with an illustrated summary of the vegetation of North America: USDA Forest Service, General Technical Report RM-73, 93 p.

Bull, W. B., 1974, Geomorphic tectonic analysis of the Vidal region, *in* Information concerning site characteristics, Vidal Nuclear Generating Station [California]: Los Angeles, Southern California Edison Company, Appendix 2.5B, amendment 1, 66 p.

Bull, W. B., and Schick, A. P., 1979, Impact of climatic change on an arid watershed; Nahal Yael, southern Israel: Quaternary Research, v. 11, p. 152–171.

Bull, W. B., Menges, C. M., and McFadden, L. D., 1979, Stream terraces of the San Gabriel Mountains, southern California: U.S. Geological Survey, Office of Earthquake Studies, Contract Report 14-08-0001-G-394.

Childs, C. W., Goodman, B. A., and Churchman, G. J., 1979, Application of Mossbauer spectroscopy to the study of iron oxides in some red and yellow/brown soil samples from New Zealand, *in* Mortland, M. M. and Farmer, V. C., eds., Sixth International Clay Conference, 1978: Amsterdam, Elsevier, p. 555–565.

Colman, S. M., 1982, Chemical weathering of basalts and andesites; Evidence from weathering rinds: U.S. Geological Survey Professional Paper 1246, 51 p.

Cooke, R. U., and Warren, A., 1973, Geomorphology in deserts: University of California Press, 394 p.

Crook, R., Kamb, B., Allen, C. R., Payne, C. M., Procter, R. J., 1978, Quaternary geology and seismic hazard of the Sierra Madre and associate faults, western San Gabriel Mountains, California: U.S. Geological Survey Contract No. 14-08-0001-15258, Final Technical Report.

Dohrenwend, J. C., McFadden, L. D., Turrin, B. D., and Wells, S. G., 1984, K-Ar dating of the Cima volcanic field, Mojave Desert, California; Late Cenozoic volcanic history and landscape evolution: Geology, v. 12, p. 163–167.

Dorn, R. I., 1984, Geomorphological interpretation of rock varnish in the Mojave Desert, California, in Dohrenwend, J. C., ed., Surficial geology of the eastern Mojave Desert, California: 1984 Annual Meeting Fieldtrip 14 Guidebook, Geological Society of America, Reno, p. 150–161.

Dorn, R. I., and Oberlander, T. M., 1981, Rock varnish origin, characteristics, and usage: Zeitschrift für Geomorphologie, v. 25, p. 420–436.

Evanari, J., Yaalon, D. H., and Gutterman, 1974, Note on soils with vesicular structure in deserts: Geomorphology, v. 18, p. 162–172.

Gile, L. H., and Grossman, R. B., 1979, The desert soil project monograph: Washington, D.C., U.S. Department of Agriculture, Soil Conservation Service, 984 p.

Gile, L. H., Peterson, F. F., and Grossman, R. B., 1966, Morphological and genetic sequences of carbonate accumulation in desert soils: Soil Science, v. 101, p. 347–360.

Gile, L. H., Hawley, J. W., and Grossman, R. B., 1981, Soils and geomorphology in the Basin and Range area of southern New Mexico; Guidebook to the desert project: New Mexico Bureau of Mines and Mineral Resources Memoir 39, 222 p.

Harden, J. W., 1982, A quantitative index of soil development from field descriptions; Examples form a chronosequence in central California: Geoderma, v. 28, p. 1–28.

Harden, J. W., and Taylor, E. M., 1983, A quantitative comparison of soil development in four climatic regimes: Quaternary Research, v. 28, p. 342–359.

Jenny, H., 1941, Factors of soil formation: New York, McGraw-Hill, 281 p.

—— , 1980, The soil resource: New York, Springer-Verlag, 377 p.

Keller, E. A., Rockwell, T. K., Clark, M. N., Dembroff, G. R., Johnson, D. L., 1982, Tectonic geomorphology of the Ventura, Ojai, and Santa Paula areas, western Transverse Ranges, California, in Cooper, I.D., ed., Neotectonics in southern California: 78th Annual Meeting of the Cordilleran Section, Geological Society of America, p. 25–42.

King, T. J., 1976, Late Pleistocene–early Holocene history of coniferous woodlands in the Lucerne Valley region, Mojave Desert, California: Great Basin Naturalist, v. 36, p. 227–238.

Ku, T. L., Bull, W. B., Freeman, S. T., and Knaus, K. G., 1977, Th²³⁰/U²³⁴ dating of pedogenic carbonates in gravelly desert soils of Vidal valley, southeastern California: Geological Society of America Bulletin, pt. 1, v. 90, p. 1063–1073.

Kukla, G., and Opkyke, N., 1975, Preliminary report on magnetostratigraphic study of sediments near Blythe, California, and Parker Valley, Arizona: San Diego Gas and Electric Company Early Site Review Report, Sundesert Nuclear Power Project, Appendix 2.5-D, 19 p.

Lattman, L. H., 1973, Calcium carbonate cemetation of alluvial fans in southern Nevada: Geological Society of America Bulletin, v. 84, p. 3013–3028.

Machette, M. H., 1978, Dating Quaternary faults in the southwestern United States using buried calcic paleosols: U.S. Geological Survey Journal of Research, v. 6, p. 369–381.

—— , 1985, Calcic soils and calcretes of the southwestern United States, in Weide, D. L., ed., Soils and Quaternary geology of the southwestern United States: Geological Society of America Special Paper 203, p. 1–21.

Marion, G. M., Schlesinger, W. H., Fonteyn, P. J., 1985, Caldep; A regional model for soil CaCO₃ (caliche) deposition in southwestern deserts: Soil Science, v. 139, p. 468–481.

McFadden, L. D., 1981, Geomorphic processes influencing the Cenozoic evolution of the Canada del Oro Valley, southern Arizona: Arizona Geological Society Digest, v. 8, p. 13–20.

—— , 1982, The impacts of temporal and spatial climatic changes on alluvial

soils genesis in southern California [Ph.D. thesis]: Tucson, University of Arizona, 430 p.

McFadden, L. D., and Bull, W. B., 1988, Quaternary soil development in the Mojave Desert, California, in Whitley, D. S., ed., Late Pleistocene archeology and environment in California: Salt Lake City, University of Utah Press (in press).

McFadden, L. D., and Hendricks, D. M., 1982, Temporal changes in the clay mineralogy of Quaternary alluvial soils forming in a xeric climate southern California: American Quaternary Association Program and Abstracts, p. 136.

McFadden, L. D., and Hendricks, D. M., 1985, Changes in the content and composition of pedogenic iron oxyhydroxides in a chronosequence of soils in southern California: Quaternary Research, v. 23, p. 189–204.

McFadden, L. D., and Tinsley, J. C., 1985, The rate and depth of accumulation of pedogenic carbonate accumulation in soils; Formulation and testing of a compartment model, in Weide, D. L., ed., Soils and Quaternary geology of the Southwestern United States: Geological Society of America Special Paper 203, p. 23–42.

McFadden, L. D., and Weldon, 1987, Rates and processes of soil development on Quaternary terraces in Cajon Pass, southern California: Geological Society of America Bulletin, v. 98, p. 280–293.

McFadden, L. D., and Tinsley, J. C., 1982, Soil profile development in xeric climates, in Tinsley, J. C., Matti, J. C., and McFadden, L. D., eds., Late Quaternary pedogenesis and alluvial chronologies of the Los Angeles and San Gabriel Mountains areas, southern California, and Holocene and faulting and alluvial stratigraphy within the Cucamonga Fault zone; A preliminary view: Field Trip No. 12, Cordilleran Section, Geological Society of America, p. 15–20.

McFadden, L. D., Wells, S. G., Dohrenwend, J. C., and Turrin, B. D., 1984, Cumulic soils formed in eolian parent materials on flows of the Cima volcanic field, Mojave Desert, California, in Dohrenwend, J. C., ed., Surficial geology of the eastern Mojave Desert, California: Field Trip 14, 97th Annual Meeting of the Geological Society of America, p. 134–149.

McFadden, L. D., Wells, S. G., and Dohrenwend, J. C., 1986, Influences of Quaternary climatic changes on processes of soil development on desert loess deposits of the Cima volcanic field, California: Catena, v. 13, p. 361–389.

McFadden, L. D., Wells, S. G., and Jercinovic, M. J., 1987; Influences of eolian and pedogenic processes on the origin and evolution of desert pavements: Geology, v. 15, p. 504–508.

Merriam, R., and Bischoff, J. L., 1975, Bishop Ash; A widespread volcanic ash extended to southern California: Journal of Sedimentary Petrology, v. 45, p. 207–211.

Metzger, D. G., Loeltz, O. J., and Irelan, B., 1973, Geohydrology of the Parker-Blythe-Cibola area, Arizona and California: U.S. Geological Survey Professional Paper 486-G, 130 p.

Muhs, D. R., 1983, Airborne dust fall on the California Channel Islands, U.S.A.: Journal of Arid Environments, v. 6, p. 223–228.

National Oceanic and Atmospheric Administration, 1978, Climatologic data; Annual summary: U.S. Department of Commerce, Environmental Data and Information Service, v. 82, no. 13, 570 p.

Olmstead, F. H., Loeltz, O. J., and Irelan, B., 1973, Geohydrology of the Yuma area, Arizona and California: U.S. Geological Survey Professional paper 486-H, 227 p.

Ore, H. T., and Warren, C. N., 1971, Late Pleistocene–early Holocene geomorphic history of Lake Mojave, California: Geological Society of America Bulletin, v. 82, p. 2553–2562.

Peterson, F. D., 1980, Holocene desert soil under sodium salt influence in a playa-margin environment: Quaternary Research, v. 13, p. 172–186.

Ponti, D. J., 1985, The Quaternary alluvial sequence of the Antelope Valley, California, in Weide, D. L., ed., Soils and Quaternary geology of the Southwestern United States: Geological Society of America Special Paper 203, p. 79–98.

Retallack, G., 1981, Fossil soils; Indicators of ancient terrestrial environments: Paleobotany, Paleoecology, and Evolution, v. 1, p. 55–102.

—— , 1983, Late Eocene and Oligocene paleosols from Badlands National Park, South Dakota: Geological Society of America Special Paper 193, 82 p.

Rogers, R. J., 1980, A numerical model for simulating pedogenesis in semiarid regions [Ph.D. thesis]: Salt Lake City, University of Utah, 285 p.

Schwertmann, J., and Taylor, R. M., 1977, Iron oxides, *in* Dixon, J. B., and Weed, S. B., eds., Minerals in soil environments: Soil Science Society of America, p. 145–180.

Schwertmann, J., Murad, E., and Schulze, D. G., 1982, Is there Holocene reddening (hematite formation) in soils of axeric temperature areas?: Geoderma, v. 27, p. 209–223.

Schlesinger, W. H., 1985, The formation of caliche in soils of the Mojave Desert, California: Geochimica et Cosmochemica Acta, v. 49, p. 57–66.

Shlemon, R. J., 1978, Quaternary soil-geomorphic relationships, southeastern Mojave Desert, California and Arizona, *in* Mahaney, W. C., ed., Quaternary soils: Norwich, England, University of East Anglia, Geological Abstracts, p. 187–207.

Smith, G. I., and Street-Perrot, F. A., 1983, Pluvial lakes of the western United States, *in* Wright, H. E., ed., Late Quaternary environments of the United States: Minneapolis, University of Minnesota Press, p. 190–212.

Soil Conservation Service, 1981, Examination and description of soils in the field, *in* Soil Survey Manual (USDA-SCS): Washington, D.C., U.S. Government Printing Office.

Spaulding, W. G., Leopold, E. B., and Van Devender, T. R., 1983, Late Wisconsin paleoecology of the America Southwest, *in* Wright, H. E., Jr., ed., Late Quaternary environments of the United States: Minneapolis, University of Minnesota Press, p. 259–293.

Torrent, J., Schwertmann, U., and Schulze, D. G., 1980, Iron oxide mineralogy of some soils of two river terrace sequences in Spain: Geoderma, v. 23, p. 191–208.

Weldon, R. J., 1985, The Late Cenozoic geology of the Cajon Pass; Implications for tectonics and sedimentation along the San Andreas Fault [Ph.D. thesis]: Pasadena, California Institute of Technology, 382 p.

Weldon, R. J., and Sieh, K. E., 1985, Holocene rate of slip and tentative recurrence interval for large earthquakes on the San Andreas fault, Cajon Pass, southern California: Geological Society of America Bulletin, v. 96, p. 793–812.

Wells, S. G., and others, 1984, Late Quaternary geomorphic history of Silver Lake, Eastern Mojave Desert, California; An example of the influence of climatic change in desert piedmonts, *in* Dohrenwend, J. C., ed., Surficial geology of the eastern Mojave Desert, California: 1984 Annual Meeting Fieldtrip 14 Guidebook, Geological Society of America, Reno, p. 69–87.

Wells, S. G., McFadden, L. D., and Dohrenwend, J. C., 1987, Influences of Late Quaternary climatic changes on geomorphic and pedogenic processes on a desert piedmont, eastern Mojave Desert, California: Quaternary Research v. 27, p. 130–146.

Yaalon, D. H., 1973, Conceptual models in pedogenesis; Can soil-forming functions be solved?: Geoderma, v. 14, p. 189–205.

Yaalon, D. H., and Ganor, E., 1973, The influence of dust on soils during the Quaternary: Soil Science, v. 116, p. 146–155.

MANUSCRIPT ACCEPTED BY THE SOCIETY JULY 1, 1987

Printed in U.S.A.

Index

[Italic page numbers indicate major references]

Typeset by WESType Publishing Services, Inc., Boulder, Colorado
Printed in U.S.A. by Malloy Lithographing, Inc., Ann Arbor, Michigan